PHYSICS
THAT WORKS

This curriculum was developed by TERC,
Cambridge, Massachusetts.
Funded in part by a grant from the
National Science Foundation.

TERC

NSF

KENDALL/HUNT PUBLISHING COMPANY
4050 Westmark Drive   Dubuque, Iowa 52002

Cover images © 2005 PhotoDisc

This material is based upon work supported by the National Science Foundation under Grant No. ESI-9618149. Any opinions, findings, and conclusions or recommendations expressed in this material are those of the authors and do not necessarily reflect views of the National Science Foundation.

Developed by TERC, Cambridge, Massachusetts

Contents

UNIT 2

Forces and Motion | On the Road Again   57

Chapter 5

Wagon Performance   76

Chapter 6

Understanding How Frictional
Forces Affect Performance   87

Chapter 7

What Makes a Vehicle Turn?   108

UNIT 3

Electricity and Simple Circuits | Restoring a Heartbeat 129

Chapter 11

The Best Circuit Design   198

Generators and Diodes | Building a Better Bike Light   213

Chapter 12

How Does a Generator Work?   216

Energy | Live from WPTW!   265

About This Student Guide

Physics That Works is not an ordinary textbook. Here you will find opportunities to explore science by using the methods scientists and engineers use every day to answer questions about our world. *You* will do the exploring in this course; you will ponder interesting questions and problems, design experiments, build apparatuses, and test them with instruments that are used in the workplace.

You will assume the roles of technicians, scientists, engineers, and inventors working on intriguing problems. You will do the kind of work they do in their jobs and work collaboratively to meet problem-solving challenges. As part of the course, you will visit these professionals where they work and see how your course work relates to the science and technology aspects of their jobs. As you tour these workplaces, you will learn about prospective careers and what qualifications are required to do these jobs.

You will work on unit projects in a hands-on way, investigating problems that deal with everyday objects like radios, speakers, tires, and bicycle lights. These long-term projects are central to each unit and model how groups of scientists or engineers work together. Because most of your work in class will be done in small groups, good teamwork is essential.

There is one major project for each of the five units. The units are:

> Unit One: Kinematics: Toys in Motion (Chapters 1, 2, and 3)
> Unit Two: Forces and Motion: On the Road Again (Chapters 4, 5, 6, and 7)
> Unit Three: Electricity and Simple Circuits: Restoring a Heartbeat
>   (Chapters 8, 9, 10, and 11)
> Unit Four: Generators and Diodes: Building a Better Bike Light
>   (Chapters 12, 13, and 14)
> Unit Five: Energy: Live from WPTW! (Chapters 15, 16, and 17)

As you can see from the names of the units, the projects are varied. For example, in one, you will design, build, and test a bike light that remains lit when you stop pedaling the bike. In another, you will build and operate a miniature radio station.

Each project is divided into several "milestones." Milestones are like stepping stones that lead you from the initial question or problem to its final solution. You can find out more about projects and the milestones by reading the unit overviews in this student guide.

STUDENT GUIDE ORGANIZATION

Your student guide is divided into five units. Your guide provides:
- a roadmap of each unit, which guides you through the activities and helps you organize your work;
- connections between important science concepts and the world of work; and
- practice problems and questions at the end of each chapter.

For each unit, this student guide provides an overview of the unit and identifies the milestones.

Each unit is made up of a series of activities. For each activity, you will find the following:
- Getting in Gear—an introduction to the activity.
- Getting to Work—a list of the steps to guide you through the activity.
- Getting the Point—required reading about important science concepts needed to understand the activity. Each of these required readings has Focus Questions to help make sure that you "get the point"!

Many activities have the following readings as well:
- Concept Connections—optional readings about everything from the physics in sports or music to the history of discoveries in physics.
- Workplace Connections—optional readings about how physics knowledge is applied in the workplace and about related careers.
- Did You Know?—interesting bits of knowledge related to the subject of the activity.

At the end of each chapter in a unit, you will find:
- What Have You Learned?—definitions and questions to help you review what you learned in each chapter. Your teacher will distribute worksheets containing Concept and Applying What you Know questions to be answered as homework assignments.

JOB SHEETS

Job sheets are "tools" you will use in every activity. There is at least one job sheet for each activity. Job sheets contain information on how to get the job done: suggestions and directions for activities, questions, project information, graphs, diagrams, and data tables.

Job sheets also provide a place for you to answer questions, make observations and reflections, draw diagrams, create graphs, and record the information you need to complete the milestones.

Your teacher will distribute the job sheets as you need them. Because you will make constant use of these sheets, and you will refer back to them often, it will be helpful to keep them organized in a binder.

KEEP IN MIND

In the end, what you get out of a course of study is mostly up to you. In *Physics That Works,* you are given the opportunity to *do* science, not just read about it. You will uncover much of the needed information yourself as you explore the physics concepts that underlie the unit projects. You will not be told all of the answers all of the time. In a real sense, you will embark on a voyage of in-depth learning and understanding that comes from an investment of your own energy in the process of discovery. Reflecting on your progress as you complete each milestone will lead you to your end goal for each unit of the course: get the job done and do it well. You cannot ask more of yourself than that. Your adventure begins now. Enjoy your journey.

Physics That Works Project Participants

Principal Investigator and Project Director
June Foster

Curriculum Developers
Jodi Asbell-Clarke
Irene Baker
Nancy Ishihara
Sara Lacy
Jeff Lockwood
Andee Rubin
Jerry Touger

Contributing Curriculum Developers
Scott Eddleman
Riley Hart
Nathan Kimball

Evaluation and Research
Katherine Paget
Amy Shulman Weinberg
Gloria Jacobs

Administration
Kate Blanchard
Valerie Martin
Sherry Soares

Cover Design Consultant
Valerie Martin

Consultants & Advisors
Steve Cremer
Leon Janikian
Paul Wagoner
Nancy Zerbey

NSF Program Director
Gerhard Salinger

Physics That Works is based on the vision of Margaret Vickers—the project's original Principal Investigator—and on her commitment to an equitable and challenging education for all students.

Contributing Teachers

Joe Clement, Beverly High School, Beverly, MA
James DeHart, West Brook High School, Beaumont, TX
Patricia Hargis, Crestline High School, Crestline, OH
JoAnne Harris, Stafford Senior High School, Falmouth, VA
Richard Hartman, North Kingstown High School, Kingstown, RI
John Payne, Pope High School, Marietta, GA
Martha Peters, Edison Preparatory School, Tulsa, OK
James Sparks, Shelbyville High School, Shelbyville, IL
Angel Tangney, Hill Regional Career High School, New Haven, CT

Kinematics | Toys in Motion

OVERVIEW

Unit One, *Kinematics: Toys in Motion,* is designed to help you learn about measuring motion while at the same time constructing and testing a toy you will design called a Creepy Crawly. When toys are produced, they undergo rigorous testing to ensure that they will be successful in the marketplace. They must be compared to other toys and to the expectations of the consumers. You will be using an instrument called a graphing motion detector to do some of this testing.

As is the case with all moving objects, your toy's motion can be quantified in terms of **position**, **velocity**, and **acceleration**. By the end of this unit, you will be able to describe each of these parameters and determine their value from graphs. Creating a Creepy Crawly and analyzing its motion to prepare it for the marketplace is your unit project, and the work on this project is divided into three project milestones.

When you read through the milestones, you'll notice that these milestones involve many facets of what is known as the design process. From your initial design of the Creepy Crawly to your ultimate testing and analysis of various toys on the marketplace, you will be practicing the work of engineers.

PROJECT MILESTONES

Your unit project is to construct and test a Creepy Crawly toy and compare it to other toys on the marketplace. This assignment is divided into three project milestones.

 Project Milestone 1   **Feasibility Report of the Creepy Crawly**

You will prepare a feasibility report. This report will include a drawing of your Creepy Crawly; a description of the testing methods you used; data on performance measures (distance, displacement, average speed, average velocity in target direction, and angle of wander); and suggestions for improvement.

Project Milestone 2   **Comparative Analysis Report**

You will prepare a comparative analysis report comparing your Creepy Crawly prototype to the consumer specifications for the ideal Perfect Prowler and to the performance specifications for the competitor's top toy, the Roving Rodent. To compare the Creepy Crawly prototype to the specifications for these other toys, you will examine the five performance measures you have already used. You will also make comparisons of a new performance measure—instantaneous velocity, and then use a graphing motion detector to obtain data and graphs for your report.

Project Milestone 3   **Product Review on Wind-up and Pull-back Toys**

You will prepare a product review report on the new wind-up and pull-back toys about to be released by Carpet Critters that includes an analysis of how they compare to their top competitors. The report will include graphs of position versus time and velocity versus time for each product with an analysis of position, velocity, and acceleration performance measurements.

ACTIVITIES AND ASSIGNMENTS

Your work on this unit project requires an understanding of kinematics, or motion. In fact, many of the milestones cannot be fully completed unless you gain familiarity with specific aspects of performance measures such as position, velocity, and acceleration. As you progress through the unit, you will complete a number of activities and assignments to help you understand these concepts, as well as graphing analysis.

Just as there are three project milestones, the activities and assignments in the unit are organized into three chapters. Each chapter focuses on a different aspect of kinematics and the toy design process.

1. In Chapter 1, you will construct your Creepy Crawly prototype and do a feasibility study to make sure it can move forward in roughly a straight line.

2. In Chapter 2, you will do more rigorous testing of your Creepy Crawly prototype using graphs of position and velocity to compare it to the performance of other competitor's toys and to consumer expectations.

3. In Chapter 3, you will use your newfound skills of graphing and motion analysis to review two new products in the Carpet Critters company's line. You will study position, velocity, and acceleration to compare these toys to their competitors.

The Feasibility of a Creepy Crawly Toy

OVERVIEW

YOU'VE LANDED EVERY KID'S DREAM JOB

You have just joined the engineering team at Carpet Critters Company, a toy company out to make a splash in the motion toys' marketplace. You are going to work with a team to design, construct, and test toys that your company is thinking of producing, specifically the Creepy Crawly. The marketing team has its visions, but you need to give the members realistic advice on whether their toy is a good idea.

The first step in toy design is a feasibility study. You will produce a prototype from the marketing team's specifications, and you need to test whether it is even a "go." Does the toy move? Does it move in the right direction? Will it stay in a relatively straight line? If not, it may be back to the drawing board.

The marketing team will meet with some consumers to ask them what they would expect out of a motion toy—How fast? How far?—and you will use a graphing motion detector to see how your prototype measures up. And don't forget the competition; the Roving Rodent is already out there and was the hottest ticket in last year's holiday shopping spree. Can your Creepy Crawly stand a chance against that big rat?

Finally, you will review the rest of the Carpet Critters' product line to do a product review of its motion toys. By this point, your engineering team will be such experts that you'll be knocking off so many position and velocity graphs that you'll be able to use them as wrapping paper!

Remember, the marketing team folks have some pretty wild ideas from time to time. The Carpet Critters Company needs you to keep them in line. With your help, they can make the next best-seller in motion toys!

Your first milestone:

Project Milestone 1   Feasibility Report of the Creepy Crawly

You will prepare a feasibility report. This report will include a drawing of your Creepy Crawly; a description of the testing methods you used; data on performance measures (distance, displacement, average speed, average velocity in target direction, and angle of wander); and suggestions for improvement.

By the end of this chapter, you should have a prototype of a Creepy Crawly that moves in a roughly straight line, and you will have measured how far it can go and how fast. To accomplish the first milestone, you will need to understand how distance, displacement, and average speed are measured and how prototype design and construction is done. You will have a chance to visit an engineer's workplace to see how he or she solves problems and works from specifications on product development.

To help you accomplish Project Milestone One, you will do the following activities:

Activity 1.1   Working as an Engineer
You will visit the workplace of an engineer to become familiar with his or her work environment and the types of problems that engineers work on.

Activity 1.2   Constructing the Creepy Crawly
The Marketing Department gives you the specifications for a toy that the Carpet Critters Company wants to develop. You will use the materials and instructions provided to construct a prototype of this motion toy.

Activity 1.3   Measuring Straight-line Motion of Your Creepy Crawly
You will learn about the first performance measures you will be using to test your Creepy Crawly: distance, displacement, and angle of wander. You make several trial runs to see how far the toy will go in one run and how closely it will stick to a straight path.

Activity 1.4   Measuring Average Speed and Average Velocity of Your Creepy Crawly
You will learn two more performance measures: average speed and average velocity. You make several more trial runs to test these.

Activity 1.5   Modifying and Testing Your Creepy Crawly
You will modify your Creepy Crawly and test it, in preparation for your feasibility report.

Activity 1.6   Preparing Your Feasibility Report
You will prepare your first report to marketing to describe the performance of your modified Creepy Crawly and to make recommendations for its improvement.

ACTIVITY 1.1

Working as an Engineer

Getting In Gear

What do engineers do? Build bridges? Make airplanes? Drill for oil? Yes, they do all of those things. But they also design household appliances, create new ways to make our lives easier, and design ways for us to have fun—toys! Almost every toy manufacturer has a team of toy engineers who designs, tests, and refines toys during their development. The engineers are the problem solvers—the ones who are charged with figuring out how to make "it" work, whatever "it" may be. In this unit, you will have a chance to assume the role of an engineer. You will test your creative and problem-solving abilities while learning about the physics you need to make your Creepy Crawly the best it can be.

To get started, you will visit the workplace of an engineer. The exact types of projects the engineer works on will depend on whom your teacher arranges for you to visit, but all engineers solve problems. As you spend time in this professional environment, imagine what it would be like to work there. Would you enjoy facing the challenges that he or she takes on every day?

Getting To Work!

To explore an engineering workplace, you will

1. Read the overview for Unit One, and discuss as a class the unit project and the outline of work throughout the unit.

2. Read the overview scenario and project milestone for Chapter 1, and discuss the scenario with your class.

3. Listen carefully to your host engineer's descriptions of the task he or she is working on and identify the specifications for the performance measures or techniques being used.

4. Answer the questions on **Job Sheet 1.1**   **A Visit with an Engineer.**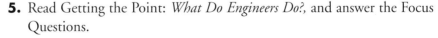
   a. Understand the reasons why the engineer has chosen to use particular techniques to perform measurements and analysis.
   b. If you find it difficult to determine the specifications of the project, ask the **Job Sheet** engineer.

5. Read Getting the Point: *What Do Engineers Do?,* and answer the Focus Questions.

6. Check out the Did You Know? reading as time permits.

Wonder about what it takes to be a toy designer? Read Workplace Connection: *Preparing for a Career in Toy Design.*

Getting The Point.

What Do Engineers Do?

There are many different fields within the field of engineering. All engineers solve problems, using very detailed specifications and using careful testing and measurement techniques, but the types of problems the solve can vary greatly. Here are just some of the different types of engineering that the Society of Women Engineers describes:

BIOMEDICAL ENGINEERING

Engineers are trained to apply techniques of mathematics and science to solving problems in medicine and biology. Engineers investigate genetic engineering, tumor biology, cellular processes, design and materials of prosthetic devices, new ways of taking images of the human body, and a wide range of other aspects of both biology and other engineering disciplines.

CHEMICAL ENGINEERING

These engineers must apply the principles of both mathematics and chemistry to solve problems, create materials, and design complex chemical systems. Chemical engineers create drug delivery systems, numerical models for atmospheric pollution problems, as well as magnetic and electronic materials. Not only do chemical and petroleum manufacturers employ them, but chemical engineers also find work in firms that produce drugs, plastics, paints, magnetic tapes, and synthetic fuels.

CIVIL ENGINEERING

The roads, dams, bridges, water treatment plants and all other public projects that affect society's daily life are developed by civil engineers. Civil engineers also perform the structural design and analysis of buildings, such as skyscrapers. Other areas of civil engineering include construction project management, construction automation, environmental engineering, traffic analysis, and mechanics of materials.

ELECTRICAL AND COMPUTER ENGINEERING

Electrical engineers explore electrical phenomena, such as determining the best methods of getting information from one place to another, and building robots that can electronically sense their surroundings. Computer engineers are involved with digital technologies like computer hardware and the development of more efficient circuitry on silicon computer chips.

MECHANICAL ENGINEERING

Mechanical engineers work with about anything that has integrated, moveable parts. They draw on knowledge from every other branch of engineering and work on a variety of projects: automobile transmissions, oil pipelines, solar heating systems, factory assembly lines, designing prosthetic devices, as well as manufacturing techniques and quality control, just to name a few.

One issue that is common in engineering classes is that there always seem to be more men than women. Although there is a higher percentage of men than women in engineering, the ratios are shifting. Women have attributes to make

good engineers. The high male-female ratio in engineering should not be a deterrent from pursuing engineering. When a senior mechanical engineer was asked to state what problems she had encountered as *female* undergraduate, she said, "I don't think that there is a problem." Although one undergraduate electrical engineer admitted to being "slightly intimidated" by the large number of men in her classes, she had experienced no major problems simply because she was a woman. A male engineering student stated that he chose lab/study partners "based on ability, not on gender."

There are some common misconceptions about engineers, such as:

- engineers are nerds
- all engineers are shy
- you have to be "super-smart" to be an engineer
- engineers have no outside interests.

These statements are no more true for engineers than they are for the population in general. Engineers are people just like you.

Adapted from *A Guide for High School Women on Becoming an Engineer: From High School To Career.* Society of Women Engineers. Reprinted with permission. http://www.swe.org/SWE/StudentServices/CareerGuidance/EngrForYou/brochure2. html (June 4, 2002)

Focus Questions

Which of these branches of engineering, if any, seem interesting to you? Why?

What are some of the ideas that people have about engineers? Are they true?

Workplace Connection: Preparing for a Career in Toy Design

The Toy Design Department, the world's first accredited baccalaureate program in toy design, opened in 1989 after three years of intensive planning with Fashion Institute of Technology and leading members of the industry. The establishment of a BFA program in toy design has provided a pool of highly skilled, socially responsible designers who respect children and delight in the creation of fun inspirational, safe toys. We are a think tank where new ideas are born and design research flourishes, on the cutting edge of the field and therefore always responsive to the needs of the marketplace.

The Toy Design Department receives more than 200 applications yearly for only 22 openings, from which we select a diverse international student body of varying ages, backgrounds and skills. Students come to the program with a mini-

Despite the advent of electronic toys and games, Hasbro, Inc. continues to employ mostly mechanical engineers, with some chemical engineers. (The company maintains an extensive chemical department in its Cincinnati location). Materials, metallurgical and electronics engineers, along with computer scientists, round out the staffing mix. "Electronics are a significant piece of quite a few of the products that we do," Smith notes, "but whether it's inside of a doll or a truck or whatever, there is a mechanism that goes along with that that is a mechanical engineering challenge."

http://www.toy-tma.com/ATI/FIT/2whoweare.html
(June 5, 2002)

mum of a two-year degree—50 percent come with four-to-six-year degrees-in such related disciplines as industrial design, mechanical engineering, illustration, advertising, graphics, fashion, fine arts and architecture. Students must demonstrate the high level of maturity and responsibility required for work as professionals. Once in the program, they bond together to form an inspiring, dynamic team.

Good design plays a critical role in the creation of really great toys. It is the responsibility of the designer to visually educate people at an early age by providing children with well-designed objects. Children will ultimately be more receptive to well-designed product in all areas as they mature into adults. The Toy Design Department emphasizes putting theory into practice. We encourage student interaction with industry professionals through our guest speaker program. Executives are invited from major manufacturers, retailers, advertisers, inventors and e-commerce to hold weekly talks with students so that they may experience the magnitude of the industry firsthand.

Adapted from *"Who We Are: The Toy Design Department."* Copyright © Toy Industry Association, Inc. (TIA). Reprinted with permission. http://www.toy-tma.com/ATI/FIT/2whoweare.html (June 5, 2002)

ACTIVITY 1.2

Constructing the Creepy Crawly

Getting In Gear

You have seen what other engineers do. Now it is your turn. Marketing has come down with a work order: you must design and construct a Creepy Crawly toy and test it for some basic motion performance measures. The first performance measures you will work with address the familiar questions "How far does the Creepy Crawly travel?" and "How straight does it travel?" You will learn two ways of describing your Creepy Crawly's change in position and a method of measuring how far off track it wanders. These types of measures give motion toy designers their first information about the performance of a new product.

Your job is to find out if it is feasible to construct a toy that will travel forward using the materials specified. Fortunately, the Marketing Department also gave you some ideas on how to start and what this toy should look like. As you design and construct your prototype Creepy Crawly, remember that this is a feasibility study for your prototype. The toy doesn't have to be perfect. You just want to construct a toy that will travel forward in a repeatable fashion.

To construct your Creepy Crawly, you will

1. Gather materials, and read $\boxed{\textbf{Job Sheet 1.2}}$ Constructing Your Creepy Crawly carefully.

2. Construct the Creepy Crawly, following the procedures outlined on Job Sheet 1.2: *Constructing Your Creepy Crawly.*

3. Make a trial run once the Creepy Crawly is constructed to test its ability to travel in a somewhat straight line and maintain control.

4. Record the results after each of five trial runs to ensure that your results are repeatable.

5. Read Getting the Point: *Making a Prototype,* and answer the Focus Questions.

6. Check out the Did You Know? reading as time permits.

7. Curious about how all this plays out in the real world? Read Workplace Connection: *Prototypes in the Computer Toy Industry* to find out.

Job Sheet

Getting The Point.

Making a Prototype

Prototyping is the process of making the first version of a product. A prototype may be made of the same or less expensive materials as the final product, but it is designed to be fully functional. A prototype allows you, the engineer, to test your design and make sure it works adequately. In the development of a commercial toy, this phase of the design process may take several years before a final design is approved for manufacturing.

The first step in making a prototype or model is to get a list of materials and to read and interpret a set of specifications for the product. Assembling materials is an important phase in the construction of a prototype. If the parts do not fit properly or do not withstand operational testing, they may have to be redesigned or manufactured in a different manner. Patience and concern for detail are important characteristics of model makers during this part of a prototype creation.

The prototype must be functional, but will not be optimal. The prototype serves to prove if the design constraints and materials are feasible. You will use your prototype to measure several performance measurements that describe its motion. You must demonstrate whether it is possible to make a toy that travels forward in a reasonably straight line with the materials provided.

Focus Questions

Why is it important to make a prototype before investing in the full-scale development of a new toy?

What questions will you be able to answer at the end of the prototyping phase?

Workplace Connection: Prototypes in the Computer Toy Industry

CONCEPTS AND PROTOTYPES

All toys start as a bright idea and then continue on through a myriad of refinements and approvals before there is any investment made to build a product. There are generally three types of prototypes used during the toy development life cycle.

During the early concept stage, product designers may make a variety of hard-foam or plastic models of potential products to help convey ideas, explore directions, and in some cases, test the concept with focus groups. While designers do some rapid foam prototyping in house, most of the models are made at outside shops by professional model makers, who employ Computer Numerically Controlled (CNC) machines and airbrush painting techniques to make photoreal, non-functional mockups.

On the engineering side, often a concept breadboard is used to validate the fundamental technical risk in the project. For example, in the case of the Intel Play Computer Microscope toy, a prototype was built using an off-the-shelf optical microscope and a digital camera joined together. This combination was used to explore and specify magnifications, light levels, and project feasibility. The goal of the concept breadboard is to quickly understand the fundamental properties of the toy, without necessarily worrying about size or cost at this stage.

The next stage of prototyping in the product life cycle is usually a form, fit, and function breadboard of the toy. This will generally consist of a Printed Circuit Board (PCB), machined or "rapid prototype" plastic parts, and software/firmware with very limited functionality. The purpose of this model is to validate the overall size of the product and provide an electronic breadboard for firmware development. This prototype presents a major challenge for the toy designer and hardware engineer, as they have to agree on an industrial design that satisfies both styling requirements and space envelope constraints. Often times, this prototype is also used at key marketing events to demonstrate the product.

In addition to the several flavors of hardware prototypes, there are also software prototypes that are developed. Software prototypes are often simply push-button Windows^{TM} applications that demonstrate the ability to either implement a software feature from scratch or demonstrate the difficulty level of integrating a third-party software package. These kinds of prototypes are very important tools when determining the software feature list. A software

Did You Know?

2002 marked the 30th anniversary of Hot Wheels. The success story starts with one man's idea to speed up the industry. In 1967 Elliot Handler, one of the original founders of Mattel, decided to add axles and working wheels to the static wheel die cast model cars of the times. What was developed was a prototype gravity-powered car that could run at a record-breaking scale speed of 300 mph downhill. The secret to such high performance racing action was low-friction wheels made of styrene which were hung on torsion bars and soon to be patented by Mattel. Handler took one look at this new, ultra-fast car, and exclaimed—"Wow, those are hot wheels"—thus, also naming the new product.

Adapted from *"Betcha Didn't Know."* Toy Industry Association, Inc. (TIA). http://www.toy-tia.org/industry/news/betcha/betcha.html (June 5, 2002)

prototype helps to crystallize the vision of the toy designer in some concrete form and helps the software engineer gauge the complexity of a software feature. By no means does the software prototype completely define a feature. It is simply a measuring stick that can be used as a piece of information when defining the software feature list, architecture, and user interface. It also serves as a resource load estimate tool when generating the project schedule.

ACTIVITY 1.3

Measuring Straight-line Motion of Your Creepy Crawly

Getting In Gear

So you've built your Creepy Crawly—let's see what it can do! Remember, this is a prototype, so don't expect perfection. But it would be nice if it would go roughly in a straight line. You must show that it can perform reliably, so you should test your toy several times for each performance specification.

You will be measuring distance and displacement, two measures of change of position. Engineers measure distance when they need to know the total length of the path traveled, for instance, when they are considering gas consumption or tire wear. They measure displacement, the change in position in a specific direction, when the start point and end point are important, for instance, when a vehicle needs to carry something from one point to another. You will learn in this activity that these two performance measures may be very different for certain paths traveled.

As you take measurements, remember to keep accurate records of your data.

Getting To Work!

To measure the first three performance measures, you will

1. Read Getting the Point: *Distance, Displacement, and Angle of Wander,* and answer the Focus Questions.

2. Select a location for a test track that provides enough space and a smooth surface for your Creepy Crawly to travel unimpeded.

3. Follow the directions on ⎜**Job Sheet 1.3**⎜ **Measuring Distance, Displacement, and Angle of Wander** to measure the first three performance measures for five runs of your Creepy Crawly.

Job Sheet

4. Check out the Did You Know? reading as time permits.

5. Do you think distance traveled is tricky? See different ways it's measured by reading the Concept Connection: *Odometers.*

Distance, Displacement, and Angle of Wander

Distance is a concept most of us feel pretty comfortable with. If somebody asks you how far away the store is from your home, you give an answer such as 1 mile or four blocks. How far did you walk to get to school this morning? These are questions we deal with every day.

Figure 1.1
How Far Did You Go?

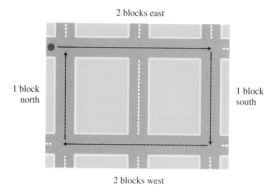

2 blocks east

1 block
north

1 block
south

2 blocks west

But suppose you go outside the school and walk two blocks east, then one block south, then two blocks west, and then one block north. How far did you go in total?

Some might say that you walked six blocks. Others might say you didn't go anywhere at all, since you ended up back at the same spot where you started. Both of these answers are true.

Your *position* is a way of specifying your location at any point. The *distance* is your total path length in your journey, which in this case is six blocks. However, your *displacement*—your change in position from the start to the finish—is zero. A distance measurement does not take direction into account. Your path can wander all over the place, and your distance traveled just keeps on increasing. The displacement is a measure of the difference in position of your end point and your starting point in any given direction.

Figure 1.2
How Far Did the
Dog Run?

100 yards

50 yards   50 yards

In another example, if a dog runs 100 yards (in a straight line) to fetch a ball and then runs halfway back along the same line, then the distance the dog ran is 100 yards + 50 yards = 150 yards. But the displacement is only 50 yards, since that is the difference between the dog's ending point and starting point.

In an ideal world, your Creepy Crawly would travel in a perfectly straight line and its distance would equal its displacement. In reality, it will probably wander and make a curved or even squiggly path.

To measure the distance that your Creepy Crawly traveled, you will need to devise a way to measure the total length of the path it traveled. To measure its displacement, you will measure the distance between its starting point and its ending point in one direction.

Figure 1.3
Measuring Distance
and Displacement

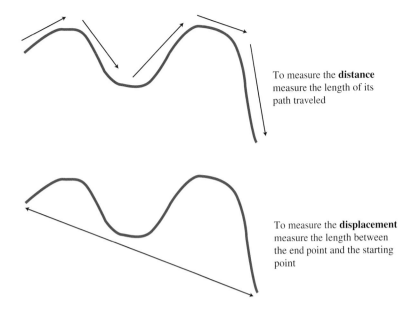

To measure the **distance** measure the length of its path traveled

To measure the **displacement** measure the length between the end point and the starting point

To quantify the amount your Creepy Crawly wanders off from a straight line, you are going to measure the *angle of wander.* This is the amount the Creepy Crawly deviates from traveling in a straight line. You will decide how to measure this. Each team may come up with a different method. Your measurements need not be exact. For example, you can say that the angle was approximately 10–20°, or whatever is appropriate for your Creepy Crawly.

Figure 1.4
Angle of Wander

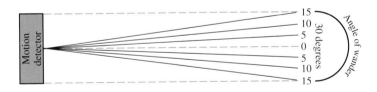

Focus Questions

If you ran around the block, ending up where you started, which would be greater: your displacement or your distance traveled?

If your toy has a large angle of wander, how would the distance traveled compare to the displacement?

Honeybees measure flight distances of hundreds of meters by sensing how many landmarks they pass on their journey. When they pass by many trees or flowers, the insects sense they have traveled a long way. They use this technique to communicate to other bees where to find food. When bees locate a meal more than 50 meters from the hive, they return to the colony and waggle their abdomens in the direction of the food source—the longer the dance, the farther the journey to food. If a meal is located closer than 50 meters, bees simply turn a few circles.

Concept Connection: Odometers

Using a string to measure the total distance your Creepy Crawly traveled worked OK in that situation, but it wouldn't do in an Olympic training session or a cross-country trip. Cars, for example, have odometers that keep track of the distance they have traveled.

In an older-style mechanical odometer a set of gears is attached to the transmission of the car. The transmission is the part of the car that takes energy from the motor and uses it to make the wheels turn. So every turn of the transmission corresponds to motion of the tires in one direction or another. The gears of the odometer are cycled along with the transmission and through a series of cables and more gears translate that motion into the motion of the little dial with numbers on the dashboard. On a bicycle, the mechanical odometer works similarly, but it is the circular motion of the wheel that drives the gears of the odometer.

Today, most bicycle and car odometers are digital. These operate by attaching a magnet to one of the wheels and an electric sensor to the frame. During each revolution of the wheel, the magnet passes by the sensor, generating a voltage in the sensor. The computer counts these voltage spikes, or pulses, and uses them to calculate the distance traveled. On a bicycle, you have to program the odometer with the circumference of the wheel. Each time the computer sense a pulse, it registers that the wheel has turned around once, which corresponds to one wheel diameter of distance traveled.

Figure 1.5
An Odometer Set within an Automobile Speedometer

ACTIVITY 1.4

Measuring Average Speed and Average Velocity of Your Creepy Crawly

Getting In Gear

By now, you should have a Creepy Crawly that moves roughly in a straight line, and you know how far it will travel in one run. You will now introduce two more performance measures, average speed and average velocity. The difference between these measures is analogous to the difference between distance and displacement. Speed is a general measure of the rate of motion of an object; velocity is looking specifically at its motion in one direction.

Remember, keep good records of all your performance measurements for all trial runs.

Getting To Work!

To measure the average speed and average velocity of your Creepy Crawly, you will

1. Read Getting the Point: *Average Speed and Average Velocity,* and answer the Focus Questions.

2. Follow the directions on Job Sheet 1.4 Measuring Average Speed and Average Velocity of Your Creepy Crawly to measure the average speed and average velocity in the target direction for five runs of the Creepy Crawly. Record all data on Job Sheet 1.4.

Job Sheet

Wonder why you should care about the difference between speed and velocity? Find out by reading Concept Connection: *Displacement or Distance?*

Getting The Point

Average Speed and Average Velocity

How fast does your Creepy Crawly go? Simple question, right? Well, it depends on what you mean by fast. Most people first think of speed to answer that question. Speed is the distance traveled divided by the time it took to get there. For instance, if you ride your bike 20 miles in 2 hours, then you have an average speed of 20 miles/2 hours, or 10 miles per hour. When talking about speed, you need not consider the direction you are traveling. You could have ridden your bike in a 20-mile circle ending up right back where you started, and your speed is still 10 miles per hour.

Velocity is a bit different. Average velocity is the displacement of an object divided by the time it took to travel. As you saw in Activity 1.3, your displacement can be quite different from the distance traveled. For example, think back to your circular bike ride. If you ended up exactly where you started from, then your displacement would be zero, so your average velocity would be zero—even though your speed was 20 miles per hour. On the other hand, if you rode your bike

20 miles in a straight line in your target direction and took 2 hours, then your average velocity in your target direction would be 10 miles per hour. To measure velocity, as opposed to speed, you must specify which direction you are considering.

You can measure the average speed of your Creepy Crawly by measuring the total length of the path it traveled in a run (its distance) and dividing by the time for that run.

average speed = total distance traveled/time interval

To measure the Creepy Crawly's average velocity in the target direction, you must be careful to measure its displacement in the target direction and divide that by the travel time (time interval) for the run.

average velocity in the target direction =
displacement in the target direction/time interval

Focus Questions

What is the difference between average speed and average velocity?

Why is it important to specify a direction when measuring the average velocity?

Concept Connection: Displacement or Distance?

Suppose you were on a bus going from the mall downtown to the movie theatre 5 miles away. You board the bus 30 minutes before your movie starts, thinking it is plenty of time for the bus to go the 5 miles. One hour later you arrive at the theatre. Fuming, you ask the driver how it could possibly take so long to go 5 miles. Couldn't he drive faster than 5 miles per hour? He replies, "Oh yes, even with stops included I average 15 miles per hour." Do you know why you missed the movie?

Although the theatre was only 5 miles from the mall where you started—and indeed 5 miles was your displacement when you got off the bus—5 miles was not necessarily the distance traveled. If indeed the bus driver was driving with an average speed of 15 miles per hour, then your bus covered a total of 15 miles in the hour you were on the bus. It may have taken a very meandering path, going several different directions along the way. If the bus had been traveling the same average speed and had headed in your target direction the whole time, it would have taken only one-third of an hour (20 minutes) to go the 5 miles, and you would have had plenty of time to get to the movie.

As it turns out, the average speed of the bus was 15 miles per hour, but the average velocity in the direction toward the movie theatre was 5 miles per hour since it took 1 hour to achieve the displacement of 5 miles between the start and end points.

ACTIVITY 1.5

Modifying and Testing Your Creepy Crawly

You have now run one set of tests on your original prototype to measure five performance measures: displacement, distance, angle of wander, average speed, and average velocity in the target direction. These give you a pretty good idea of what your Creepy Crawly can do.

In this activity, you will modify your Creepy Crawly. You'll make some changes to see if you can improve on your Creepy Crawly's performance. Perhaps you can make it travel farther, faster, or in a straighter line. It is important to change only one characteristic at a time, such as the type of rubber band or the amount of modeling clay. This will allow you to determine which characteristic actually affects the motion of the Creepy Crawly.

Then you will test the performance of your modified Creepy Crawly and create a table of the results. Be sure to record your data carefully, because the data will be used in your upcoming feasibility study.

Getting To Work!

To optimize your Creepy Crawly prototype, you will

1. Follow the instructions on | **Job Sheet 1.5** | Modifying and Testing Your **Creepy Crawly Prototype** to change one characteristic.

2. Retest your Creepy Crawly, and record all data on Job Sheet 1.5.

3. Read Getting the Point: *Controlling Variables.*

Job Sheet

Getting The Point.

Controlling Variables

Suppose you suddenly developed an allergic reaction to something you ate, but had no idea what caused it. How would you find out? There are so many possibilities—where do you begin? Allergists (doctors who test for and treat allergies) recommend that you remove as many candidates as possible from your daily life and then add them back one by one. This may mean that you stop eating dairy products, certain grains, nuts, and shellfish, since those are all likely candidates for food allergies. Suppose as soon as you do that, your reaction goes away. Great! You feel better, but what have you learned? The food that you are allergic to is one (or maybe two) of these many items that you stopped eating.

To identify which food caused the reaction, you introduce one of the candidates back into your diet each week. In the first week, you may try dairy products and find that you have no reaction—phew, you're not allergic to milk. The next week you try grains and still no reaction. Then the third week, you try shellfish and sure enough, you get the reaction again. By controlling the variables and introducing only one at a time, you were able to clearly identify that it is shellfish that causes your allergic reaction.

You should use a similar kind of procedure when experimenting with the construction of your toy. Suppose on your first run the toy spun around in circles. To correct it, you might try to adjust the position of the rubber bands, try thicker rubber bands, or add modeling clay to the inside of the canister. If you did all three of these at once and then the toy moved in a straight line, how would you know which of the changes you made was helpful?

You need to change just one variable at a time to be able to state conclusively what makes a difference in the toy's ability to go in a straighter line. If you change the types of rubber bands and the toy still goes in a circle, you can assume that the problem is not with the type of rubber bands. If you then adjust the position of the original rubber bands and the car goes in more of a straight line, then you are beginning to hone in on the variable that might make a difference.

Sometimes you must make combinations of changes to affect the result. For instance, maybe it is only when weight is added to the canister and when the rubber bands are separated by more than an inch on the canister that the toy will travel in a straighter line. In this case, you will have to be very careful to record the results after each individual change so that you can correctly identify the exact combination that gives you the best result.

Focus Question

What are the problems associated with changing too many variables at once when testing a new product?

ACTIVITY 1.6

Preparing Your Feasibility Report

Getting In Gear

You have now constructed a prototype Creepy Crawly, measured five performance measures, modified one characteristic to attempt to improve its performance, and measured five performance characteristics of the modified Creepy Crawly. As the milestone for this chapter, you will prepare a feasibility report that describes your Creepy Crawly and its performance, and poses conclusions about the strengths and weaknesses of the modified toy. You will use the data you have collected for your modified Creepy Crawly and information from previous activities as you write your feasibility report.

Your report need not be elaborate, but it should be clear and organized.

Getting To Work!

To complete Project Milestone One, you will

1. Follow the instructions on ┌ **Job Sheet 1.6** ┐ **Preparing Your Feasibility Report** to gather data from previous activities.

2. Ensure that all diagrams and data tables are labeled so that someone not familiar with your project could understand them.

3. Make sure your feasibility conclusions about the modified toy's strengths and weaknesses are based on the data shown.

4. Read Getting the Point: *Why Create a Feasibility Study?*

5. Review the concepts and answer the questions in What Have You Learned?

6. Check out the Did You Know? reading as time permits.

Job Sheet

Getting The Point.

Why Create a Feasibility Study?

To go from an idea to a product on a shelf in a store can take years and lots of money. Toys need to be designed, tested, redesigned and retested (several times), and prepared for market. Before a company invests too much money and resources into a product, it wants to make sure the product will work. *Feasibility* means capable of being accomplished or brought about. A feasibility study indicates what a product can accomplish, what its strengths and weaknesses are, and whether it can accomplish particular tasks set forth.

You will need to report how feasible your Creepy Crawly prototype is in the areas of the five performance

Did You Know?

In a Hot Wheels "Action Pack," Mattel, Inc., was marketing toy models of NASA's missions to Mars: the Mars Climate Orbiter and the Mars Polar Lander. These toys had gone through all the regular testing and marketing of the other Hot Wheels products and were expected to be a huge success once the spacecraft were making headlines with their fabulous images and scientific discoveries. The toys hit the shelves in stores everywhere, and then the unexpected happened. The Climate Orbiter was destroyed as it entered Martian orbit. The Polar Lander failed while landing on Mars. No testing or preparation on the part of Mattel could have avoided this disaster; the fate of its toys was in the hands of NASA. Instead of becoming the hottest holiday toy for tikes, the Hot Wheels space probes were the item of choice by collectors of space paraphernalia—the missions of doom.

measures. In this chapter, you measured maximum distance traveled with one windup, displacement in the target direction, average speed, average velocity in the target direction, and angle of wander. You learned that the difference between distance and displacement, as well as the difference between speed and velocity, is whether or not they depend on the direction traveled.

Among the eventual goals for the Creepy Crawly is for it to travel in a straight line. The performance measure angle of wander, as well as the difference between the displacement and the distance (or difference between the average speed and average velocity), will give the marketing team a sense of how close your Creepy Crawly prototype is to being market-ready. Later, you will compare your Creepy Crawly in more detail to the competitor's product and to consumer expectations.

Focus Questions

What is the purpose of a feasibility study?

What are some performance measures that will indicate that the Creepy Crawly is a feasible product?

What Have You Learned?

Position. Position is the location of a point in space. It can be expressed in many different ways. For example, we can express position by naming the object's location on a number line, in other words its distance from the 0 point, or origin. In this unit, you will determine a starting point for your motion toys and measure position relative to that point. In real-life engineering contexts, position can be expressed as either a positive or negative number, depending on whether it falls to the right or the left of an origin. But because this unit deals only with straight-ahead motion, all positions have positive values.

Displacement. A displacement is the change in position in a given direction and has a sign, depending on which direction an object moves. For example, if an object moves from 2 meters to 6 meters, its change in position is 4 meters. If it moves from 6 meters to 2 meters, its change in position is −4 meters. In this unit, we are dealing primarily with forward motion, with no backtracking, so most changes in position will have positive values.

Distance. Distance is the length of the path traveled. The distance is the same as displacement only if the object has gone forward in one direction. If an object changes direction, however, it may have a large distance, but small or even zero displacement. Distance measurements do not depend on direction and therefore have no sign; that is, distance is always a positive quantity.

Target direction. When dealing with displacement and velocity, you must specify the direction of interest. The target direction is the direction for which you are measuring the change of position.

Interval. An interval is the amount of time that elapses between one clock reading and another. It is calculated by subtracting the second clock reading from the first.

Speed. Speed is a measure of how fast something is moving. It is the distance traveled divided by the time of travel (time interval). It tells you nothing about direction. In this unit, we deal with both average speed and instantaneous speed.

Average speed. To find average speed, divide the distance the object traveled by the time it spent traveling. To do that calculation, you need to know the starting and ending positions (so you can find the distance) and the starting and ending clock readings (so you can find the elapsed time). Notice that an average speed value cannot tell you whether an object is speeding up or slowing down at any given moment or any information about the direction the object is traveling.

Instantaneous speed. Instantaneous speed is the speed of an object at a single point in time. Instantaneous speed cannot be measured precisely, but you can get closer and closer to it by taking measurements over shorter and shorter time intervals. In practice, this is difficult to do by hand; the motion detector is the best tool we have for performing these calculations.

Velocity. Velocity is the rate of motion of an object in the target direction. When the displacement is measured in a given direction, the velocity in that direction is the displacement divided by the time of travel. When using the motion detector, positive velocity represents any motion in a direction *away from* the motion detector. Negative velocity represents any motion *toward* the motion detector.

Average velocity. To find average velocity, divide the object's total displacement in the target direction by the time it spent traveling. To do that calculation, you need to know the starting and ending positions (so you can find the displacement in the target direction) and the starting and ending clock readings (so you can find the elapsed time). In calculating average velocity, make sure you note the sign of the change in position, as well as its value. In one dimension, the result will be positive or negative, depending on what direction the object is moving. Notice that for straight-line travel with no reversals of direction, the average speed and average velocity are the same.

Instantaneous velocity. Instantaneous velocity is the velocity of an object at a single point in time. Like instantaneous speed, it cannot be measured precisely, but you can get closer and closer to it by taking measurements over shorter and shorter time intervals. The motion detector can give a good approximation of instantaneous velocity because it measures distance over very tiny time intervals.

CONCEPT QUESTIONS

1. Select which statements are true for the diagram in Figure A. (There may be more than one answer.)

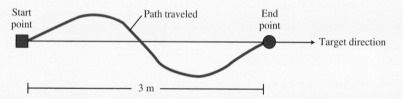

Figure A
Path of Motion

a. The distance traveled by the object is 3 meters.
b. The distance traveled by the object is greater than 3 meters.
c. The displacement of the object is 3 meters.
d. The displacement is greater than the distance traveled by the object.
e. The displacement is not in the target direction.

2. Suppose you start out on a walk by heading north for 0.5 kilometer. You then turn and walk east for 1.5 kilometers and then walk south for 0.2 kilometer.
a. What is your displacement in the northern direction (if north is your target direction)?
b. What is your distance traveled?

3. Under what circumstances are distance traveled and displacement equal?

4. Suppose you drove 100 miles east and then 50 miles south and then 50 miles west and then 50 miles north. It took you 5 hours to do the whole trip.
a. What was your average speed during the trip?
b. What was your average velocity in the eastern direction for the entire trip?
c. What was your average velocity in the northern direction for the entire trip?

Continued

5. What type of engineer did you visit, and what were the performance measures he or she used when studying his or her products?

6. What characteristics of your Creepy Crawly were important in maximizing its displacement during trial runs?

APPLYING WHAT YOU KNOW

1. Is it possible for the displacement of an object to be greater than its distance traveled during a run? Why or why not?

2. Describe in detail a path you might walk that would have the displacement equal to half of the distance traveled.

3. Describe a scenario where you would run more than 100 miles and have a displacement of zero.

4. How does the angle of wander affect the difference between distance and displacement?

5. An airplane flies between two cities that are 1000 miles apart. If the average speed of the airplane is 400 miles/hour, how long will it take for the plane to fly the trip?

6. If you could make further modifications to your Creepy Crawly to improve its performance, what would you do and why?

Comparative Analysis Review of the Creepy Crawly

OVERVIEW

HOW DOES YOUR CREEPY CRAWLY MEASURE UP TO THE COMPETITION?

Your prototype is done, and you have decided on the feasibility of the Creepy Crawly based on the first five performance measures: distance, displacement, angle of wander, average speed, and average velocity in the target direction. Now the tough stuff begins. The Creepy Crawly's top competitor, the Roving Rodent, is flying off the shelves of toy stores everywhere—kids can't get enough of them. Will the Creepy Crawly be able to compare?

Marketing has pulled together several focus groups of typical consumers—kids, parents, day-care providers—to ask them what they would look for in an ideal motion toy, tentatively named the Perfect Prowler.

You will be given the desired performance measures for the Perfect Prowler, as specified by the focus groups, and two graphs of the performance measures of the Roving Rodent. You need to see how your prototype will compare. To compare graphs, you will need to learn how to make graphs of the data from your Creepy Crawly. You will be using a graphing motion detector to do the detailed analysis of its motion.

Remember, your model is a prototype. We wouldn't expect it to behave like the commercial Roving Rodent or like the dream toy of a consumer group. But does it even come close?

Your next milestone:

Project Milestone 2 | Comparative Analysis Report

You will prepare a comparative analysis report comparing your Creepy Crawly prototype to the consumer specifications for the ideal Perfect Prowler and to the performance specifications for the competitor's top toy, the Roving Rodent. The report will include analysis of data and graphs of position versus time and velocity versus time generated by a graphing motion detector. Based on your analyses, you will make a recommendation about whether to proceed with the development of the Creepy Crawly.

By the end of this chapter, you will have compared your Creepy Crawly prototype to the performance of its top competitor, the Roving Rodent, and also to the expectations of the consumer focus groups.

You will be able to describe the instantaneous velocity in the target direction of the Creepy Crawly during trial runs. You will use graphical data from the graphing motion detector of position versus time and velocity versus time to do this analysis.

To help you accomplish Project Milestone Two, you will do the following activities:

Activity 2.1   Comparing Your Prototype to Consumer Preferences
You will receive a set of specifications gathered from several consumer focus groups on the type of performance they would expect from an ideal motion toy, nicknamed the Perfect Prowler. You will use the five performance measures you learned about in Chapter 1 to compare your Creepy Crawly prototype to their Perfect Prowler specifications.

Activity 2.2   Measuring Instantaneous Velocity
To understand instantaneous velocity, you will measure the motion of one or more of your classmates running a 100-meter sprint.

Activity 2.3   Creating a Position versus Time Graph
To become familiar with how position and time are commonly displayed on a graph, you will plot the data from your classmates' runs and use that graph to analyze their instantaneous velocity.

Activity 2.4   Using a Graphing Motion Detector
You will learn how to use an instrument that records motion data and creates graphs. Using the motion detector and graphs during the rest of the unit will help you understand various facets of motion. You will create a position versus time graph of your Creepy Crawly. You will also receive a similar graph showing the motion of the Creepy Crawly's top competitor, the Roving Rodent. You will use these graphs to compare the motion of the two toys, in particular the performance measure of changing instantaneous velocity.

Activity 2.5   Graphing Velocity versus Time
You will study how velocity versus time graphs correspond to position versus time graphs for various types of motion.

Activity 2.6 Measuring Maximum Velocity of the Creepy Crawly

You will create a velocity versus time graph of the motion of your Creepy Crawly and compare it to that of its competitor, the Roving Rodent. You will analyze the velocity versus time graphs to determine the maximum value of the instantaneous velocity.

Activity 2.7 Preparing Your Comparative Analysis Report

For Project Milestone Two, you will prepare a report on the detailed performance of your Creepy Crawly for the Marketing Department. This will include the analysis of six performance measures (the five from Chapter 1 plus instantaneous velocity) as they compare to the specifications for the Perfect Prowler and the specifications of the Roving Rodent.

ACTIVITY 2.1

Comparing Your Prototype to Consumer Preferences

Getting In Gear

The Marketing Department appreciated your feasibility study and is now ready to proceed with a comparative analysis of the Creepy Crawly product. The first thing you will do is compare your Creepy Crawly to the specifications outlined by the consumer focus groups. The Marketing Department has given you the focus groups' specifications for what they think would constitute an ideal wind-up toy (nicknamed the Perfect Prowler) that they would buy.

To begin your comparative analysis, you will review the data for each of the performance measures provided for the Perfect Prowler. These should be familiar to you from your work in Chapter 1. They include the distance traveled, the displacement, the angle of wander, the average speed, and the average velocity in a target direction. You will use the data from your feasibility report to compare the Creepy Crawly's performance measures to those of the Perfect Prowler.

Keep in mind that the Perfect Prowler is a fictitious toy created in the minds of the customers. It may be impossible to match their expectations, but let's see if the Creepy Crawly can even come close.

Getting To Work!

To compare your Creepy Crawly prototype to the Perfect Prowler specifications, you will

1. Read the overview scenario and project milestone for Chapter 2, and discuss the scenario with your class.

2. Review with your teacher the specifications for the Perfect Prowler on **Job Sheet 2.1** How Does Your Creepy Crawly Measure Up?

Job Sheet

3. Read Getting the Point: *Comparing Data.*

4. Review the Creepy Crawly data from your feasibility report, and decide which data to enter in the table on Job Sheet 2.1. Enter the data.

5. Summarize the strengths and weaknesses of your Creepy Crawly in comparison to the Perfect Prowler specifications (Item 2 on the job sheet).

6. Check out the Did You Know? reading as time permits.

7. Wonder how consumer groups are used in the toy industry? Read Workplace Connection: *Focus Groups and Testing.*

Getting The Point.

Comparing Data

When given data from many trial runs and from different toys, all the numbers may seem like a big jumble at first. The first step in comparing data is to sort and organize. For instance, you might make a table that has a row for each toy represented and a column for each performance measure. Then you can decide whether you should put all the data in the table or just some selected measurements.

You have several choices in determining how to select measurements to report. Suppose you performed five trial runs and your distance measurements results were

Table 2.1
Example 1 of distance measurements from trial runs.

Trial one: 0.55 m	Trial two: 0.70 m	Trial three: 0.70m	Trial four: 0.60 m	Trial five: 0.65 m

You might want to choose the maximum value for each performance measure, which in this case means that you would report a distance of 0.70 meters. You may choose to take an average measurement (the mean), then sum all values for the performance measure and divide that total by the number of values. For example, for the measurements shown above, the average = (0.55 m + 0.70 m + 0.70 m + 0.60 m + 0.65 m)/ 5 = 0.64 m. (We have divided by 5 since there are five measurements used.) Another method is to take the median value (the value that falls in the middle of the range of data), which in this case is 0.65 meters, since there are two values below 0.65 meters and two values above it.

Now suppose your results of the distance measurements from five trial runs were

Table 2.2
Example 2 of distance measurements from trial runs.

Trial one: 0.55 m	Trial two: 0.70 m	Trial three: 0.05m	Trial four: 0.60 m	Trial five: 0.65 m

You might be suspicious that the run that resulted in a measurement of 0.05 meters had a problem. You may choose to throw out a data point that is very far from the rest.

However you report your data, be sure you have a solid rationale for your choice.

Workplace Connection: Focus Groups and Testing

Once a product has demonstrated feasibility (that it can be built), the next question is will it be marketable—will people buy it? This type of testing often begins with a small group of people who are likely customers, called a focus group. Focus group testing is often conducted in testing rooms with a two-way mirror to the observation room so that outsiders can watch unnoticed.

A target audience may be chosen for the toy. The marketers may want to observe children from a certain age range and in specific economic, racial, or ethnic groups if they are considering a particular market. Or they may want to make sure their focus group is very diverse to include potential customers from a variety of backgrounds.

For focus groups in the early stages of design of a new product, the marketers may only have drawings or ideas for the new toy. In this case, they may show a series of pictures and ask the children which colors or features they prefer and how they would want the toy to behave. In later stages of development, a prototype of the new toy may be brought to the groups along with several of its competitors. Observers watch to see which toy kids immediately reach for, which they play with the longest, which make them most engaged, and which they seem happiest with. Afterwards, the observers ask the children a series of questions about their feelings toward the toys.

Another important set of focus group participants is the parents, guardians, and caregivers. These are generally the people who actually purchase the toy. They may be asked questions about whether they see the toy as long-lasting, a good value, educational, promoting a good message, and safe for their children. In later stages of production, they might also be asked to suggest a price for the toy.

At the conclusion of the test, a detailed written report on the test results is prepared.

Did You Know?

In 1974, four engineers at Pilot Pen Corp. of Japan began searching for a dustless chalkboard. What they found would eventually become one of the world's most popular drawing toys—Magna Doodle. The Magna Doodle uses magnetic attraction between a magnet and iron filings to create drawings on a screen. Over 40 million Magna Doodles have been sold to date. Magna Doodle also has a knack for showing up in some of the most unlikely places: Hal Hunter, offensive line coordinator for the Cleveland Browns, uses Magna Doodle on the sidelines to diagram his plays, and hospital patients often use Magna Doodle when they cannot communicate vocally.

Adapted from "Betcha Didn't Know." Toy Industry Association, Inc. (TIA). http://www.toy-tia.org/industry/news/betcha/betcha.html (June 5, 2002)

ACTIVITY 2.2

Measuring Instantaneous Velocity

In Chapter 1, you worked with average velocity, which gives you an idea of the overall rate that an object moves in a specific direction. In this chapter, we are going to study a new performance measure called *instantaneous velocity*. This is the velocity that an object has at a specific point or interval of time. If an object starts and stops, or speeds up and slows down, then the average velocity may not be a good representation of how fast the object can go. The marketing group will want to know the maximum velocity that your Creepy Crawly can attain at any given instant, and compare this to the maximum instantaneous velocity of its competitor, the Roving Rodent.

To get a feeling for what instantaneous velocity means, you and your classmates will first measure the instantaneous velocity of a runner in your class. By studying the way his or her instantaneous velocity changes over the duration of a 100-meter sprint, and in the next activity by graphing that data, you will come to understand the similar data you will be analyzing from your Creepy Crawly and the Roving Rodent.

Getting To Work!

To measure the instantaneous velocity of a runner, you will

1. Go outside with your class to the track or area that your teacher provides.

2. Follow the directions on │ **Job Sheet 2.2** │ **Measuring Instantaneous Velocity** to measure time splits during a 100-meter run.

3. Calculate the instantaneous speed for each split by dividing the distance (10 meters) by the time interval for the split. Record the data on Job Sheet 2.2.

Job Sheet

4. Examine your data and decide at which part of the race the runner was running the fastest.

5. Read Getting the Point: *Understanding Instantaneous Velocity.*

6. Check out the Did You Know? reading as time permits.

7. Think it's easy to determine the fastest runner? Read Concept Connection: *Who Was Fastest?*

Getting The Point.

Understanding Instantaneous Velocity

Humans have been recorded to run over 27 miles per hour when running their fastest split of a 100-meter run. However, the world record for a 1-mile race is approximately 16 miles per hour. And the world's best marathon runners run about 12.5 miles per hour. Why the difference? Well, those sprinters may be fast, but they couldn't keep that pace up for a longer distance.

How fast you are running depends on the length of the race and how you pace yourself and also at which point of the race you are being timed. Racers generally start from a starting block where they are motionless, so at their start their velocity is zero. This clearly must change over the course of the race if they are going to get anywhere, not to mention break any records. Different racers will have different changes in instantaneous velocity over the course of their race; this is generally referred to as their pace. Some racers may increase their velocity right out of the blocks, hit their peak early, and run as hard as they can until they peter out at the end. Others might save some strength for a burst of velocity at the end to pass the other racers.

To measure the racer's velocity at any point in the race, you must divide the race up into intervals, known as splits. You can time how long it takes the runner to go the first 10 meters, then the second 10 meters, the third 10 meters, and so on. The process from there is the same as calculating the average velocity. You divide the displacement in the target direction during the interval by the time of the interval.

instantaneous velocity =
   displacement during a time interval/the time of the interval

In other words, the instantaneous velocity is just the average velocity over a very short part of the race. Naturally, it would be great to know an object's velocity at an exact moment in time. But just by the nature of how we define velocity (displacement divided by the time interval), you need to average over some nonzero interval of time to calculate velocity. However, the smaller you can make your interval, the more "instantaneous" the velocity is.

You may notice that we are using the term velocity throughout this reading, and you might be wondering what happened to speed? Remember, velocity is the displacement in a specific direction divided by the time traveled (or time interval). Speed is the total distance traveled divided by the time of travel (or time interval). If the runner is always moving in the target direction, then the instantaneous velocity in the target direction is the same as the speed. From this point forward in this unit, the motion you will be measuring for your Creepy Crawly and other toys is going to be straight-line motion only. Thus, we are using the term velocity. It is important that your runner runs in a straight line for your measurements of instantaneous velocity. Otherwise, you will be calculating the speed, not velocity.

Focus Questions

What is the difference between average velocity and instantaneous velocity?

Why do you want to use the smallest time interval possible when measuring instantaneous velocity?

Concept Connection: Who Was Fastest?

Table 2.3
Ten meter split times for 1999 men's world championship runners.

	10m	20m	30m	40m	50m	60m	70m	80m	90m	100m
A	1.86	1.03	0.92	0.88	0.86	0.84	0.85	0.85	0.85	0.86
B	1.88	1.00	0.91	0.89	0.85	0.85	0.86	0.86	0.86	0.88
C	1.87	1.02	0.92	0.90	0.86	0.84	0.88	0.89	0.89	0.90

The data in Table 2.3 represent the 10-meter splits for the top three men in the world championship for the 100-meter sprint in 1999. If you add up all the times, you will see that Runner A (Maurice Green from the USA) won this race with a time of 9.80 seconds. That means his average velocity was 10.2 meters/second. Sure enough, Maurice also had the fastest start split at 0.86 seconds (instantaneous velocity for that interval of 5.38 meters/second) and the fastest final split at 0.86 seconds (instantaneous velocity of 11.6 meters/second). But notice that at the 60-meter split, the third place racer, C (Dwain Chambers from England), had the same instantaneous velocity as Green. Therefore, for a split second of an interval, Chambers was tied for fastest man of the moment.

Notice also that it takes about half the race for the runners to reach their peak instantaneous velocity, and they only sustain that velocity for about 10 or 20 meters, eventually dropping down at the end of the race.

Did You Know?

In 1896, the world record for the men's 100-meter sprint was 12.0 seconds. By 1960, the record dropped to 10.0 seconds, which is only 0.13 seconds greater than Maurice Green's record in 2000. In Green's fastest split, he had a velocity of 11.6 meters/second, which converts to 26 miles/hour. A cheetah can run 70 miles per hour, and a lion and gazelle can run 50 miles per hour and can sustain those velocities for 100–200-meter distances. Looks like people are still no match for the big cats.

ACTIVITY 2.3

Creating a Position versus Time Graph

Getting In Gear

You now have data from Olympic racers and runners in your own class that give splits for their times and from which you calculated instantaneous velocity. In this activity, you will create a graph of your class data to see patterns in how the velocity changes over the race. This will help you understand the graph that you will be getting from an instrument called a motion detector in the next few activities.

Engineers, scientists, and other people who work with data often use graphs to see trends and patterns in the data. From making a graph of a parameter (such as position), you can often see how that pattern changes with respect to another parameter (such as time). For example, by plotting position versus time, you will see where the runner has the greatest (or lowest) instantaneous velocity.

Getting To Work!

Job Sheet

To plot your instantaneous velocity data, you will

1. Read Getting the Point: *Creating a Position versus Time Graph.*

2. Get the instantaneous velocity data table(s) you created on Job Sheet 2.2 *Measuring Instantaneous Velocity.*

3. Follow the directions on ⟨Job Sheet 2.3⟩ Creating a Position versus Time Graph to create a position versus time graph from your class runner data.

Getting The Point.

Creating a Position versus Time Graph

Plotting data on a graph often allows us to see patterns or trends that might not stand out when looking at the data in a table or list. Sometimes a graph is produced by a measurement instrument (such as the motion detector you will use in upcoming activities), and you must interpret the graph to understand what is happening.

In general, a graph is created using two axes, the y-axis, which is vertical, and the x-axis, which is horizontal. The x-axis is usually used for the independent variable, such as time. One way to think of this is that time would keep ticking whether we were running a race or not, so it is an independent variable. The y-axis is used for the dependent variable, which is the variable that changes with the experiment. In this case, it is the position of the runner that changes over time as we run the race.

Here is the graph of the data from the championship run of Maurice Green.

Figure 2.1
Position versus Time Graph for Maurice Green's Championship Run

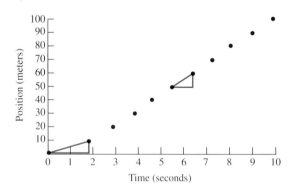

Notice that the points on the graph make roughly a line going from lower left to upper right, however, there is some curvature to that line, especially in the lower left. Studying the shape of this imaginary curve can provide insight to how the runner's velocity changes over time. Drawing a line between one point and the next allows us to study each interval. The slope of that line, the rise over the run, tells us the change in the independent variable with respect to the dependent variable.

In the case of the graph of the runner's position versus time, the slope of each line represents the distance traveled during the interval divided by the time of the interval. This is the same as the definition of the instantaneous velocity for that interval.

slope = displacement in the time interval/time of the interval = instantaneous velocity

Notice in the first 10-meter interval (shown by a blue line) that the slope of the line is relatively shallow. This means that his instantaneous speed was less than during the rest of the race. This makes sense since the runner was starting from a dead stop. During the midpoint of the race, the interval shown by the yellow line shows a much steeper slope where the runner was going at top velocity.

Other than at the beginning of the race, the amount of variation of instantaneous velocity is hard to detect. Maurice Green's velocity was changing slightly during the midpoint and near the end of the race, but for the most part his speed was roughly constant, so it appears as a straight line.

Focus Questions

What quantity is equivalent to the rise over run or the slope of a position versus time graph?

What does a shallow slope in a position versus time graph indicate?

ACTIVITY 2.4

Using a Graphing Motion Detector

Getting In Gear

In the last two activities, you measured velocity via the brute force method, by measuring the displacement and timing how long it took to travel. Now you are going to let an instrument do the work for you. But first you must understand how the instrument communicates the information to you. You will start by moving in front of a motion detector yourself and analyzing the graphs from the motion detector. Then you will use the motion detector to measure the motion of your Creepy Crawly.

You will be creating graphs in this activity much like the way an engineer would. Whether measuring velocity, temperature changes, or the reaction rates of chemicals, engineers often use probes and sensors and make graphs of their data. Graphs enable you to see patterns and determine maximum and minimum points more easily. As you saw in the last activity, the slope of a line on a graph yields a value for the rate of change of one variable with respect to another. For the data from your runner, the rate of change of position versus time yields a measure of velocity. This is the same measurement that you will do now with a motion detector.

Getting To Work!

Job Sheet

To begin your studies of the graphing motion detector, you will

1. Read Getting the Point: *Using Graphing Motion Detectors.*

2. Follow the instructions on **Job Sheet 2.4** **Making Position versus Time Graphs with a Graphing Motion Detector** to create graphs from the motion detector and analyze the motion of an object that created graphs from the motion detector.

3. Make a position versus time graph of your Creepy Crawly with the motion detector and compare with the position versus time graph for the Roving Rodent provided on Job Sheet 2.4.

4. Read for homework Getting the Point: *The Relationship between Velocity and Position* in Activity 2.5, and answer the Focus Questions. You need to read this to prepare yourself for Activity 2.5.

5. Check out the Did You Know? reading as time permits.

6. Wonder how motion detectors are used by the police? Read Concept Connection: *Speed Busters.*

Getting The Point.

Using Graphing Motion Detectors

What is a graphing motion detector? A graphing motion detector is an instrument that measures motion. A graphing motion detector can usually

1. sense the presence of an object within a certain range;

2. measure important characteristics of an object's motion, for example, how far or fast it is moving; and

3. display a graph of the motion.

Some motion detectors have additional capabilities, for example, they may print out copies of the graphs they make. Your teacher will explain the important features of the equipment you are using.

How do motion detectors work? Motion detectors operate on the same principle that allows bats to sense objects at night and submarines to detect objects under the sea. The motion detector emits a short burst of high-frequency sound, then records how long it takes to receive an echo back. It can then calculate how far away the object is by multiplying this time interval by the speed of sound.

Detection. The sound waves emitted by the motion detector must strike an object large enough to return an echo that can trigger the measurement. The artwork that you made for your Creepy Crawly is not just for fun; it increases the toy's surface area so that its motion can be measured more easily. Make sure your cutout is the size specified on the toy request form from Job Sheet 1.2. Constructing Your Creepy Crawly; otherwise, the motion detector won't "see" it.

The motion detector produces a cone of sound with a spread of approximately 30°. It measures the distance to the *closest* object it detects, so it is important to keep the area in front of the motion detector clear. (Otherwise, you could detect the wrong object.) The farther from the detector, the wider the area that must be kept clear (see diagram).

Figure 2.2
Detecting the Sail of the Creepy Crawly

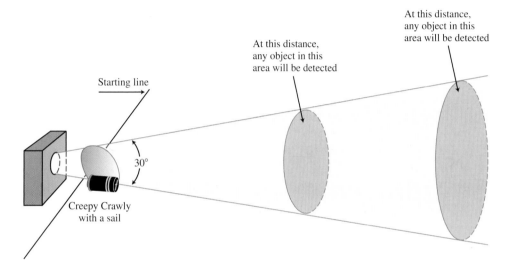

Setting up your motion detector. You must set up your motion detector behind the test track, not alongside it.

Range. Motion detectors generally work best with small objects moving in a range between 0.2 meters from the motion detector and 3 meters from the motion detector. It is a good idea to set up a test area on the floor with these distances marked. Place the motion detector on one mark, and make a second mark 0.2 meters in front of it. Don't try to measure distances shorter than this. A third mark at 3 meters defines the limit of the detector's useful range.

Distance readings. When you are measuring how far a toy can travel, use the 0.2-meter mark as your starting line. The farther an object moves away from the motion detector, the larger the measurement will be.

Sampling rate. The sampling rate controls how many measurements the motion detector will take in a given interval of time. Most motion detectors allow you to change sampling rate. If your graphs seem jagged instead of smooth, you might try increasing the sampling rate. A good rate to try is 20 measurements per second.

Did You Know?

Bats use a natural device similar to a motion detector to help them find their prey in the dark. Bats emit very high-pitch sounds from their mouth or nose, which echo off surfaces in front of them. The bat's brain processes the returning information to measure how long it takes a noise to return, and then the bat's brain figures out how far away the object is.

The bat can also determine where the object is, how big it is, and in what direction it is moving. By sensing whether the echo hits its right or left ear first, it determines which side the prey is on. By measuring the intensity (strength) of the echo, the bat infers the size of its prey. And by hearing the pitch of the echo, the bat can tell if the prey is moving toward or away from the bat and how fast.

Concept Connection: Speed Busters

The graphing motion detector you are using operates on the same principle as the radar detectors the police use to catch drivers who are speeding. A basic speed gun is just a radio transmitter and receiver combined into one unit. The speed gun sends out an electromagnetic wave that bounces off the moving object.

When the echo of the wave is picked up by the receiver on the gun, the distance to the object is calculated by determining how long the echo took to return to the gun. The velocity of the car in the direction toward or away from the speed gun is measured through the Doppler shift of the radar waves. This is similar to the effect when you hear a car horn or train whistle increase in pitch as it is coming toward you and decrease in pitch as it moves away from you.

When the car is moving away from the radar gun, the electromagnetic waves appear to stretch out away from the observer, which lowers its frequency. If the car is moving toward the radar gun, the peaks and valleys of the wave get squeezed together and the frequency increases. Based on how much the frequency changes, a radar gun can calculate how quickly a car is moving toward it or away from it.

ACTIVITY 2.5

Graphing Velocity versus Time

Getting In Gear

In the previous activity, you saw how an instrument such as a graphing motion detector is used to create a graph of position versus time. Engineers use this type of equipment often to provide visual graphs of parameters. From the graphs, they can see patterns and trends that provide information about maximum and minimum values of parameters, and changes or trends in the data.

In this activity, you will learn about another useful graph, that of velocity versus time. Velocity, the change of position in a specific direction over time, is related to position. By studying the graphs of position versus time and velocity versus time together, you can get a better picture of the motion of an object.

In particular, the graphing motion detector can give you a much more accurate instantaneous velocity because it uses split-second time intervals for its measurements. This is much shorter than the time interval you could measure by hand. This is a good example of how instruments can enhance observation and analysis.

Getting To Work!

To continue your studies of the graphing motion detector, you will

1. Attend to your teacher's discussion about speed and velocity and about direction of displacement.

2. Refer to Job Sheet 2.5 Graphing Velocity versus Time, and follow the instructions under the heading Making the Graphs Come to Life.

Job Sheet

Getting The Point.

The Relationship between Velocity and Position

In contrast to the runners you timed going around a track, the graphing motion detector can only measure motion along a straight line leading to or from its sensors. The detector measures the motion of an object as it moves directly toward or away from the detector, so it is appropriate to use the term *velocity* in this context, as opposed to the word *speed.*

As you learned in earlier activities, velocity is the change in displacement divided by the time of travel. Stated another way, velocity is the *rate of change* of the position.

You have already been dealing with rate of change of position, especially when you examined the plots of the sprinters in the 100-meter race.

Figure 2.3
Position versus Time Graph of a Sprinter in a 100-meter Race

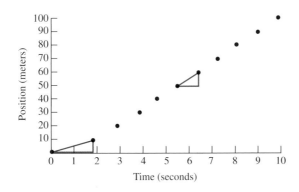

You saw that the racer's rate of change of position (speed, in this case) was less in the first 10-meter interval than during the sixth interval. The slope of the line between the two points is an indicator of the rate of change. A shallow line that goes from the lower left to the upper right indicates a slow forward movement. A steeper line from the lower left to the upper right indicates a faster forward movement.

You can use position versus time data to then create a velocity versus time graph. Suppose you were studying the motion of an object that had a position versus time graph that looked like the following:

Figure 2.4
Position versus Time Graph of One Example Object

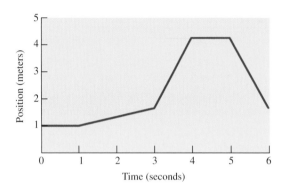

Notice that in the first interval the position did not change. This means its rate of change of position is zero. In the second and third interval, it begins to have a small positive rate of change, meaning it is moving forward slowly. Suddenly in the fourth interval, it starts moving rapidly in the forward direction. In the fifth interval, it stops changing position. Finally, in the sixth interval, it moves backward rapidly.

This would yield a velocity versus time graph resembling the following:

Figure 2.5
Position versus Time Graph of Another Example Object

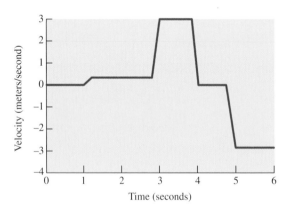

Notice that there are both positive and negative velocities. These correspond to the forward (positive) and backward (negative) motion of the object. When the object is not changing position, its velocity is zero. When the object is moving at a constant velocity, the graph shows a flat line at a positive or negative value.

Focus Questions

If an object was moving forward at a constant speed during a time interval, what would the graph of the velocity versus time graph look like for that interval?

Describe the behavior of an object for which the velocity versus time plot is a straight line at the 0 meter/second value.

ACTIVITY 2.6

Measuring Maximum Velocity of the Creepy Crawly

Getting In Gear

Now that you have been working with velocity versus time graphs and understand how they contribute to telling the story of an object's motion, it is time to put your Creepy Crawly back to work. In this activity, you will use the graphing motion detector again with five trial runs of your Creepy Crawly.

The graphing motion detector will measure the velocity of the Creepy Crawly as it moves on a line away from the detector. Any sideways wandering of the Creepy Crawly will not be accounted for, so a Creepy Crawly that goes fast and straight will have the highest velocity reading.

You will also be given a velocity versus time graph of the Roving Rodent, the Creepy Crawly's top competitor already on the market. You will be asked to compare graphs from the Creepy Crawly to that of the Roving Rodent to see how they measure up.

Getting To Work!

To measure the maximum velocity of your Creepy Crawly with the graphing motion detector, you will

1. Follow the instructions on | **Job Sheet 2.6** | **Measuring Maximum Velocity with the Motion Detector** to make five trial runs of your Creepy Crawly and obtain graphs of the velocity versus time from the graphing motion detector.

2. Analyze the velocity versus time graph for the Roving Rodent provided on Job Sheet 2.6 and compare it to that of your Creepy Crawly.

3. Answer the questions on Job Sheet 2.6 to figure out the value of the maximum velocity and the interval in which it occurred.

Job Sheet

ACTIVITY 2.7

Preparing Your Comparative Analysis Report

You now have user-defined specifications of the Perfect Prowler and performance measurements for the top competitor, the Roving Rodent. How does your prototype Creepy Crawly measure up? Gather your data and prepare a report for the marketing team.

Your comparative analysis report should include
- data tables from the Perfect Prowler and the Creepy Crawly, showing data for the first five performance measures: distance, displacement, angle of wander, average speed, and average velocity; and
- graphs of position versus time and velocity versus time for both your Creepy Crawly and the Roving Rodent. The graphs should be annotated with comments about changes in velocity and how the position and velocity correspond to each other at various times during the run.

You should present data to back up any claims you make in response to the questions, and your report should be neat, organized, and clear.

To complete Project Milestone Two, you will

1. Obtain the Perfect Prowler versus Creepy Crawly data table from Job Sheet 2.1: How Does Your Creepy Crawly Measure Up?

2. Gather the best of your position versus time graphs of the Creepy Crawly you created on Job Sheet 2.4: *Making Position versus Time Graphs with a Graphing Motion Detector* and the best of your velocity versus time graphs of the Creepy Crawly you created on Job Sheet 2.6: *Measuring Maximum Velocity with the Motion Detector.*

3. Compare these graphs to the corresponding graphs provided for the Roving Rodent on Job Sheets 2.4 and 2.6.

4. Answer the questions about your data on **Job Sheet 2.7** Preparing the **Comparative Analysis Report.**

Job Sheet

5. Write a conclusion about whether you think the Creepy Crawly will be well accepted by consumers based on their specifications for the Perfect Prowler. Will your Creepy Crawly compete well against the Roving Rodent?

6. Organize all of this information in a clear and neat format to present to the marketing team.

7. Review the concepts and answer the questions in What Have You Learned? for homework.

What Have You Learned?

KEY CONCEPTS

Instantaneous velocity. Instantaneous velocity is the velocity of an object at a single point in time. Like instantaneous speed, it cannot be measured precisely, but you can get closer and closer to it by taking measurements over shorter and shorter time intervals. The motion detector can give a good approximation of instantaneous velocity because it measures distance over very tiny time intervals.

Graphing. A graph is a method of displaying data. In general, axes are used to display a range of parameters. For example, time may be displayed horizontally on the *x*-axis, and position may be displayed vertically on the *y*-axis. In this manner, data points are plotted at the places in the graph corresponding to the values of each parameter. Graphs are useful to see patterns and trends in data.

Dependent variable. The parameter displayed on the *y*-axis is called the dependent variable. In general it is the variable being tested or measured and may be influenced by the change in the independent variable.

Independent variable. The parameter displayed on the *x*-axis is called the independent variable. This is selected to be the parameter that is being measured solely for the purpose of measuring change in the dependent variable.

Slope. The slope of a graph is the ratio of the vertical change between points (the rise) and the horizontal change (the run). The slope yields the rate of change of the dependent variable with respect to the independent variable.

CONCEPT QUESTIONS

1. Describe what happens to a runner's instantaneous velocity over the course of a typical race.

2. Explain why the duration of a time interval is important in the precision of an instantaneous velocity measurement.

3. What are the two parameters measured by the graphing motion detector in this unit?

4. What characteristics of the Creepy Crawly design were most important in increasing its instantaneous velocity? Why?

5. Suppose you started from a dead stop, ran down the street, stopped to tie your shoe, and then resumed your pace. Which velocity versus time plot in Figure A shows this motion the best?

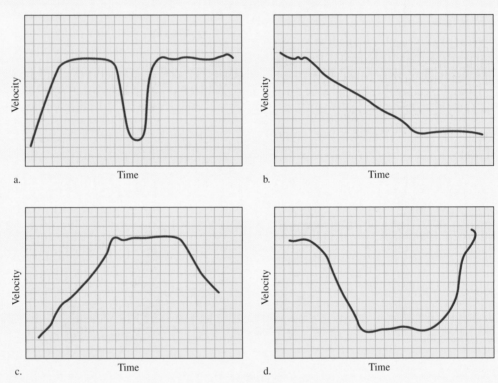

Figure A
Velocity versus Time Graphs

Continued

APPLYING WHAT YOU KNOW

1. When is the instantaneous velocity of an airplane the greatest—during takeoff, mid-flight, or during landing?

2. What characteristics, other than motor power, do you think are important in making cars travel fast and in a straight line? Explain your answers.

3. Make a graph that shows your estimate of how the average temperature varies with time over the course of a year in your region.

4. Figure B shows three position versus time graphs and three velocity versus time graphs. Draw an arrow to connect the graphs that correspond to the same motion of an object.

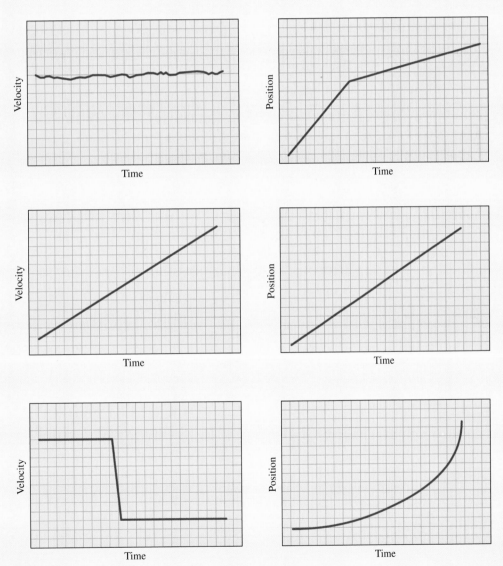

Figure B
Velocity versus Time Graphs and Position versus Time Graphs

Sizing Up the Competition

OVERVIEW

LET'S CHECK OUT THE REST OF CARPET
CRITTERS' PRODUCT LINE

You have sharpened your skills with the Creepy Crawly, and the manufacturing team is off and running with your recommendations. The members of the marketing team are so impressed with your battery of performance tests, they want you to study some of the other toys they have been working on.

They are going to send down two of Carpet Critters' top sellers, a wind-up toy and a pull-back toy. They are also gathering the data from each of these toy's top competitors. Use the graphing motion detector and your analysis expertise to give them a product review of these toys.

Your last milestone:

Project Milestone | Product Review on Wind-up and Pull-back Toys

You will prepare a product review on the new wind-up and pull-back toys about to be released by Carpet Critters that includes an analysis of how they compare to their top competitors. The report will include graphs of position versus time and velocity versus time for each product with an analysis of position, velocity, and acceleration performance measurements.

By the end of this chapter, you will have compared two new toys to their competitors, reporting on their performance measures including those you have dealt with in the past two chapters plus acceleration.

You will use graphical data from the graphing motion detector of position versus time and velocity versus time to do this analysis.

To help you accomplish Project Milestone Three, you will do the following activities:

Activity 3.1   Examining Carpet Critters' Other Line of Toys

You will be given two new toys from the Carpet Critters Company, a wind-up toy and a pull-back toy, which are nearly ready to go to market. You will also receive graphs of the position versus time and velocity versus time data for the top competitors for each of these toys. You will create similar plots for each of the Carpet Critters toys to analyze and compare to the competition.

Activity 3.2   Becoming Familiar with Acceleration

You will examine a series of velocity versus time graphs to learn how to interpret the change of rate of velocity over time, otherwise known as acceleration.

Activity 3.3   Analyzing the Acceleration of Motion Toys

You will examine the velocity versus time graphs from the Carpet Critters toys and their competitors to obtain information about their acceleration during trial runs.

Activity 3.4   Preparing Your Product Review Report on Wind-up and Pull-back Toys

You will compile a final report to marketing on the comparison of the two new Carpet Critters toys with their competitors.

ACTIVITY 3.1

Examining Carpet Critters' Other Line of Toys

The Marketing Department would like you to do some tests on another line of toys it is considering. You will receive working models of Carpet Critters' new wind-up and pull-back toys. These toys have already gone through the prototype phase and are nearly ready for distribution. Marketing will also provide you with motion graphs of similar toys from the competition.

To do your product review of each toy, you will have to create position versus time and velocity versus time graphs using the graphing motion detector. You will compare these to position versus time and velocity versus time graphs provided for the top competitor of each toy. After becoming familiar with the new toys in the Creepy Crawly product line, you will review how to analyze graphs to determine the performance measures such as maximum distance and maximum instantaneous velocity. Because you do not have the actual competitors' toys, you will need to use only the graphs to determine these performance measures for the competitors.

Getting To Work!

To compare the motion of the competitors' toys with the motion of the new toys from Carpet Critters, you will

1. Read the overview scenario and project milestone for Chapter 3, and discuss the scenario with your class.

2. Watch your teacher's demonstrations of each of the new Carpet Critters' toys.

3. Decide on a name for each toy within your group.

4. Read Getting the Point: *How Do You "Read the Story" of a Graph?,* and discuss it with your teacher.

5. Examine the graphs of the competitors' toys, and answer the associated questions under Interpreting the Competition's Graphs, in **Job Sheet 3.1** Sizing Up the Competition.

Job Sheet

6. Use the graphing motion detector to create at least one position versus time graph and one velocity versus time graph for each Carpet Critters toy. Append the graphs to Job Sheet 3.1.

7. Complete the questions for Comparing the Toys in Job Sheet 3.1. You will analyze and compare graphs of the Carpet Critters wind-up toy with the competitor's wind-up toy, and then compare the Carpet Critters pull-back toy to that of its competitor.

8. Check out the Did You Know? reading as time permits.

9. Wonder what the competition is like in the real world? Read Workplace Connection: *Competition in the Toy Industry.*

Getting The Point.

How Do You "Read the Story" of a Graph?

In Chapter 2, you worked with position versus time graphs and the velocity versus time graphs. Let's review how to read those graphs.

As you read a graph from left to right, you should think of it as telling a story about the motion it is describing. The events in the story may be things like "at this point the toy stops" or "between here and there the toy is speeding up."

When position versus time and velocity versus time graphs are available for the same trip, the information you get is always connected. Say a toy is moving away from the motion detector at constant velocity; by definition, its position must be increasing. The position versus time graph below shows the position increasing between points A and B (Graph A). The velocity versus time graph shows the velocity remaining constant between points A and B (Graph B). This must be the case, because points A and B represent the *same moments of time* in both graphs.

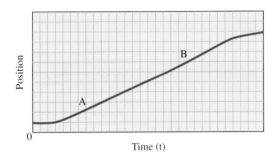 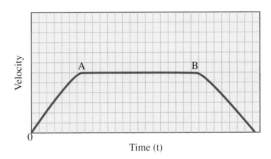

Figure 3.1
Corresponding Position versus Time and Velocity versus Time Graphs

You can identify individual points of time (or intervals of time) by putting your own letters on your graphs. Be sure that you use the same letters if the points represent the same time.

Focus Questions

During what interval is the object slowing down?

At what point does the object stop?

During what interval on the position graph is the object not moving? Is the position zero during this interval?

Workplace Connection: Competition in the Toy Industry

Competition is fierce throughout the toy industry. At a recent American International Toy Fair, an industry event managed by the Toy Manufacturers of America, David Miller, president of TMA, noted that total industry sales in the past year rose only about 4% to $20.3 billion. Though there are small companies that nibble out a corner of this market for themselves, most have been consumed by the two industry giants, Mattel and Hasbro, which oversees brands including Playskool, Kenner, Tonka, Milton Bradley, Parker Brothers and Tiger Electronics.

From a business perspective, toys are anything but a game. Manufacturers work feverishly to create the next hot item that kids beg their parents to buy them. Bill Smith, vice president of engineering at Hasbro in Cincinnati, Ohio, notes the impact that this has on the toy engineer's job. "It's a fad industry, so in addition to [providing] the technology lead on product development, it's a project management and leadership role" for the engineer, he says.

Technical professionals in Smith's department deal largely with industrial design, safety analyses and even work with the marketing and packaging departments. "The challenges are having fresh and innovative product in a timely manner, but above all, being safe and reliable," Smith explains. "We are very aggressive in time-to-market. In this business, if you're not first, you're not there. It's stressful, but rewarding."

A similarly industrious environment pervades at San Mateo, Calif.-based Zowie Entertainment Inc., a start-up company developing "smart toys" that combine traditional play with advanced technology. Zowie's inaugural products, Zowie PlayZones, integrate action figures and PCs allowing a child to play with the figures and control the action on the computer screen. Marcos Vescovi, the company's co-founder and chief architect, explains that the development cycle of such products—from concept definition, to design, to pre-production and production—takes 10 to 12 months.

"It's very fast-paced because of competition," he affirms.

The embrace of computers by the industry has allowed companies to perform many of those functions more quickly, however. Smith notes that technology drives much of Hasbro's product development process. Computers allow for 3-D designs and simulated tests for tension, and the technology has advanced through work with movie and television studios that employ the latest special effects. "Licensed product is our mainstay here," Smith explains, "so we work with [George] Lucas's and [Steven] Spielberg's studios.

We did the initial work on the Jurassic Park line" of action figures, for example. Other product lines that have been licensed for toy development by Hasbro include Star Wars and NASCAR.

At Hasbro, taking an idea from blue-sky concept to finished product involves a team of professionals representing quality assurance, manufacturing, product development, marketing and industrial design, and support groups from other areas. The whole process will generally be completed in about a year. "Some products of opportunity are driven considerably shorter than that, such as holiday shipments of the Furby last year," Smith adds.

Adapted from "Fun and Games: Engineers and Computer Scientists Are Turning Their Passion for Play into Exciting Careers at Toy Companies," by Paula Lipp and Lory A. Frenkel. Copyright © 2002 Career Recruitment Media, Inc. Reprinted with permission. http://www.graduatingengineer.com/articles/feature/07-28-00.html (June 5, 2002)

Did You Know?

The great 1984 cookie wars is an extreme case of competition. Procter & Gamble sued competitors for flying over a bakery plant in an effort to analyze smokestack effluent for clues to P&G's "soft inside, crunchy outside" cookie formula.

http://www.tompeters.com/toms_world/t1985-1986/022886-getting.asp

ACTIVITY 3.2

Becoming Familiar with Acceleration

Getting In Gear

Just as velocity is the change of rate of position in a given direction, acceleration is the change of rate of velocity. You will use the concepts and skills you have gathered over the past several activities and apply them to determine the acceleration of the various toys you are studying. You will learn in the next unit that acceleration is a very important quantity because it is related directly to the force that is causing the object to move.

You will be given velocity versus time graphs for several types of motion to determine the rate of change of velocity over time, or acceleration. You will be building the skills necessary to analyze plots in the next activity for the Carpet Critters toys and those of their competitors.

Getting To Work!

To learn about acceleration, you will

1. Study the velocity versus time graphs in the warm-up activity on
   Job Sheet 3.2 | Becoming Familiar with Acceleration, and answer
   the associated questions.

2. Study the velocity versus time graphs in the section Acceleration with Numbers on Job Sheet 3.2, and answer the associated questions.

3. Study the velocity versus time graphs in the section Acceleration in Pictures on Job Sheet 3.2, and answer the associated questions.

4. Read Getting the Point: *Acceleration* for homework.

Job Sheet

Want to find out about Maurice Green's acceleration? Read Concept Connection: *Calculating a Racer's Acceleration.*

Getting The Point

Acceleration

Acceleration is the change of rate of velocity over time. It is the amount the velocity changed during an interval divided by the time of that interval.

acceleration =
     change in velocity during a time interval/time of the interval

A common way of referring to acceleration of an object is speeding up. This is partially correct, but not entirely. It is important to remember that acceleration is actually the *rate* at which the object speeds up. There are some other little twists to the story. When an object slows down, it is also accelerating. In common language, this rate of its slowdown is often called deceleration, but engineers and physicists would call this an acceleration. The difference is that it is a negative acceleration.

Recall that a negative velocity means that the object is moving backward. A negative acceleration can occur when the object is still moving in a forward direction but just with a reducing velocity. A zero velocity means that an object is at rest. But a moving object may have a zero acceleration, which means that its velocity is constant.

Also, the acceleration of an object can be nonzero if the object is traveling at a constant speed but is changing direction. This is because as the object is turning, its velocity in the target direction is changing.

Acceleration may seem like an obscure concept to you right now. Why would you really care about the rate at which the velocity is changing? You will see in the next unit on forces and motion that acceleration of an object is directly related to the force acting upon it. For example, consider an apple falling from a tree. (This is reported to be the thought experiment that Sir Isaac Newton used when first developing his ideas of force and acceleration.) When the apple first leaves the branch, it starts out with zero velocity since it was at rest when it was hanging from the branch. As it falls, it picks up speed. The rate at which its velocity toward the ground increases is its acceleration in that direction. It will constantly increase its speed until it hits the ground. This constant acceleration is caused by the force of gravity that is pulling the apple toward the center of the Earth. All objects near the surface of the Earth experience the same force of gravity from the Earth's mass and, as long as no other forces are acting upon them, they will have the same acceleration toward the center of the Earth.

Concept Connection: Calculating a Racer's Acceleration

Recall the championship race data for Maurice Green that we saw in earlier activities (Table 3.1).

Table 3.1
Distance versus time for Maurice Green's ten-meter time splits.

	10m	20m	30m	40m	50m	60m	70m	80m	90m	100m
A	1.86	1.03	0.92	0.88	0.86	0.84	0.85	0.85	0.85	0.86

As you browse through the data, where does it look like he was speeding up? Where was his speed constant? Where was he slowing down?

The rate of change of velocity in the target direction is called acceleration in the target direction. We can calculate this in a similar way as you have calculated velocity—by comparing one interval to the next. You have already calculated the instantaneous velocity for a runner by dividing distance traveled during a time interval by the time of that interval. To calculate the acceleration of the runner, you will find the difference in the instantaneous velocities for two intervals and divide by the time between the two intervals:

acceleration = change in instantaneous velocity/time between intervals

The time between intervals is a bit tricky, since the velocity of the runner is changing throughout each interval. To find an average, you need to determine the midpoint time of each interval and use the difference between the midpoint of one interval and the midpoint time of the previous interval.

As an example, consider again the data from the championship race of Maurice Green (Table 3.2). For the purpose of this exercise, we will assume that Green was running in a straight line so we can use velocity in the target direction instead of speed.

This time, along with the time for each interval shown in the first row, there is also the instantaneous velocity for that interval shown in the second row.

Table 3.2

Ten meter splits of time and velocity for sprinter Maurice Green.

	10m	20m	30m	40m	50m	60m	70m	80m	90m	100m
T (s)	1.86	1.03	0.92	0.88	0.86	0.84	0.85	0.85	0.85	0.86
v (m/s)	5.38	9.71	10.87	11.36	11.63	11.90	11.76	11.76	11.76	11.63

During the first interval, Green had an instantaneous velocity of 5.38 meters/second. During the second interval, his instantaneous velocity was 9.71 meters/second, quite a bit faster. This tells you he was accelerating between the first and second interval, but by how much?

His change in instantaneous velocity between the first and second interval was

$$9.71 \text{ m/s} - 5.38 \text{ m/s} = 4.33 \text{ m/s}$$

That is how much his velocity increased. To get his acceleration, you need to calculate the rate of change of his velocity.

How long did it take him to increase his velocity by that much? To figure that out, we need to expand our data table (Table 3.3) and add the midpoint times (the time of the half-way point during the interval).

Table 3.3

Distance, velocity, and acceleration data for Maurice Green's race.

	Time for interval	Instantaneous velocity for interval	Cumulative time for this interval	Midpoint for this time interval	Acceleration between this interval and the previous
10m	1.86 s	5.38 m/s	1.86 s	0.93 s	
20m	1.03 s	9.71 m/s	2.89 s	2.38 s	2.99 m/s/s
30m	0.92 s	10.87 m/s	3.81 s	3.35 s	1.20 m/s/s
40m	0.88 s	11.36 m/s	4.69 s	4.25 s	0.54 m/s/s
50m	0.86 s	11.63 m/s	5.55 s	5.12 s	0.31 m/s/s
60m	0.84 s	11.90 m/s	6.39 s	5.97 s	0.32 m/s/s
70m	0.85 s	11.76 m/s	7.24 s	6.82 s	0.17 m/s/s
80m	0.85 s	11.76 m/s	8.09 s	7.67 s	0 m/s/s
90m	0.85 s	11.76 m/s	8.94 s	8.52 s	0 m/s/s
100m	0.86 s	11.63 m/s	9.80 s	9.37 s	−.015 m/s/s

The midpoint of the first interval was 0.93 seconds. This is obtained by dividing the first interval (1.86 seconds) in half. The midpoint of the second interval was 2.38 seconds. This is obtained by taking half of the second interval (1.03 seconds/2 = 0.52 seconds) and adding it to the end of the first interval:

midpoint of second interval = 0.52 s + 1.86 s = 2.38 s

So his acceleration between the first and second intervals is the change in velocity divided by the time between intervals:

acceleration = change in velocity/time between intervals =
(4.33 m/s) / (2.38 s) = 2.99 m/s/s

Notice that the units of acceleration are m/s/s. Since acceleration is change in velocity divided by time, the units are meters/second divided by second. Sometimes you will see this written as m/s^2.

Calculating the acceleration for the next several intervals follows the same pattern. But something changes with the 80- and 90-meter intervals. Notice that the instantaneous velocity does not change between the seventh, eighth, and ninth intervals, so there is zero acceleration at that point. Then in the last interval, Green's velocity actually decreased, so the acceleration is negative.

ACTIVITY 3.3

Analyzing the Acceleration of Motion Toys

Now that you have learned about acceleration, you will analyze the graphs from the competitors' toys and compare them to the toys of the Carpet Critters Company. You will use the velocity versus time graphs that you created for your Carpet Critters wind-up and pull-back toys, along with the analogous graphs that were provided for each of their top competitors. You will analyze these graphs to determine the rate of change of velocity over time—acceleration—and use this information to compare the toys to their competitors.

Getting To Work!

To compare the acceleration of each of the toys being evaluated, you will

1. Examine the velocity versus time graph for each of the competitors' toys provided on | **Job Sheet 3.3** | Acceleration of Motion Toys and the velocity versus time graph you generated in Activity 3.1 for each of the Carpet Critters' toys.

Job Sheet

2. Answer the associated questions on Job Sheet 3.3.

ACTIVITY 3.4

Preparing Your Product Review Report on Wind-up and Pull-back Toys

Getting In Gear

You have now completed all the analysis for the marketing team on its new line of wind-up and pull-back toys. You just need to prepare a final product review report, and your job will be complete. Your report should (1) compare the Carpet Critters' wind-up toy with the competitor's wind-up toy in terms of certain performance measures, and (2) compare the Carpet Critters' pull-back toy with the competitor's pull-back toy in terms of certain performance measures. To ensure that your report is complete, gather all your data and graphs on the wind-up and pull-back toys, both from the competition and from the Carpet Critters Company. By organizing your data and graphs into groups that follow a story you choose to tell, you can create a clear and informative report for the marketing team.

Getting To Work!

To complete Project Milestone Three, you will

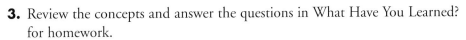

1. Gather the materials you need as suggested in | **Job Sheet 3.4** | Preparing **Your Product Review Report for Wind-up and Pull-back Toys.**

2. Make sure you address each of the report components listed in Job Sheet 3.4.

Job Sheet

3. Review the concepts and answer the questions in What Have You Learned? for homework.

KEY CONCEPTS

Acceleration. Acceleration is the rate at which the velocity (not the speed) of an object changes. Think about a car whose manufacturer brags that it can go "from 0 to 60 in 10 seconds." This means that the car will be standing still at 0 seconds and going 60 miles per hour at 10 seconds. Just how fast is the car speeding up? In this case, the car would on average be speeding up 6 miles per hour in each second in order to reach 60 miles per hour in 10 seconds. The acceleration would then be 6 miles per hour/second. (In general, we would write this as 6 miles/hour/second; the units are read as "miles per hour per second.")

Acceleration can also be negative, as when a car is slowing down. If the same car has powerful brakes, it might go from 60 miles per hour to 0 miles per hour in 3 seconds. Then its average acceleration would be −20 miles/hour/second. But the car may not be slowing down at the same rate throughout the 3 seconds. In that case, we may wish to look at its instantaneous acceleration at various points in time.

Instantaneous acceleration. Instantaneous acceleration is the acceleration of an object at a single point in time. It cannot be measured precisely, but you can get closer and closer to it by taking measurements over shorter and shorter time intervals. This is how the motion detector produces graphs of acceleration. What kind of information can we get from instantaneous acceleration that we can't get from average acceleration? The average acceleration reflects a situation where the car is speeding up or slowing down uniformly. It is always possible, however, that the acceleration is not the same over the whole time interval. For example, maybe the car gets going somewhat more slowly, then jumps ahead in the last few seconds of reaching 60 miles per hour. Instantaneous acceleration can capture those differences.

CONCEPT QUESTIONS

1. Describe the differences in velocity and acceleration for the wind-up toys and the pull-back toys over the course of their runs.

2. As the velocity of a moving object increases,
   a. does its acceleration necessarily increase?
   b. is its motion necessarily in the forward direction?
   c. is its acceleration necessarily nonzero?

3. If an object has a nonzero acceleration, is its speed necessarily changing? Why or why not?
   Continued

4. Describe the acceleration of an object when its motion yields the graph in Figure A.

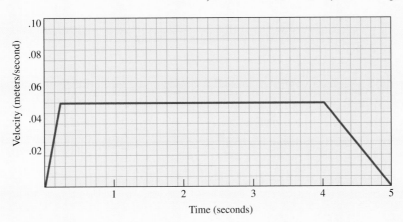

Figure A
Velocity versus Time Graph

APPLYING WHAT YOU KNOW

1. If an object is moving in the positive direction and slowing down, what is the sign (positive or negative) of its velocity and its acceleration?

2. If an object is moving backward (in the negative direction) and is slowing down, what is the sign of its velocity and acceleration?

3. Write a story that describes an object's motion when its velocity is positive and its acceleration is negative.

4. Write a story that describes an object's motion when its acceleration is zero, but it is moving very fast.

5. Draw the position versus time plot and the velocity versus time plot on blank graphs, and describe the acceleration of an object that is moving back and forth on a pendulum, like a swing (see Figure B).

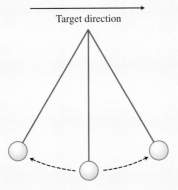

Figure B
A Pendulum

Forces and Motion | On the Road Again

OVERVIEW

In Unit Two, *Forces and Motion: On the Road Again,* you will test the tires manufactured by Wheelers and Dealers for its all-terrain vehicles (ATVs). These vehicles need high-performance treads and tires of just the right design to do the back-road driving expected by Wheelers and Dealers customers. This unit builds on the kinematics that you learned in Unit One, as you will once again study the **motion** of a vehicle, but this time under more varied conditions.

A wagon will be used as a test vehicle to try out your tire designs. While designing and performing tests you will learn about **friction** and other **forces** that relate to tire performance and about the various types of terrain an ATV might encounter.

The project milestones in this unit will guide you from setting up the conditions of the performance tests of an ATV, such as different types of terrain, to planning the data collection and implementing the tests. Finally, you will encounter the ultimate vehicular challenge—turning a corner. That may sound easy now, but just you wait and see!

PROJECT MILESTONES

The project for this unit includes designing, planning, and implementing a performance test for ATV tires for a variety of conditions and types of motion. This assignment is divided into four project milestones.

Project Milestone 1 — **Choosing Terrain Conditions for a Performance Test of Tires**

You will draw up a list of terrain conditions (for example, sand, mud, dry pavement, or wet pavement) for the ATV tire test. You will choose at least two conditions to investigate in the tire performance test. You will also decide on a method for locking the motion of a wagon's wheels, in order to simulate locked brakes on an ATV, and for attaching samples of tire material to the wagon's wheels. Finally, you will create a list of materials you need to conduct your test.

Project Milestone 2 — **Planning Data Collection Procedures for Evaluating Tire Performance**

You will describe the desired behavior of an ATV's tires when its brakes are locked. You will plan data collection procedures for the tire performance test with locked wheels, then justify your choices using the physics concepts of force and motion.

Project Milestone 3 — **Conducting the Performance Test**

You will implement the performance test, making force or motion measurements of the wagons and varying the terrain conditions and the tire treads. You will evaluate how well the test works in showing performance differences among tire treads in various terrain conditions, and suggest improvements to your tests as needed. Then you will make a presentation about your tests.

Project Milestone 4 — **Evaluating a Tire's Performance during Cornering**

You will describe the desired behavior of an ATV's tires when the vehicle is turning a corner. You will design data collection procedures for a test during cornering, under the same terrain conditions you investigated in milestone three. You will implement the test, evaluate how well it works, and then report your findings to the other engineering groups.

ACTIVITIES AND ASSIGNMENTS

To succeed at the project for this unit, you must become familiar with various forces that tires experience. As you work through this unit, you will complete a number of activities to help you understand what causes forces and how to measure them.

There are four chapters in this unit, each having a corresponding project milestone. Each chapter deals with a different facet of tire performance testing and design.

1. In Chapter 4, you will choose a set of terrain conditions to investigate for the tire performance test and conduct three sets of experiments with your test vehicle.

2. In Chapter 5, you will use Newton's Second Law of Motion to decide how to measure vehicle performance for the ATV tire performance test. After conducting the trials, you will use what you have learned about speed, velocity, and acceleration to analyze the experimental results.

3. In Chapter 6, you will explore how wheeled vehicles travel forward. After examining tires as they roll and skid, you will measure frictional forces using several pairs of materials. Then you will plan and implement your ATV tire performance test and explain how static and sliding frictional forces affect performance.

4. In Chapter 7, you will develop and try out ways to test the performance of a line of ATV tires during "cornering" (going around a corner or sharp turn) on different road surfaces. By focusing on an object when it's turning, you will begin to understand what happens when forces are exerted on an object in two dimensions.

Wagons in Motion

OVERVIEW

WHEELING AND DEALING

Welcome to Wheelers and Dealers, the manufacturer of "Sporty Tires," a new line of tires for all-terrain vehicles (ATVs), designed to work better under locked-brake conditions. Wheelers and Dealers has hired your engineering group to design a performance test of the prototype treads as they are developed. The tests must compare the performance of various treads under locked-brake conditions. The tires are already in development, and we want to test each prototype of tread material the moment the R&D Department produces it. We need you to begin work right away, so we have arranged for you to use wagons for your test vehicles rather than an actual ATV. During the performance test, the wagon wheels will be fitted with sample tire treads. It's good to have you aboard. Now get this project rolling!

In this chapter, you will decide what terrain conditions to investigate. First, you will all work together as a class, making a list of terrain conditions that an ATV might encounter. From that list, your group will choose two or more conditions to investigate in depth. You will also decide what materials you will need to build your test track.

Your first milestone:

Project Milestone 1

Choosing Terrain Conditions for a Performance Test of Tires

You will draw up a list of terrain conditions (for example, sand, mud, dry pavement, or wet pavement) for the ATV tire test. You will choose at least two conditions to investigate in the tire performance test. You will also decide on a method for locking the motion of a wagon's wheels, in order to simulate locked brakes on an ATV, and for attaching samples of tire material to the wagon's wheels. Finally, you will create a list of materials you need to conduct your test.

You now work at Wheelers and Dealers, a tire company, to develop a performance test for the company's new line of tires for ATV users. Most ATVs, and many trucks as well, don't have antilock brakes, so these tires are designed to perform well during locked-brake conditions. By the end of this chapter, you will have conducted three sets of experiments using a wagon for your test vehicle. The experiments involve starting and traveling at a constant velocity. You will observe and measure what happens to the wagon's motion as it encounters different forces. Then you will use your knowledge of speed, velocity, and acceleration to analyze the results.

To help you accomplish Project Milestone One, you will do the following activities:

Activity 4.1   Starting a Wagon
You will begin to learn about force as you experiment with ways to start your test wagon. You will invent different ways to start the wagon using bungee cords, springs, ropes, pulleys, and your own muscle power. You will try to start your wagon the same way each time you push or pull it. You will try out your best method in three test trials. You will then start to sort out what kinds of forces produce what kinds of motions.

Activity 4.2   Pushing on Each Other
You will learn about Newton's Third Law of Motion. Working with a teammate, you will explore what happens when two people push against each other, one riding in a wagon, the other kneeling on the floor.

Activity 4.3   Achieving Constant Velocity
Here you will learn about net force and Newton's First Law of Motion. You will work on an experiment designed to get your test wagon moving at constant velocity. You will predict the force required, then do the experiment and discuss the results. At the end of this activity, you will summarize what you have learned from what you observed when starting, stopping, and moving your wagons at constant velocity.

Activity 4.4   A Visit to a Tire Business
You will meet on-site with a professional in the tire business. You will find out about how ATV tires are designed to meet various terrain and weather conditions safely. And you will examine tire tread designs that meet particular performance specifications.

Activity 4.5   Choosing Test Conditions

To develop the tire performance test, you will draw up a list of terrain conditions to investigate. You will examine your test wagons and test areas, and decide what materials you will need to build a test track and to attach various tire materials to the wheels. Along the way, your group will complete milestone one.

ACTIVITY 4.1

Starting a Wagon

Getting In Gear

Have you ever had something you had to do, say a homework assignment, and you felt like it was just too hard to get started? You needed some kind of push to get going—maybe the reminder that if you don't get it done you won't be able to watch TV. Vehicles also need a push to get started. And as you can imagine, a large truck in deep sand would need a much bigger push than a bicycle on smooth pavement.

Forces can be caused by many things. You can exert a force on a wagon by pushing or pulling it with your arms. When a vehicle is going downhill, the force of gravity pulls it down. In a motorized ATV, the motor drives an axle that exerts a force on the wheels to make them move. These are only a few examples of forces that we encounter every day.

To begin learning about forces, you will make a wagon start moving using your muscles and some helpful tools. You will make several trial runs and measure the motion of the wagon as a result of various forces. Becoming familiar with these measurements and the idea of forces will help you design your tire performance tests.

Getting To Work!

To explore how to get a wagon started, you will

1. Read the overview for Unit Two, and discuss as a class the unit project and the outline of work throughout the unit. Your teacher will give you a demonstration of a performance test that he or she developed.

2. Read the overview scenario and project milestone for Chapter 4, and discuss the scenario with your class.

3. Work in groups and obtain Job Sheet 4.1 How Do You Start a Wagon?; follow the directions.

4. Read Getting the Point: *The Nature of Force*, and answer the Focus Questions.

5. Check out the Did You Know? reading, as time permits.

Job Sheet

Wonder what Newton was doing in high school? Read Concept Connection: *Isaac Newton Was a Poor Student!*

The Nature of Force

In physics, the word *force* has a very particular meaning. When one object is pushing, pulling, or pressing on another object, we say it is *exerting a force* on the other object. Even an inanimate, stationary object (like a book) can exert a force on another object, for example, by resting on it or supporting it.

The *magnitude* of the force tells how hard one object is pushing or pulling another object at a particular instant. Magnitude can be measured with a spring scale or other device. Hanging scales, like those found in produce markets, are examples of stretching spring scales. Bathroom scales are examples of compressing spring scales. The magnitude of a force is expressed as a numerical value given either in metric units called *newtons* (n)—after Sir Isaac Newton—or English units, which are common in the United States, called *pounds* (lbs.).

To characterize a force fully, we must also identify its *direction*. Force is a quantity, in fact, that demands a direction to be assigned to each numeric magnitude. You apply a force *up* or *down,* or *north,* or to the *left,* or at a certain angle to the floor. You will notice that the direction you apply the force is always the direction of motion. Quantities such as force, which require a magnitude and direction to be fully expressed, are called *vector* quantities.

A third important quality of a force as it is exerted on an object is the *duration* of the force. You may have noticed that when rockets blast off, their engines only burn for a particular interval of time, then shut down. The space shuttle liquid and solid fuel engines "burn" for only about 2 minutes to boost the shuttle into Earth's orbit. After this short interval of applying extreme force, no additional force is needed to keep the space shuttle in orbit. In subsequent activities, you will explore the laws of physics that allow that to happen.

Focus Questions

What is meant by the magnitude of a force?

Why must a direction be specified for a force when it is applied?

What is a vector quantity?

Concept Connection: Isaac Newton Was a Poor Student!

When Isaac Newton attended the Grammar School in Grantham, England, he did not excel academically. His school reports described him as "idle" and "inattentive." Perhaps his mind was on other things.

Apparently his studies improved in university. Isaac paid his way through college for the first 3 years by waiting tables and cleaning rooms for the professors and the wealthier students. Just at the time he was granted a scholarship to pay for his education, the plague spread throughout England and closed the universities, so Newton returned home. There he continued to work on problems in mathe-

Figure 4.1
"Give Me a Place to
Stand and I Will Move
the Earth."

Image from Mechanics Magazine, London 1824. http://www.mcs.drexel.
edu/~crorres/Archimedes/Lever/LeverIntro.html (June 10, 2003)

matics and physics. It was during this time that
he began to develop his ideas about gravita-
tion and the theory of optics. (He was the
first to realize that white light is made up
of the colors of the rainbow.) He con-
ceived much mathematics, both integral
and differential calculus and infinite
series. He was slow to publish his work;
other mathematicians were doing similar
work and almost beat him to it.

Newton's book *Quaestiones
Quaedam Philosophicae* (Certain Philo-
sophical Questions) begins with a statement in Latin meaning, "Plato is my
friend, Aristotle is my friend, but my best
friend is truth." In 1687, Newton published
the *Philosophiae Naturalis Principia Mathematica*,
or *Principia* as it is always known. This work is the
origin of calculus and much of classical physics.

**Did You
Know?**

What does pushing have to do with
lifting? Archimedes (287–212 B.C.E.) is generally regarded as the greatest mathematician
and scientist of antiquity, and one of the three
greatest mathematicians of all time, together
with Isaac Newton and Friedrich Gauss.

When you push on something, it
pushes back. Archimedes figured out how
to make your push more effective. He
was the father of efficient pushing.

ACTIVITY 4.2

Pushing on Each Other

Getting
In
Gear

In this activity, you actually have permission to push each other around! While
your partner is sitting in the wagon, you are going to push on it to feel just
what Sir Isaac Newton meant by "equal but opposite" forces. When you push the
wagon, what do you feel? Is it the same as pushing on a cement wall? On a balloon? What is the difference?

Getting To Work!

To investigate Newton's Third Law of Motion, you will

1. Discuss the three important components of force.

2. Work in groups and obtain **Job Sheet 4.2** Pushing Me, Pushing You?; follow the directions. Please note all safety precautions.

Job Sheet

3. Read Getting the Point: *Newton's Third Law of Motion,* and answer the Focus Question.

4. Check out the Did You Know? reading as time permits.

Wonder how you get started on ice skates? Read Concept Connection: *The Physics of Ice Skating.*

Getting The Point

Newton's Third Law of Motion

Newton's Third Law of Motion presents the idea that physical interactions are never one way: whenever one thing affects another, the second thing also affects the first. Formally, the law states that in every interaction between two objects, the two objects exert forces on one another that are equal in magnitude and opposite in direction. This is true regardless of which object is more "active" in any way. In practice, this means that you can set a wagon in motion by sitting in it and pushing off against a wall; essentially, you are forcing the wall to push the wagon away.

Consider a book lying at rest on a table. How do we know that the force of the book on the table is equal and opposite to the force of the table on the book? Consider what would happen if the force of the book on the table was greater than the force of the table on the book. In that situation, the book would move through the table (in the direction of the unbalanced force) and hit the floor. Now consider what would happen if the force of the table on the book was greater than that of the book on the table. What would happen to the book in this case?

Focus Question

You performed a pushing experiment in which one person (A) was on a wheeled vehicle and another person (B) was not. When A pushed on B, B didn't move; instead, A rolled away in the wagon. Use Newton's Third Law of Motion to explain how B made A roll away—without so much as moving a muscle!

Concept Connection: The Physics of Ice Skating

The basic stroke in ice skating provides a good example of Isaac's 3rd law in action. When you "stroke" (the basic push in ice skating), you apply a backwards force to the ice. The ice applies an equal, forward force on you, so you go forward. Skaters stroke at an angle, so part of the stroke is wasted. You're pushing forward and to the side. The side push is resisted by the edge of your other blade. The forward push is resisted only by ice/blade friction, so you go forward.

Actually, this is exactly why sailboats go forward, not sideways. The wind pushes the boats forward and to the side. The sideways push is resisted by the long keel, but the forward push is relatively unresisted. Boats are designed to be aerodynamic (actually, "hydrodynamic") to forward motion and are intentionally unhydrodynamic to sideways motion.

Note that these forces apply only to direct pairs of objects. I push on the ice; it pushes on me. As I push in on the wall, it pushes me outward. Third law reactions never involve a third body.

Adapted from *"The Physics of Ice Skating—Isaac's Third Law,"* by Karen Knierman and Jane Rigby. http://satchmo.as.arizona.edu/~jrigby/skating/3rdlaw.html (June 10, 2003)

Did You Know?

The Father of the Rocket Was Ridiculed
Another demonstration of Newton's Third Law is rocket propulsion. Rockets are propelled by "pushing off" of their exhaust, i.e., the rocket pushes the exhaust in one direction and it is pushed in the other. Thus, even in outer space where there is nothing from which to push, a rocket can move. One of the early pioneers in rocketry, Robert Goddard, was ridiculed for stating that a rocket would operate in outer space. A quotation from a New York Times editorial in 1921 stated:

"That Professor Goddard with his chair at Clark College and the countenance of the Smithsonian Institution does not know the relation between action and reaction, and the need to have something better than a vacuum against which to react—to say that would be absurd. Of course, he only seems to lack the knowledge ladled out daily in high schools."

Adapted from "Newton's Laws of Motion" by John M. Pratte. http://a-s.clayton.edu/pratte/jmp5.html (June 10, 2003)

ACTIVITY 4.3

Achieving Constant Velocity

Now that you have that wagon moving, how do you keep it moving? What happens to its motion when you stop pushing? Why? In this activity, you will discover just what to do to keep the wagon moving at a constant speed. Later, you will conduct the experiment and measure the force, so keep your prediction and data table handy.

Getting To Work!

Job Sheet

To explore how to keep your wagon moving at a constant speed, you will

1. Work in groups and obtain | **Job Sheet 4.3** | **How Do You Keep a Wagon Moving at a Constant Velocity?**; follow the directions to perform the activity. Please note all safety precautions.

2. Read Getting the Point: *Net Force and Newton's First Law of Motion,* and answer the Focus Question.

3. Check out Did You Know? reading as time permits.

Wonder if there are places in space where the forces cancel each other? Read Concept Connection: *Lagrange Points in Space* as time permits.

Heard of space railroads? Read Workplace Connection: *Zero Gravity Railroad* as time permits.

Getting The Point.

Net Force and Newton's First Law of Motion

When an object is pushed or pulled equally in two opposite directions, the overall effect is just as if there were no force exerted on it at all. We would then say there is a *net force* of zero. For this reason, when we consider the combined effect of two or more forces, we let the forces in one direction be positive and those in the opposite direction be negative. A force's magnitude is given by its absolute value; its direction is given by its sign. For forces operating along a straight line, we can find the net force operating on an object simply by adding the signed values of the forces (as measured in units of force known as newtons). For example, if a force of 20 newtons is applied straight up (positive direction) on an object that weighs 20 newtons (negative direction), then the object would not move. When the net force on an object equals zero, the object is said to be in *equilibrium.*

Newton's First Law of Motion is usually stated as "An object has a constant speed and direction unless a (nonzero) net force is exerted on it." This force must be exerted by something outside the object itself. That is, it must be an *external force.* The fact that most objects eventually come to rest, in human experience, is evidence that an unopposed, external force is being exerted on the object. That force is usually friction or air resistance, or a combination of both. In these familiar circumstances, an additional force must be exerted on the object to oppose the frictional force and to keep an object moving at a constant velocity. In exotic situations in which there is essentially no friction at all, as in the nearly total vacuum of space, objects would "coast" indefinitely.

Focus Question

What is a net force?

In an earlier activity, you performed an experiment in which one person (A) was sitting in a wagon and another person (B) was kneeling on the floor. A pushed on B, but B didn't move. Using what you have learned about net force and Newton's First Law of Motion, explain why B didn't move.

Concept Connection: Lagrange Points in Space

The Italian-French mathematician Josef Lagrange discovered five special points in the vicinity of two orbiting masses where the net force from these masses on a third, smaller mass would be zero so the third object will maintain an orbit at a fixed distance from the larger masses. These points are denoted with L-numbers in the figure below.

The L1 point of the Earth-Sun system affords an uninterrupted view of the sun and is currently home to the Solar and Heliospheric Observatory Satellite SOHO. The L2 point of the Earth-Sun system will soon be home to the MAP Satellite and (perhaps) the Next Generation Space Telescope. The L1 and L2 points are unstable on a time scale of approximately 23 days, which requires satellites parked at these positions to undergo regular course and attitude corrections.

NASA is unlikely to find any use for the L3 point since it remains hidden behind the Sun at all times. The idea of a hidden "Planet-X" at the L3 point has been a popular topic in science fiction writing. The instability of Planet X's orbit

Figure 4.2
Lagrange Points of
Sun-Earth System

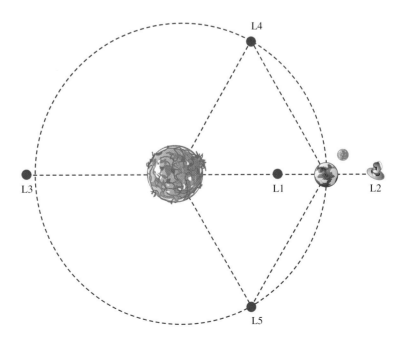

(on a timescale of 150 days) didn't stop Hollywood from turning out classics like The Man from Planet X.

The L4 and L5 points are home to stable orbits so long as the mass ratio between the two large masses exceeds 24.96. This condition is satisfied for both the Earth-Sun and Earth-Moon systems, and for many other pairs of bodies in the solar system. Objects found orbiting at the L4 and L5 points are often called Trojans after the three large asteroids Agamemnon, Achilles and Hector that orbit in the L4 and L5 points of the Jupiter-Sun system. (According to Homer, Hector was the Trojan champion slain by Achilles during King Agamemnon's siege of Troy). There are hundreds of Trojan Asteroids in the solar system.

From *"The Lagrange Points."* Courtesy of NASA, Map Science Team, and Neil Cornish. http://map.gsfc.nasa.gov/m_mm/ob_Techorbit1.html (June 10, 2003)

Workplace Connection: Zero Gravity Railroad

Expanding the new frontier just as they did the old, railroads will take flight soon as the first space railroad is launched aboard Space Shuttle Atlantis.

Circling Earth aboard the International Space Station, the car on this railway will have a top speed of only 300 feet per hour, but the entire line—tracks and all—will travel almost nine times faster than a speeding bullet, a constant speed of over 17,000 miles per hour, in orbit! The rail line eventually will stretch almost 100 yards along the structural backbone of the station, serving as a mobile base from which the station's Canadian-built robotic arm can assemble and maintain the complex.

"To build the rails that linked the east and west coasts of the United States, thousands of workers endured desert heat, frigid mountains and countless obstacles. These rails in space will run in temperatures far hotter than any desert and far colder than any mountain," said NASA Mobile Transporter Subsystem Manager Tom Farrell at the Johnson Space Center in Houston. "And just like the transcontinental rails pulled together our country, these rails pull together 16 nations around the world, cooperating in orbit."

Atlantis will launch the railcar, called the Mobile Transporter, and an initial 43-foot section of track as it delivers the first segment of the International Space Station's exterior truss. Designated "S0 (S-zero)," the first section of truss will be carried aloft by Atlantis on shuttle mission STS-110 in April. More sections of track will be added during the next two years as eight segments of the girder-like truss are launched aboard the shuttle. By the end of this year, the tracks already will stretch more than 130 feet. When completed, the truss will stretch over 360 feet, the longest structure ever built in space.

An additional base system will be attached atop the flatcar-like Mobile Transporter during a shuttle flight in May, but the space train will leave the depot for its inaugural run during Atlantis' April mission. After spacewalkers loosen launch restraints and attach electrical and computer cable reels, Mission Control will command the Mobile Transporter railcar to inch its way up and down the 43-foot section of track.

"It's built for precise positioning and smooth velocity control; it's not built for speed," said Randy Straub, subcontract technical manager for the system with The Boeing Company in Huntington Beach, Calif.

The operation of the railway is critical for continued assembly of the station. It will allow the station's Canadarm2 robotic arm to carry future truss segments and solar arrays down the tracks to install them. Part flatcar and part locomotive, the Mobile Transporter weighs 1,950 pounds and is a horse made of aluminum, not iron. The Mobile Transporter was built by TRW Astro in Carpinteria, Calif., for Boeing, the prime contractor for station construction. It measures three feet high, nine feet long and eight feet wide and moves along two parallel rails attached to the station truss at speeds varying from one-tenth of an inch to one inch per second. Although driven by dual electric motors that generate only about a hundredth of one horsepower, the transporter can move 23 tons of cargo down the rails.

What is the hardest part about building a zero-gravity railroad?

"We've done a lot of work to make certain it can't jump the tracks," said Farrell. "We have to be sure it will be safe during all the station's activities, like rebooting its orbit or having visiting vehicles dock."

The transporter stays on track with three sets of wheels, one set that propels it and two sets in roller suspension units, spring-loaded units that have rollers on both sides of the track to ensure the transporter can't float loose. The railcar will have 10 stops, specific locations called worksites where it can be locked down with a 7,000-pound grip, allowing the robotic arm to safely maneuver cargo. Although it can be driven from the station or from the ground, the engineers for NASA's space railroad will normally reside in Mission Control, Houston, driving the train from thousands of miles away and hundreds of miles below.

Although the Mobile Transporter will be a freight train and not a passenger train, space-walking astronauts will have their own form of personal rail transportation aboard the station. Astronauts will operate a small handcar to maneuver up and down the rail line, a car that they will pull along the zero-gravity railway by hand to move themselves and their gear from place to place. Called the Crew and Equipment Translation Aid, two such carts will be delivered to the station before the end of the year.

From *"Space Shuttle to Launch First Space Railroad in April."* NASA News Release H02-58 (March 19, 2002). Courtesy of NASA. http://www.jsc.nasa.gov/news/releases/2002/H02-58.html (June 10, 2003)

Did You Know?

You are moving at 1,000 mi/hr at this moment.

When your velocity changes over time, you feel acceleration, and that's where the fun really begins. Cornering, speeding up, rotating, slowing down—these are all accelerations. Right now we're all moving at roughly 1,000 mph, but we don't feel the effects because the Earth spins at a constant velocity—meaning we spin the same speed every day without accelerating.

Adapted from "Physics Is Your Friend," by Shidan Towfiq. http://www.shidan.com/Writing/physics_text.htm (June 10, 2003)

ACTIVITY 4.4

A Visit to a Tire Business

Getting In Gear

So far, you have been working with your test vehicle, a wagon. How does that relate to how an ATV works on different kinds of terrain? Wish you had an expert around to whom you could ask all your questions? In this activity, you will visit a tire business where you can ask away.

Getting To Work!

To explore this workplace, you will

Job Sheet

1. Contribute to a class discussion about the visit, and review the questions on **Job Sheet 4.4** A Visit to a Tire Business.

2. Work in your groups to develop other questions that interest you, and then have your teacher review them.

3. Hand in all permission forms, and review the transportation arrangements and how you will make up missed classes.

4. Meet with your tour leader during the visit, ask your questions, and note answers on your job sheet.

5. Read Concept Connection: *Testing Your Tires* and Workplace Connection: *Real-World Tire Testing*, which your teacher may assign for homework after the tour.

6. Write a thank-you letter to your tour leader.

Concept Connection: Testing Your Tires

"What" is tested is just as important as the test itself. Without testing the right parameters the test can be an invalid indicator of actual real world performance.

Components of Tire Testing

REAL WORLD ROAD RIDE RATINGS
Ride Comfort
Noise Comfort
Handling
Overall Road Rating

PERFORMANCE TEST TRACK DRIVE RATINGS
Cornering Stability
Steering Response
Braking Modulation
Handling Predictability
Overall Track Rating
Combined Road & Track Rating

Lap Time (Seconds)

Average Cornering (g-Force)

Slalom Time (Seconds)

Braking Distance (50-0 mph in Feet)

Can you think of other things, that you want to know before you buy tires that were not tested?

Adapted from *"It Takes Longer Names To Identify Today's Ultra High Performance Tires."* The Tire Rack, Inc., South Bend, Indiana. http://www.tirerack.com/tires/tests/longer_names.jsp (June 10, 2003) and http://www.tirerack.com/tires/tests/longer_names_charts.html (June 10, 2003)

Workplace Connection: Real-World Tire Testing

What does it take to test a tire?

Since experience is said to be the best teacher, The Tire Rack goes to the extreme to make certain that our team members experience as many of the products they sell as possible. Annually our team participates in over 20 Ride & Drives, allowing them to experience and compare at least 60 different products. Our Real World Road Rides and Performance Test Track Drives are typically conducted over a four-day period in order to allow each team member to experience all of the products back-to-back.

To keep their evaluations consistent we are currently using three identical Lexus IS300 sport sedans, the same Real World Road Ride route, and same Performance Test Track Course. For that matter, the only thing that really changes are the tires, wheel, suspension or brake components that we are testing.

The Real World Road Ride allows every team member to drive each vehicle around the approximate 4-1/2 mile Real World Road Ride loop we have established to experience the ride, noise and light handling qualities in the same conditions our customers do every day. Fortunately the state of Indiana has provided a generous variety of roads to select from around our South Bend headquarters. We have two-lane roads, four-lane roads and expressways with surfaces including chipped stone in tar (rough and irregular), asphalt (some areas are very smooth while others are patched) or concrete (smooth, but complete with expansion joints and some studded tire wear). The vehicle conditions that would affect the results of a Real World Road Ride are kept to a minimum by keeping the radio off, windows up and climate control fan on its lowest setting. This allows us to focus on the product's contribution to ride, noise, and light handling qualities without unnecessary distractions. This is 90% of the lesson. NOTE: Only the Real World Road ride is used to evaluate light truck tires.

The Performance Test Track Drive uses our new purpose-built test track that is located on a ten-acre site adjacent to our South Bend headquarters and dedicated to our testing during the week and used for autocross competition by local car clubs on the weekends. Since it is never used as a parking lot, we don't have to worry about parked cars dripping oil and antifreeze creating isolated slick spots. Our approximately 1/3 of a mile per lap test course challenges the car's steering response, handling, braking, and cornering capabilities and allows us to compare the products.

New for 2002, will be our ability to turn on the track's sprinkler system to evaluate traction and handling under consistent wet road conditions. Additionally we will be able to measure braking distances and time specific track segments that will help quantify the product's contributions to responsiveness and maximum cornering capability. The test track allows our team to experience how well the tires handle at their performance limit, or how they would react to an emergency situation on the road. Admittedly, this is 90% of the fun!

Following each Ride & Drive, our team's evaluation of each product's comfort and performance is scored on a 1 to 10 scale, with 10 being the highest. Additionally, each driver's lap times are recorded with a competition lap timer and the fastest laps are averaged to help quantify the tire's performance capabilities on the track. We have found that our team's driving experience and insight reflects that of our customers. They are a combination of racers, autocrossers, and enthusiasts whose evaluations provide an excellent overview of the variety of products we test.

ACTIVITY 4.5

Choosing Test Conditions

Getting In Gear

You are now ready for your first milestone of this unit, setting up a tire performance test. What kind of terrain conditions do you think an ATV might encounter? How can you simulate these in your classroom? In this activity, you take on the challenge to create a test track that best measures the performance of an ATV tire.

Getting To Work!

To complete Project Milestone One, you will

1. Participate in a class discussion on what kinds of terrain conditions a tire for an ATV might encounter in both road and off-road surfaces, and for different weather conditions.

2. Work in groups and obtain ⎹ **Job Sheet 4.5** ⎸ **How Do We Set Up the Performance Test?**, then perform the activity.

Job Sheet

3. Review the concepts and answer the questions in What Have You Learned? for homework.

4. Check out the Did You Know? reading as time permits.

Wonder how this relates to the tires on cars and motorcycles? Take time to read Concept Connection: *Tires and Friction.*

Concept Connection: Tires and Friction

Friction plays a very important role in our lives. You may not think about it, but without friction everything would be free. Friction uses up stored energy, and storing energy costs money. Every different type of vehicle and every different type of road requires a different type of tire. A tire designed for use on a flat road differs greatly from a tire designed for use on the dirt.

What do you have to take into account when designing a tire?

Did You Know?

Charles Goodyear–U.S. inventor of the vulcanization process that permitted the commercial use of rubber. He was born in New Haven, Conn. Interested in treating rubber so that it would lose its adhesive quality and not melt, he discovered vulcanization in 1839 when he accidentally dropped a rubber-sulfur mixture onto a hot stove. The process would prove profoundly important for the future uses of rubber. He patented it in 1844, but had to fight numerous patent infringements in the U.S. and Europe. He never profited from his discovery and died in debt. The Goodyear Tire and Rubber Co. (founded 1898) honors his name.

From "Goodyear Charles" The Britannica Concise.
http://www.britannica.com/ebc/article?eu=391143 (June 10, 2003)

Figure 4.3
On Road and Off Road Motorcycles and Tire Treads

© 2005 PhotoDisc, Inc.

Courtesy of Corel

Why are the tires used on these motorcycles so different? Each is used on a different surface, and each surface has different friction characteristics.

What Have You Learned?

Force. When one object is pushing, pulling, or pressing on another object, we say it is exerting a force on the other object. (Even an inanimate, stationary object can exert a force on another object, for example, by resting on it or supporting it.) The magnitude of the force tells how hard one object is pushing or pulling another object at a particular instant. To identify a force fully, we must also tell its direction, specifying what is exerting the force on what. Force is measured in metric units called newtons (n) and English units called pounds (lbs.).

Newton's Third Law of Motion. This law states that physical interactions are never one way: whenever one thing affects another, the second thing also affects the first. Formally, the law states that in every interaction between two objects, the two objects exert forces that are equal in magnitude and opposite in direction. This is true regardless of which object is more "active" in any way. In practice, it means that you can set a wagon in motion by sitting in it and pushing off against a wall.

Newton's First Law of Motion. This law states that an object will have a constant speed and direction unless an external (nonzero) net force is exerted on it. The fact that most objects do come to rest (in human experience) is evidence that some unopposed force, usually friction or air resistance, or both, is being exerted on them. In these familiar circumstances, an additional force must be exerted on an object to oppose the frictional force and to keep an object moving at a constant velocity. In exotic situations in which there is essentially no friction, as in the nearly total vacuum of space, objects would "coast" indefinitely.

Net force and equilibrium. When an object is pushed or pulled equally in two opposite directions, it behaves as if no force was being exerted on it at all. (We say in such cases that there is a net force of zero.) For that reason, when we consider the combined effect of two or more forces, we let the forces in one direction be positive and those in the opposite direction be negative. A force's magnitude is given by its absolute value; its direction is given by its sign. For forces operating along a straight line, we can find the net force on an object simply by adding the signed values of the forces. When the net force on an object equals zero, the object is said to be in equilibrium.

CONCEPT QUESTIONS

1. When you push on a wall, it does not seem like the wall is pushing on you because the change is too small to see. What could you do to prove to yourself that the wall is, in fact, pushing on you?

2. Explain why it is harder to push something on a rug than on a skating rink.

3. When a skater brakes while on roller blades, how does that help the skater stop?

4. Why would the skater eventually coast to a stop without applying the brakes?

5. Why is it easier to walk on concrete than on ice?

APPLYING WHAT YOU KNOW

1. If the brake pads are worn down on roller blades or on a 10-speed bike, would the skater's or rider's ability to stop be affected? Why? How could the skater or rider control her ability to stop?

2. Suppose you were trying to push a box of books across the floor, and the box does not budge. What does that suggest about the net force on the books? Besides the force that you exert, is anything else exerting a force on the books? If so, what?

3. If you were floating in midair, and there was nothing for you to push off from, would you be able to propel yourself forward? Why or why not?

Wagon Performance

OVERVIEW

GIVE ME A BRAKE!

Although antilock brakes are becoming more and more common, they are still rare in all-terrain vehicles (ATVs), which are used for off-road recreation on rough terrain. ATV drivers need complete control over braking in the quickly changing conditions they encounter, and antilock brakes would remove some of that control. It is important, then, that tires on ATVs perform well when the driver locks the brakes by braking so hard that the wheels can no longer turn.

The Wheelers and Dealers tire company needs you to run performance tests with antilock brakes on a variety of terrains. You have already selected the different types of terrain; now you need to figure out how to control the motion of the vehicle to simulate antilock braking behavior. You wouldn't want to be responsible for any cliff-hanging or tree-hugging incidents, so design and plan carefully!

Your next milestone:

Planning Data Collection Procedures for Evaluating Tire Performance

Project Milestone 2

You will describe the desired behavior of an ATV's tires when its brakes are locked. You will plan data collection procedures for the tire performance test with locked wheels, then justify your choices using the physics concepts of force and motion.

By the end of this chapter, you will have developed an understanding of Newton's Second Law of Motion and decided how to measure vehicle performance for the ATV tire tread project. Your working knowledge will come from a series of six wagon-pulling trials. After conducting the trials, you will use what you have learned about speed, velocity, and acceleration to analyze the experimental results. You then will apply your understanding of force and motion to the task of designing data collection methods for the ATV tire performance test.

To help you accomplish Project Milestone Two, you will do the following activities:

Activity 5.1   Pulling a Wagon with Constant Force

You will learn about Newton's Second Law of Motion. You will conduct an investigation in which one student pulls a wagon and rider over a distance of 20 meters, using a pulley, while other students time their progress. You will conduct the investigation six times, varying the mass and the magnitude of the force. For each of the six trials, you will record your observations and measurements.

Activity 5.2   Predicting a Wagon's Reaction to a Force

You will learn more about Newton's Second Law of Motion. Using the data you collected from the six trials of the test wagon in Activity 5.1, you will calculate the velocity and acceleration using a calculator or a spreadsheet program. You will then look for patterns in the relationships among force, mass, and acceleration. By the end of this activity, you will know whether acceleration increases or decreases when force or mass is increased. You will also be able to express these relationships mathematically.

Activity 5.3   Planning Data Collection Procedures for Evaluating Tire Performance

Engineers need to set performance standards when building and testing products. In this activity, you will return to the ATV tire tread project. You will describe the desirable performance of a tire in locked-wheel conditions and develop a plan for collecting data under the terrain conditions your group has chosen to study. Then you will use the concepts of force, position, distance, velocity, acceleration, and mass to ensure that your data collection methods will accurately show differences in performance among different tire treads in different terrain conditions. With this activity, you will complete Project Milestone Two.

ACTIVITY 5.1

Pulling a Wagon with Constant Force

Getting In Gear

In this activity, it isn't how fast you can pull, it is how steadily you can pull a wagon for 20 meters. Suppose you pull the wagon with exactly the same force for the whole time. How do you think the wagon will behave? Will it move at a constant speed? slow down? speed up? Why?

You will have the help of a pulley system to keep an even force on the wagon as you pull. This investigation will help you discover what Sir Isaac understood when he created Newton's Second Law of Motion.

Getting To Work!

To explore Newton's Second Law of Motion, you will

1. Read the overview scenario and project milestone for Chapter 5, and discuss the scenario with your class.

2. Work in groups and obtain [**Job Sheet 5.1**] **Can You Predict What Will Happen When You Pull a Wagon with a Constant Force?**; follow the directions.

Job Sheet

3. Read Getting the Point: *States of Motion and Mass versus Weight,* and answer the Focus Questions.

4. Check out the Did You Know? reading as time permits.

Getting The Point.

States of Motion and Mass versus Weight

As you have seen in Newton's First Law, an object can be in two different states of motion when there is no net force acting on it—at *rest,* or traveling at *constant velocity.* When a net force does act on an object, a different state of motion results—acceleration.

From your previous work in kinematics, you may recall that acceleration is the change of velocity over time. Most of your work with wagons in this unit will focus on *uniform acceleration* in response to a uniform, steady force. There are physical situations, such as a rocket being launched, in which *nonuniform acceleration* results. Why does that occur? To exhibit a uniform acceleration, the mass "of the object being accelerated must be constant. Think what would happen if a classmate that you were pushing in a wagon with a constant force suddenly jumped out. The wagon certainly would not accelerate at the same rate as before, assuming you applied the same force to it! In a similar way, a rocket expels fuel and exhaust every second during liftoff, thereby changing the rocket's total mass and resulting acceleration every second as well.

An equal arm balance measures mass. An object will balance the same set of standard masses on Earth or on the Moon. In contrast, a bathroom scale measures weight. Weight depends on the strength of the gravitational pull on an object; an object will therefore weigh less on the Moon than on Earth. The gravitational field of the Moon is one-sixth as strong as Earth's. Since the moon pulls on a mass with one-sixth the strength of Earth, the weight of every object would register as one-sixth its magnitude on Earth. The point is that while an object's weight may be different in different locations, its mass is always the same. So the same net force is required to give the same mass a particular acceleration anywhere. This is not a true statement if we substitute weight for mass.

Did You Know?

Heavy Facts about Jupiter

The mass of Jupiter is 318 times the mass of Earth. This means that if Jupiter were the same size as Earth, the gravitational force would be 318 greater on Jupiter than on the surface of Earth. Jupiter is much larger, however; you could fit more than 1000 Earths inside Jupiter. So the mass is distributed over a larger sphere. The result is that your weight on Jupiter would be a bit more than 2.5 times your weight on Earth.

Focus Questions

What are the four states of motion common in nature?

How much would you weigh on the Moon compared to on Earth?

Why is it incorrect to say, "I have a mass of 100 pounds"?

ACTIVITY 5.2

Predicting a Wagon's Reaction to a Force

Getting In Gear

Now that you know what happens when you keep the force steady, what do you think will happen when you vary the force? In this activity, you'll have a chance to play around. (Not too rough; we don't want any collisions!) By pulling the wagon harder and softer, you can study the wagon's behavior under varying forces. Can you predict a particular motion variation for the wagon and then make it happen by exerting different forces over the course of a trial run?

Getting To Work!

Job Sheet

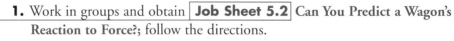

To explore varying motion as a result of forces, you will

1. Work in groups and obtain | **Job Sheet 5.2** | **Can You Predict a Wagon's Reaction to Force?**; follow the directions.

2. Read Getting the Point: *Newton's Second Law of Motion,* and answer the Focus Questions.

3. Check out the Did You Know? reading as time permits.

Wonder how Newton's laws apply to rocket science? Read Concept Connection: *Rocket Principles.*

Getting The Point.

Newton's Second Law of Motion

Newton's Second Law of Motion describes what happens to an object when a net force is exerted on it: *it accelerates.* Although you may realize that speeding up and slowing down are both kinds of acceleration, it might surprise you to consider that *changing direction* is a type of acceleration as well.

Newton's second law also tells us, mathematically, exactly how much acceleration a force can produce. This relationship is $F_{net} = ma$, where F_{net} is net force, m is mass, and a is acceleration. This equation tells you that

1. the harder you push an object, the more quickly it speeds up, slows down, or turns (these are all types of acceleration); and

2. if you push two different objects equally hard, the object with less mass will accelerate more.

Once you know the force equation, $F_{net} = ma$, it is easy to see where the units of force, particularly the newton, are derived from. In the metric system, mass is measured in kilograms and acceleration is measured in meters/second^2, so the units of force must be

$$ma = kg \times m/sec^2 = kgm/sec^2$$

Since "kilograms times meters over seconds squared" is a mouthful to say—and to honor its formulator, Sir Isaac Newton—it has been renamed a *newton* (abbreviated n). Whenever you are manipulating variables in the equation, remember that the *real* units of force are the mouthful!

**Focus
Questions**

In words and pictures, identify and describe the force exerted on a test wagon that is coasting to a stop.

Explain why this scenario is an example of Newton's Second Law of Motion.

Concept Connection: Rocket Principles

A rocket in its simplest form is a chamber enclosing a gas under pressure. A small opening at one end of the chamber allows the gas to escape, and in doing so provides a thrust that propels the rocket in the opposite direction. A good example of this is a balloon. Air inside a balloon is compressed by the balloon's rubber walls. The air pushes back so that the inward and outward pressing forces are balanced. When the nozzle is released, air escapes through it and the balloon is propelled in the opposite direction.

When we think of rockets, we rarely think of balloons. Instead, our attention is drawn to the giant vehicles that carry satellites into orbit and spacecraft to the Moon and planets. Nevertheless, there is a strong similarity between the two. The only significant difference is the way the pressurized gas is produced. With space rockets, the gas is produced by burning propellants that can be solid or liquid in form or a combination of the two.

One of the interesting facts about the historical development of rockets is that while rockets and rocket-powered devices have been in use for more than two thousand years, it has been only in the last three hundred years that rocket experimenters have had a scientific basis for understanding how they work.

The science of rocketry began with the publishing of a book in 1687 by the great English scientist Sir Isaac Newton. His book, entitled *Philosophiae Naturalis Principia Mathematica,* described physical principles in nature. Today, Newton's work is usually just called the *Principia.* In the *Principia,* Newton stated three important scientific principles that govern the motion of all objects, whether on Earth or in space. Knowing these principles, now called Newton's Laws of Motion, rocketeers have been able to construct the modern giant rockets of the 20th century such as the Saturn V and the Space Shuttle. Here now, in simple form, are Newton's Laws of Motion.

1. Objects at rest will stay at rest and objects in motion will stay in motion in a straight line unless acted upon by an unbalanced force.

2. Force is equal to mass times acceleration.

3. For every action there is always an opposite and equal reaction.

As will be explained shortly, all three laws are really simple statements of how things move. But with them, precise determinations of rocket performance can be made.

This law of motion is just an obvious statement of fact, but to know what it means, it is necessary to understand the terms rest, motion, and unbalanced force.

Rest and motion can be thought of as being opposite to each other. Rest is the state of an object when it is not changing position in relation to its surroundings. If you are sitting still in a chair, you can be said to be at rest. This term, however, is relative. Your chair may actually be one of many seats on a speeding airplane. The important thing to remember here is that you are not moving in relation to your immediate surroundings. If rest were defined as a total absence of motion, it would not exist in nature. Even if you were sitting in your chair at home, you would still be moving, because your chair is actually sitting on the surface of a spinning planet that is orbiting a star. The star is moving through a rotating galaxy that is, itself, moving through the universe. While sitting "still," you are, in fact, traveling at a speed of hundreds of kilometers per second.

Motion is also a relative term. All matter in the universe is moving all the time, but in the first law, motion here means changing position in relation to surroundings. A ball is at rest if it is sitting on the ground. The ball is in motion if it is rolling. A rolling ball changes its position in relation to its surroundings. When you are sitting on a chair in an airplane, you are at rest, but if you get up and walk down the aisle, you are in motion. A rocket blasting off the launch pad changes from a state of rest to a state of motion.

The third term important to understanding this law is unbalanced force. If you hold a ball in your hand and keep it still, the ball is at rest. All the time the ball is held there though, it is being acted upon by forces. The force of gravity is trying to pull the ball downward, while at the same time your hand is pushing against the ball to hold it up. The forces acting on the ball are balanced. Let the ball go, or move your hand upward, and the forces become unbalanced. The ball then changes from a state of rest to a state of motion.

In rocket flight, forces become balanced and unbalanced all the time. A rocket on the launch pad is balanced. The surface of the pad pushes the rocket up while gravity tries to pull it down. As the engines are ignited, the thrust from the rocket unbalances the forces, and the rocket travels upward. Later, when the rocket runs out of fuel, it slows down, stops at the highest point of its flight, then falls back to Earth.

Objects in space also react to forces. A spacecraft moving through the solar system is in constant motion. The spacecraft will travel in a straight line if the forces on it are in balance. This happens only when the spacecraft is very far from any large gravity source such as Earth or the other planets and their moons. If the spacecraft comes near a large body in space, the gravity of that body will unbalance the forces and curve the path of the spacecraft. This happens, in particular, when a satellite is sent by a rocket on a path that is parallel to Earth's surface. If the rocket shoots the spacecraft fast enough, the spacecraft will orbit Earth. As long as another unbalanced force, such as friction with gas molecules in orbit or the firing of a rocket engine in the opposite direction from its movement, does not slow the spacecraft, it will orbit Earth forever.

Now that the three major terms of this first law have been explained, it is possible to restate this law. If an object, such as a rocket, is at rest, it takes an unbalanced force to make it move. If the object is already moving, it takes an unbalanced force, to stop it, change its direction from a straight line path, or alter its speed.

NEWTON'S THIRD LAW

For the time being, we will skip the second law and go directly to the third. This law states that every action has an equal and opposite reaction. If you have ever stepped off a small boat that has not been properly tied to a pier, you will know exactly what this law means.

A rocket can lift off from a launch pad only when it expels gas out of its engine. The rocket pushes on the gas, and the gas in turn pushes on the rocket. The whole process is very similar to riding a skateboard. Imagine that a skateboard and rider are in a state of rest (not moving). The rider jumps off the skateboard. In the third law, the jumping is called an action. The skateboard responds to that action by traveling some distance in the opposite direction. The skateboard's opposite motion is called a reaction. When the distance traveled by the rider and the skateboard are compared, it would appear that the skateboard has had a much greater reaction than the action of the rider. This is not the case. The reason the skateboard has traveled farther is that it has less mass than the rider. This concept will be better explained in a discussion of the second law.

With rockets, the action is the expelling of gas out of the engine. The reaction is the movement of the rocket in the opposite direction. To enable a rocket to lift off from the launch pad, the action, or thrust, from the engine must be greater than the mass of the rocket. In space, however, even tiny thrusts will cause the rocket to change direction.

One of the most commonly asked questions about rockets is how they can work in space where there is no air for them to push against. The answer to this question comes from the third law. Imagine the skateboard again. On the ground, the only part air plays in the motions of the rider and the skateboard is to slow them down. Moving through the air causes friction, or as scientists call it, drag. The surrounding air impedes the action-reaction.

As a result rockets actually work better in space than they do in air. As the exhaust gas leaves the rocket engine it must push away the surrounding air; this uses up some of the energy of the rocket. In space, the exhaust gases can escape freely.

NEWTON'S SECOND LAW

This law of motion is essentially a statement of a mathematical equation. The three parts of the equation are mass (m), acceleration (a), and force (f). Using letters to symbolize each part, the equation can be written as follows:

$$f = ma$$

By using simple algebra, we can also write the equation two other ways:

$$a = f/m$$

$$m = f/a$$

The first version of the equation is the one most commonly referred to when talking about Newton's second law. It reads: force equals mass times acceleration. To explain this law, we will use an old style cannon as an example.

When the cannon is fired, an explosion propels a cannon ball out the open end of the barrel. It flies a kilometer or two to its target. At the same time the cannon itself is pushed backward a meter or two. This is action and reaction at work (third law). The force acting on the cannon and the ball is the same. What happens to the cannon and the ball is determined by the second law. Look at the two equations below.

$$f = m(cannon) * a(cannon)$$

$$f = m(ball) * a(ball)$$

The first equation refers to the cannon and the second to the cannon ball. In the first equation, the mass is the cannon itself and the acceleration is the movement of the cannon. In the second equation the mass is the cannon ball and the acceleration is its movement. Because the force (exploding gun powder) is the same for the two equations, the equations can be combined and rewritten below.

$$m(cannon) * a(cannon) = m(ball) * a(ball)$$

In order to keep the two sides of the equations equal, the accelerations vary with mass. In other words, the cannon has a large mass and a small acceleration. The cannon ball has a small mass and a large acceleration.

Let's apply this principle to a rocket. Replace the mass of the cannon ball with the mass of the gases being ejected out of the rocket engine. Replace the mass of the cannon with the mass of the rocket moving in the other direction. Force is the pressure created by the controlled explosion taking place inside the rocket's engines. That pressure accelerates the gas one way and the rocket the other.

Some interesting things happen with rockets that don't happen with the cannon and ball in this example. With the cannon and cannon ball, the thrust lasts for just a moment. The thrust for the rocket continues as long as its engines are firing. Furthermore, the mass of the rocket changes during flight. Its mass is the sum of all its parts. Rocket parts include engines, propellant tanks, payload, control system, and propellants. By far, the largest part of the rocket's mass is its propellants. But that amount constantly changes as the engines fire. That means that the rocket's mass gets smaller during flight. In order for the left side of our equation to remain in balance with the right side, acceleration of the rocket has to increase as its mass decreases. That is why a rocket starts off moving slowly and goes faster and faster as it climbs into space.

Newton's second law of motion is especially useful when designing efficient rockets. To enable a rocket to climb into low Earth orbit, it is necessary to achieve a speed, in excess of 28,000 km per hour. A speed of over 40,250 km per hour, called escape velocity, enables a rocket to leave Earth and travel out into deep space. Attaining space flight speeds requires the rocket engine to achieve the greatest action force possible in the shortest time. In other words, the engine must burn a large mass of fuel and push the resulting gas out of the engine as rapidly as possible.

Newton's second law of motion can be restated in the following way: the greater the mass of rocket fuel burned, and the faster the gas produced can escape the engine, the greater the thrust of the rocket.

PUTTING NEWTON'S LAWS OF MOTION TOGETHER

An unbalanced force must be exerted for a rocket to lift off from a launch pad or for a craft in space to change speed or direction (first law). The amount of thrust (force) produced by a rocket engine will be determined by the mass of rocket fuel that is burned and how fast the gas escapes the rocket (second law). The reaction, or motion, of the rocket is equal to and in the opposite direction of the action, or thrust, from the engine (third law).

From *"Rocket Principles."* Glenn Learning Technologies Project. Courtesy of NASA. http://www.lerc.nasa.gov/WWW/K-12/TRC/rockets/rocket_principles.html (June 10, 2003)

Did You Know?

What is a slug? Even though Americans are familiar with the English system of units (feet, yards, quarts, etc.), almost no one knows or uses the English unit of mass. The "slug" is our official unit of mass, and the pound is our unit of force. According to Newton's second law then, 1 slug of mass weighs about 32 pounds on Earth $(F = ma = 1 \text{ slug} \times 32 \text{ ft/sec}^2 = 32 \text{ sl.ft/sec}^2 = 32 \text{ lbs.})$.

ACTIVITY 5.3

Planning Data Collection Procedures for Evaluating Tire Performance

Getting In Gear

So now that you are all revved up and ready to go, we are going to apply the brakes—antilock brakes, that is. How do you think an ATV will react to antilock brakes in the sand? Is it different on pavement? What if the pavement is wet? In this activity, you will plan how to collect data to evaluate tire performance when antilock brakes are used in a variety of conditions.

Getting To Work!

To complete Project Milestone Two, you will

1. Participate in a class discussion about what happens when ATV wheels lock.

2. Work in groups and obtain │ **Job Sheet 5.3** │ **Planning Data Collection Procedures for Evaluating Tire Performance**; follow the directions.

3. Review the concepts and answer the questions in What Have You Learned? for homework.

Job Sheet

What Have You Learned?

KEY CONCEPTS

Newton's Second Law of Motion. An unopposed force exerted on an object will always bring about some change in the motion of that object. Whenever there is a change in velocity (even if there is no change in speed), there is acceleration. Newton's Second Law of Motion relates an object's acceleration to the net force exerted on it.

States of motion. In Newton's laws, there are four basic "motions" of an object: rest, constant velocity, uniform acceleration, and nonuniform acceleration.

Mass. A measure of a body's resistance to acceleration. According to Newton's laws of motion, if two unequal masses are allowed to collide, in the absence of any other forces both will experience the same force of collision. If the two bodies acquire accelerations, they will do so in proportion to their respective masses. Mass is measured in grams in the metric system.

Weight. The downward force on a body created by the gravitational field upon which the body is situated. Proportional to the strength of this field, weight is absent when the field is absent. Weight is measured in newtons in the metric system and in pounds in the English system of units.

CONCEPT QUESTIONS

1. Give an example of an object undergoing uniformly accelerated motion. Give an example of an object that undergoes nonuniform acceleration.

2. What are the units of a newton?

3. Why is Newton's second law often called the definition of mass?

APPLYING WHAT YOU KNOW

1. How would you measure the mass of an object in a spaceship in which the acceleration due to gravity was zero?

2. If a force of 100 newtons is exerted on a mass of 50 kilogram, what would the acceleration of the mass be?

Understanding How Frictional Forces Affect Performance

OVERVIEW

TAKING THE TEST

Your engineering team has been hard at work learning about Newton's laws of motion and getting ready for the big test on your tires. The reputation of the Wheelers and Dealers tire company is on the line. Can they make an ATV tire that will perform under all kinds of terrain conditions when the antilock braking system is on?

Get your terrain-condition designs and your data collection plans ready. It is time to see what these test vehicle tires can do. Your presentation will speak for itself—and decide whether or not you get the next big contract for the company.

Your next milestone:

3 Project Milestone | Conducting the Performance Test

You will implement the performance test, making force or motion measurements of the wagons and varying the terrain conditions and the tire treads. You will evaluate how well the test works in showing performance differences among tire treads in various terrain conditions, and suggest improvements to your tests as needed. Then you will make a presentation about your tests.

You will continue your work as an engineering team and explore how wheeled vehicles travel forward. You will learn about frictional forces as the forces that surfaces exert on each other. By examining tires and discussing rolling and skidding tires, you will learn that there are two types of frictional forces, static and sliding. You will measure these forces using several pairs of materials. By the end of the chapter, you will have planned and implemented your ATV tire performance test and explained how static and sliding frictional forces affect performance.

To help you accomplish Project Milestone Three, you will do the following activities:

Activity 6.1 From Spinning to Gripping: Friction on the Road
You will begin to investigate different situations involving forces and motion. The knowledge you gain will ultimately help you design and carry out your performance test. You will explore what happens between a vehicle's wheels and the surface they travel on when the wheels begin to rotate. First, you will think about a problem involving a bicycle's wheels spinning in place. Then you will simulate the problem—experimenting with different kinds of wheeled vehicles and different surfaces—and learn about the frictional forces involved.

Activity 6.2 Measuring Static and Sliding Frictional Forces
You will continue to investigate frictional forces, this time by attempting to drag a book or block of wood across a table and by measuring the different frictional forces involved in getting started and moving forward. You will write about why it is useful to measure maximum static frictional force when assessing the performance of a vehicle. After observing a wheeled vehicle coasting to a stop, you will consider the importance of frictional forces in stopping and share your ideas about what caused the vehicle to stop.

Activity 6.3 How Does Weight Affect Frictional Forces?
Engineers take into account the weight of a vehicle when designing features for particular traveling conditions. In this activity, you will predict and then test how weight affects sliding and static frictional forces. Using the pairs of materials from the last activity, you will conduct five trials, increasing the weight for each trial. By the end of this activity, you will understand and write about how and why the "pressing against" force affects sliding and static frictional forces.

Activity 6.4 Finding the Coefficient of Friction from a Graph

You will plot the data from Activity 6.2 on a graph of frictional force versus normal force. By calculating the slope of the line on this graph, you will determine the coefficient of friction for various materials.

Activity 6.5 Conducting and Presenting the Performance Test of Tires

The deadline for your ATV tire test project is approaching! Your test should show the differences in tire performance between various types of tire tread, on different terrain conditions, when a wagon's wheels are locked. You'll evaluate how well the test works and suggest improvements if needed. You will complete Project Milestone Three by making a presentation about your performance test. Finally, you will respond to the question you answered earlier about Officer Brown's bicycle.

ACTIVITY 6.1

From Spinning to Gripping: Friction on the Road

Suppose you are at a playground with a long slide. You have a handful of flat rocks, and your friend has a handful of marbles. Which do you think would go faster down the slide? Why? What other examples of rolling and sliding friction can you think of?

In this activity, you will study the motion of toy vehicles on different surfaces to see when they roll, when they slide, and why.

To explore sliding and rolling friction, you will

1. Read the overview scenario and project milestone for chapter 6, and discuss the scenario with your class.

2. Read Part 1 of Job Sheet 6.1 Why Doesn't Officer Brown's Bicycle Move Forward?; try to answer the questions.

Job Sheet

3. Simulate Officer Brown's situation, using materials provided by your teacher.

4. Discuss Officer Brown's situation with your class.

5. Answer the questions for Part 2 on Job Sheet 6.1.

6. Read Getting the Point: *Frictional Force* for homework, and answer the Focus Question.

7. Check out Workplace Connection: *Friction of Molecules* and the Did You Know? reading as time permits.

Wonder how friction affects gas mileage? Read Concept Connection: *Energy Technology and Fuel Economy.*

Frictional Force

To understand the different static and sliding frictional forces that two surfaces exert on each other, you need to understand something about the differences between materials at a molecular level.

When two surfaces are in contact, we can see with the naked eye whether the surfaces are rough or smooth. If we pull an object with a rough surface over another rough surface, we see that the bumps and indentations catch on each other. If the bumps and indentations fit reasonably well together, then a large part of the surfaces are in contact with each other.

To understand friction, we have to imagine what is happening at the microscopic level. All materials are made up of atoms of one or more elements. Atoms of different elements can be joined together to form molecules.

A frictional force is a force that each of two touching surfaces exerts on the other. How do these molecules exert force on each other? One other important fact about most molecules and atoms will help to identify the force that each surface exerts on the other surface. *Molecules usually have areas that are charged positive and negative, much like the positive and negative poles of a magnet.* The positive parts of molecules on the first surface form temporary bonds with the negative parts of molecules on the second surface. And the negative parts of molecules on the first surface form temporary bonds with the positive parts of molecules on the second surface. The positive and negative parts are attracted to each other just as the positive and negative ends of magnets are attracted to each other. These bonds are called electrostatic bonds.

The bumps and crevices of a material create more surface area, and allow more bonds to form. Bumps and crevices at the surfaces of objects get caught on one another, and temporary electrostatic bonds form between the molecules on each surface. For the same type of material, a rough surface increases the surface area that then forms more temporary bonds with another surface. Even if the surfaces of two objects appear smooth under a microscope, the molecules on each surface can form temporary bonds.

Focus Question

Why is friction sometimes called the invisible force?

Concept Connection: Energy Technology and Fuel Economy

Only about 15% of the energy in the fuel you put in your gas tank gets used to move your car down the road or run useful accessories like air conditioning or power steering. The rest of the energy is lost. Because of this the potential to improve fuel economy with advanced technologies is enormous.

Figure 6.1
Energy Usage of a Car
Engine

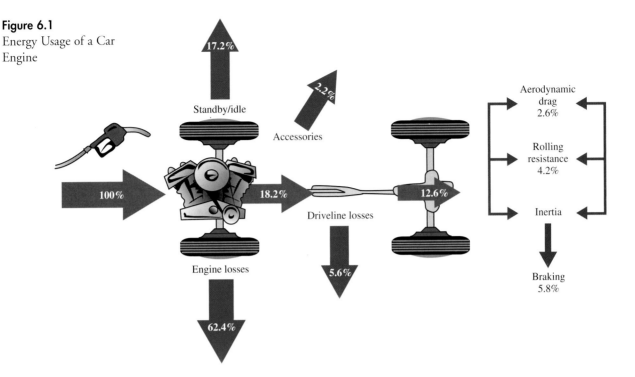

Motor vehicles need energy to accelerate (overcome inertia), to push the air out of their way (aerodynamic drag), and to overcome the friction from tires, wheels and axles (rolling resistance). Fuel provides the needed energy in the form of chemicals that can be combusted (oxidized) to release heat. Engines transform heat released in combustion into useful work that ultimately turns the vehicle's wheels propelling it down the road.

Even modern internal combustion engines convert only one third of the energy in fuel into useful work. The rest is lost to waste heat, the friction of moving engine parts or to pumping air into and out of the engine. All of the steps at which energy is wasted are opportunities for advanced technologies to increase fuel economy.

The figure above illustrates the paths of energy through a typical gasoline-powered vehicle in city driving. Of the energy content in a gallon of gasoline, 62% is lost to engine friction, engine pumping losses, and to waste heat. In urban driving, another 17% is lost to idling at stop lights or in traffic. Accessories necessary for the vehicle's operation (e.g., waterpump) or for passenger comfort (e.g., air conditioning) take another 2%.

Just over 18% of the energy in gasoline makes it to the transmission. Losses in the drive train to friction and slippage claim more than 5%, leaving a bit less than 13% to actually move the vehicle down the road. The laws of physics will not permit all of these losses to be entirely eliminated. But improvements are possible at every step.

The 12.6% of original fuel energy that makes it to the wheels must provide acceleration (5.8%) and overcome aerodynamic drag (2.6%) and rolling resistance. In stop and go city driving it is not surprising that acceleration is the biggest need, rolling is next, followed by aerodynamic drag. On the highway the order is reversed: aerodynamic drag, which increases at an increasing rate with speed requires the most energy (about 10.9%). Each of these final uses of energy also represents an opportunity to improve fuel economy. Substitutions of high strength lightweight materials can reduce vehicle mass and thus the energy required for acceleration. Smoother vehicle shapes have already reduced drag significantly, but further reductions of 20-30% are possible. Advanced tire designs can cut rolling resistance.

From *"Energy Technology and Fuel Economy."* Fuel Economy Guide, Model Year 2002. U.S. Department of Energy. http://www.fueleconomy.gov/feg/atv/shtml (June 10, 2003)

Workplace Connection: Friction of Molecules

Engineers hope to make microscopic engines and gears as ordinary in our lives as microscopic circuits are today. But before this dream becomes a reality, they will have to deal with laws of friction that are very different from those that apply to ordinary-sized machines. Last year, a group of surface scientists has demonstrated that friction can arise between two surfaces even before they press against one another, through the formation of adhesions on the molecular level.

In classical physics, the amount of friction between two objects is proportional to the force that squeezes them together, called the "load." This empirical observation, called Amonton's Law after the 17th-century physicist who discovered it, works well for large objects, but "it really doesn't work at the molecular level," says Alan Burns of Sandia National Laboratories in Albuquerque, New Mexico. Two surfaces that are less than a nanometer apart can actually attract each other via molecular interactions, creating a paradoxical situation known as "negative load," where the surfaces have to be pulled apart rather than squeezed together. 17th-century physics gives no guidance on how friction works in such a case.

In recent years, physicists have studied molecular friction with atomic force microscopes (AFMs), in which a scanning tip is pulled across a surface like an old-fashioned record needle. But, according to Burns, AFMs have one drawback: when the tip gets too close to the surface, the molecular forces make it jump into contact—thus passing right through the interesting negative-load regime. To overcome this problem, he and three colleagues designed an apparatus that carefully controlled the gap between the probe and the surface.

As a result, the researchers were able to study for the first time how friction varies with a negative load. The results depended strongly on the chemistry of the surface, a one-molecule-thick layer of alkanethiol lubricant attached to a gold film. This layer, Burns says, is like a "molecular brush," consisting of long molecules that fasten to the gold at one end. Depending on the chemical makeup of the free end of the molecule, the hairs of the brush interact differently with a glass probe. When the "hairs" ended with a methyl group, the attraction was weak, and the amount of friction at negative loads was insignificant. But when the "hairs" ended with a carboxyl group, they formed hydrogen bonds with the probe and tugged strongly at it, creating measurable friction even at negative loads.

Figure 6.2
Galileo Galilei

Galileo Galilei (1564–1642)

Friction is a force that slows down moving things. Galileo was the first scientist we know of that really identified what friction was. When he wasn't dropping objects off the top of the leaning tower of Pisa, Galileo was doing experiments rolling balls down inclined planes. He noticed that a ball picked up speed if rolled down a ramp, and it lost speed when it rolled up a ramp. Finally, he asked himself the question "If the ball rolled down a plane and onto a completely level surface, how far would the ball travel?" The answer, theoretically, was—forever! Any moving body, even a moving body rolling across a seemingly flat plane, will roll forever, an effect Galileo called inertia. Friction is the force that interferes with this motion. In this case, friction caused by the slightly uneven surface of the tabletop creates a drag on the rolling object, which will eventually come to a stop.

From *"Montshire Minute: Friction."* Montshire Museum of Science (Norwich, VT). http://www.montshire.net/minute/mm990503.html (June 10, 2003)

"This is a really fine experimental contribution," says Jacqueline Krim, an atomic friction researcher at North Carolina State University in Raleigh. "The next step would be for someone to reproduce these results in a computer simulation," so that theorists could tell whether their models accurately predict the friction observed by Burns's experiment. In the long run, engineers of micromachines—machines on a computer chip— will also need to know how friction works at the atomic level. "Strong adhesion will prevent the gears from turning smoothly," Burns says, "or prevent them from turning at all."

Mackenzie, D., Phys. Rev. Focus 3, story 9 (1999) *"Friction of Molecules."* http://focus.aps.org. Copyright © 1999 by the American Physical Society. Reprinted with permission.

ACTIVITY 6.2

Measuring Static and Sliding Frictional Forces

Getting In Gear

Imagine that you are trying to push a heavy box across the floor. Why is it that if you push lightly the box doesn't move, but a bit more and it starts sliding? How much force is enough? In this activity, you will use a pulley and bucket setup to find that limit, called the maximum static friction force. Once you get the bucket moving, you will measure the sliding frictional force. The force may be caused by the same thing, but it has different names depending on whether the object is moving or staying still.

Getting To Work!

Job Sheet

To investigate static and sliding friction, you will

1. Work with your group and follow the instructions on 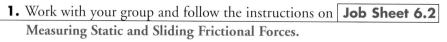 **Job Sheet 6.2** **Measuring Static and Sliding Frictional Forces.**

2. Read Getting the Point: *Normal Force,* and answer the Focus Question.

3. Check out Concept Connection: *Skating Is All Wet!,* and the Did You Know? reading as time permits.

Wonder about the economic cost of wear and friction? How is that cost connected to tribology. What is tribology? Read Workplace Connection: *Friction in the Workplace.*

Getting The Point.

Normal Force

Manufacturers of wheeled vehicles take into account the loaded weight (including riders and cargo) of a vehicle when designing features for particular traveling conditions. This is particularly important for special-use vehicles such as ATVs.

Frictional forces increase as the two surfaces in question press harder against each other. The "pressing against" forces that they exert on each other (usually called normal forces) are perpendicular to the two surfaces. Think about the following:

It's harder to push a bureau across a floor when it is full than when it is empty. The greater weight when it is full means the earth is pulling down harder on the bureau and its contents. So for the bureau to remain in equilibrium, the floor has to press upward harder against the bottom of the bureau. When this "pressing against" force increases, the frictional force that the floor exerts on the bottom of the bureau also increases.

Focus Question

Why do you think weight affects frictional force? Describe as completely as you can, and use diagrams or sketches to illustrate your thinking.

Concept Connection: Skating Is All Wet!

Water has many unusual properties. One is that the low pressure solid form (what we know as ice) has a volume per mole that is ~10% larger than that of liquid water into which it melts. An everyday consequence of this fact is that ice cubes float near the surface of water, with about 10% of their volume above the water-air surface and 90% below.

Another consequence of this decrease in volume upon melting is that the melting temperature of ice decreases when one increases the pressure on the ice. This can be rationalized by Le Châtelier's Principle. An increase in pressure on a sample of ice can be partially removed by melting the ice and thus lowering the sample volume. However, the effect is a small one in that it takes a pressure of ~121 atmospheres (1.22 MPa in SI units) to reduce the melting temperature by a mere 1 degree Centigrade.

It is often claimed that one can skate on ice because the pressure of the skate causes the ice to melt, thus dramatically reducing the friction between skate and ice. While this makes a good story, it is not quite correct. If one takes the skater to have a mass of 75 kg (weight of 165 lbs), and the skate to be 3 mm wide and 20 cm long, one can calculate that the entire gravitational force exerted on the area of one skate is only a pressure of about 12 atmospheres. While one can imagine that the force is concentrated in a somewhat smaller area, the effect of pressure alone is clearly enough to shift the melting temperature of the ice by at most a few tenths of a degree. Since common experience is that ice skating is possible even when the ambient temperature is well below the normal freezing point, the pressure induced lowering of the melting point clearly does not explain this every day observation.

What is responsible then? Scientists have far from a complete understanding of this everyday phenomenon. It is likely partially related to an effect known as surface melting. The stability of solids is due to the regular structure that allows for each molecule to have multiple attractive interactions. At the surface of a solid, this is not the case, since there are no molecules 'above' the surface to bind to. As a result, the surface molecules will often distort to make the best of a bad situation by trying to increase their bonding to each other and those below. This is known as surface reconstruction. It is also known that the molecules on the surface can become disordered and liquid like at a temperature below the normal melting point of a solid, this is the phenomenon known as surface melting. Bringing up another surface (such as the metal of a skate) will influence this surface melting, since now the water molecules on the surface can bind to the metal surface atoms as well. Another important effect is friction, which can generate enough heat to melt a thin layer of ice in contact with the skate.

Adapted from *"Common Theory of Ice Skating is all Wet!"* by Kevin K. Lehmann, Department of Chemistry, Princeton University. Reprinted with permission. http://www.princeton.edu/~lehmann/BadChemistry.html#Skating (June 10, 2003)

Workplace Connection: Friction in the Workplace

TRIBOLOGY

Tribology is the science and technology of interacting surfaces in relative motion and all practices related thereto. In other words, it is that interdisciplinary field which concerns the friction, lubrication, wear, and surface durability of materials and mechanical systems. Tribology is an important, enabling subject which is closely-tied to progress in transportation, manufacturing, energy conversion, agriculture, and mining industries. Typical tribological applications include bearings, gears, bushings, brakes, clutches, chains, human body implants and protheses, floor tiles, seals, piston engine parts, sports equipment (for example, skis and skates), and cosmetics (for example, lubrication in shampoo and skin creams). The basic disciplines involved in tribology are:

Table 6.1

Disciplines involved in tribology.

mechanical engineering	materials engineering
lubrication engineering	metallurgy and ceramics
polymer science	surface chemistry
contact mechanics	surface physics
chemical engineering	surface engineering

Did You Know?

Friction in Billiards

Because the weight and mass of the cue ball and object ball are the same, when the cue ball "slides" into the object ball at no angle (0 degrees) and with no top, bottom or side spin, the cue ball will stop dead, regardless of velocity. Not might. It will. It is the law. 100% of the energy (weight, mass & velocity) of the cue ball is surrendered to the object ball, and there is no energy remaining to carry the cue ball further in any direction. The use of english and spin changes the result, but nonetheless, by the use of physics.

The friction of the cloth will put forward (never backward) roll on the balls. The leather cue tip is used to increase friction with the cue ball, which in turn provides control over the friction of the cloth. This is physics. Believe it. Trust it. Use it. Many players feel using top or no english provides better control. Why? Because top spin works with the natural friction of the cloth and not against it.

Advanced players know how to use conflicting forces (laws of physics) to move the cue ball in magical ways. A novice should work with the laws, at least until they have learned to understand, or at least trust them. Faith in the physics of the game will allow you to concentrate more on improving the human factor.

Adapted from *"Physics and Pool,"* by Jim Meador. http://www.bil-liardworld.com/physics.html (June 10, 2003)

Figure 6.3
Elements Studied in
Tribology

The economic cost of wear and friction to the U.S. easily exceeds $ 100 Billion per annum. The magnitude of the impact of tribology becomes easily apparent considering that $ 1 Billion per annum is involved in warranty costs for automotive brakes alone. Consider the annual maintenance costs for automobiles, aircraft, trucks, and ships due to worn parts or to oil and grease changes. Friction losses decrease the efficiency of many machines and, if reduced, could preserve dwindling natural resources like coal, oil, and natural gas.

From *"Tribology."* U.S. Department of Energy. Oak Ridge National Laboratory. http://www.ms.ornl.gov/research-groups/SPM/methods/Tribology/Tribology.htm (June 10, 2003)

ACTIVITY 6.3

How Does Weight Affect Frictional Forces?

Now that you understand the difference between static and sliding friction, what about when you change the weight of the object? You learned that Newton's Second Law of Motion states that a greater force is needed to accelerate a greater mass by the same amount, but what about when the object isn't moving? What do you think happens to the maximum static friction force of an object when its weight increases? Let's find out.

To learn about the effect of weight on frictional forces, you will

1. Work with your group and follow the instructions on Job Sheet 6.3
   Testing the Effect of Weight on Frictional Force.

2. Read Getting the Point: *Coefficients of Friction,* and answer the Focus Questions.

3. Check out the Did You Know? reading as time permits.

Job Sheet

Wonder what squeaky clean hair has to do with friction? Read Concept Connection: *The Secret of Squeaky Clean Hair.*

Coefficients of Friction

What is a coefficient of friction?

Engineers who design bike routes need to predict the frictional force that will be generated between the tire and the road under typical conditions. Route surfaces vary, and different pairs of materials exert different amounts of frictional force for a particular "pressing against" force. You have already tested the frictional force for different pairs of materials in your lab, and in your engineering investigation you may wish to test frictional force using bikes on road surfaces. Engineers need a way to rate the frictional force of pairs of commonly used materials (such as rubber and asphalt) at any given "pressing against" force.

When you graphed frictional force versus "pressing against" force, your data fell in a straight line. Because the graph had a straight line, you were able to calculate a slope for the line. The slope of the line is the ratio of the frictional force to the "pressing against" force (F_{friction}/N). This ratio is a way to rate every pair of materials, and it is called the coefficient of friction between the two materials.

The coefficient of friction is represented by the Greek character μ (pronounced "myou"). Coefficients of friction have no units, since both the frictional force and the "pressing against" force are measured in newtons. They cancel out during division.

How can the coefficient of friction be used?

Since $\mu = F_{\text{friction}}$/N, the frictional force between any two objects can be calculated if you know μ and the "pressing against" or normal force N:

$$F_{\text{friction}} = \mu N$$

If you want to calculate the critical static frictional force, you use the coefficient of static friction for μ. If you want to calculate the sliding frictional force, you use the coefficient of sliding friction for μ. These coefficients can often be found in a standard text of science and math information.

Focus Questions

Why doesn't the coefficient of friction have units?

How would you calculate the coefficient of friction of wood and wood in your science class?

Concept Connection: The Secret of Squeaky Clean Hair

Why is human hair like a stack of polystyrene coffee cups and how can knowing that help you play the violin better or design a new best-selling food product? Understanding the friction forces between two surfaces sliding over each other and how this is affected by adding conditioner to hair or rosin to a violin bow was discussed at the Institute of Physics Annual Congress in Brighton on Tuesday 28 March, by Dr. Simon Johnson, a scientist with Unilever Research.

Tribology—the study of friction and how wear can be reduced by lubrication—is an area that is fairly well understood in mechanical engineering applications. In the cosmetics industry, though, research is aimed at identifying and enhancing friction characteristics that we find pleasurable. What makes hair feel soft or "squeaky clean," for example, or what makes a moisturiser feel creamy?

An important target for cosmetics research is keratin, a fibrous protein that is the major constituent of hair, wool, nails, feathers, hooves, horns and the stratum corneum—the surface layer of human skin. This layer, which is about a hundredth of a millimeter thick over most of the body is made up of dead cells closely packed together to form a thin membrane supported by a bed of connective tissue.

Studies have shown that, when dry, the stratum corneum behaves, from a friction viewpoint, like a glassy polymer (such as Perspex); when wet, it behaves more like a soft elastomer (like rubber). We all know from washing our hands that the friction of wet skin is much greater than that of dry skin and that wet skin shows "stick-slip" behavior which disappears in the presence of soap. According to physicists, the slippery wet feel of soap on skin or of conditioners on hair partly arises from the electrical repulsion between molecules on the absorbing surfaces.

Human hair fibres are typically a fifteenth of a millimetre thick and have a cuticular cell morphology—in other words, they have a surface similar to that formed by a stack of polystyrene coffee cups or overlapping tiles on a roof.

Each hair is covered with six layers of cuticles and these overlap in such a way to produce quite regular steps on the hair surface that are about half a thousandth of a millimetre in height. When one fibre slides over another in a direction that is towards the cuticle edges (from tip to root), the friction is greater than that in the opposite direction. The same kind of friction effects are also seen in wool. This increase in friction for sliding against the cuticles results from a process called Coulombic interlocking and is similar to the effect of sliding two pieces of abrasive paper across each other. Crossed hair fibres usually show a stick-slip motion. Adding hair conditioner provides lubrication, just like adding oil to an engine.

But perhaps the most commercially important aspects of lubricated skin contacts lie in the food industry. The taste sensation we recognize as "creaminess" comes from the way a thin layer of a food product behaves when we shear it against

Did You Know?

Gripping is important in space as well. In the movie *2001: A Space Odyssey*, director Stanley Kubric and writer Arthur C. Clark recognized that there would be a problem walking in a spacecraft. They came up with an elegant, simple solution to walking in a zero gravity (zero net force) environment. With no net force on a person, there is no way for a person to walk. The person can push off something and float but cannot walk like we do here on Earth. It would be impractical on a commercial passenger spacecraft to have flight attendants flying all over the passenger cabin. The filmmakers had the occupants use boots with a Velcrolike substance on the bottom. This gave them the traction they needed to walk normally on carpeted surfaces.

the roof of our mouth with our tongue. So next time you're caught snacking on a Creme Egg, explain that you're simply investigating the physics of friction.

Adapted from *"Secrets of Squeaky-Clean Hair"* by Simon A. Johnson. Institute of Physics and IOP Publishing Ltd. Reprinted with permission. http://physics.iop.org/IOP/Congress/2000/preleasemon3.html (June 10, 2003)

ACTIVITY 6.4

Finding the Coefficient of Friction from a Graph

Getting In Gear

Measuring the frictional forces, like you did in Activity 6.3, gives you some information to predict the motion of an object. But is there a way to predict how an object on a surface will behave no matter what weight it has? This is what the coefficient of friction buys you. You will graph your data from Activity 6.3, from which you will calculate the coefficients of sliding and static friction for your setup.

Getting To Work!

To calculate the coefficients of friction for your setup, you will

Job Sheet

1. Follow the instructions on │ **Job Sheet 6.4** │ How Can You Calculate the Coefficient of Friction from a Graph?

2. Read Getting the Point: *Coefficient of Friction Revisited*—and Getting the Point: *Friction and Your Tires—Locked and Unlocked,* and answer the Focus Questions.

3. Check out the Did You Know? reading as time permits.

Wonder about the aerodynamics of bicycle racing? Read Workplace Connection: *Friction and Professional Cycle Racing.*

Getting The Point

Coefficient of Friction Revisited

Friction is an enemy of motion. Any time an object attempts to move across a surface, friction opposes the motion or attempted motion. As you have seen, friction depends on the texture of both the object and the surface the object is attempting to move on. It also depends on the weight, the "pressing against," or normal force exerted on the surface.

The ease or difficulty with which an object slides over another surface can be measured and described by the *coefficient of friction.* This number is symbolized by the letter μ or μ_k for sliding or kinetic friction.

To determine the coefficient of friction for any pair of materials, divide the force of friction by the normal force, or F_f/N. If an object were to slide on a frictionless surface (approached but never attained on the surface of the Earth), the coefficient would be zero. So, you would expect that slippery combinations of materials such as steel on ice (ice skates) would have very low coefficients (less than .1), while rough, textured ones like wood on gravel would have fairly high coefficients (greater than .5).

For example, if a wood block weighing 10 newtons sliding on a felt billiard table has a 20 newtons frictional force exerted on it, the coefficient of friction would be $F_f/N = 10$ n/20 n $= .5$. The coefficient of friction is a unit/less number (also called dimensionless) since it is a ratio of two forces and the units, in this case newtons, cancel out.

What if you doubled the normal force? What would happen to the coefficient of friction? At first glance, it would appear that the coefficient would double. But remember, doubling the normal force would in turn double the amount of frictional force. So, in the example above, doubling the normal force would lead to a calculation of $\mu k = Fk/N = 2 \times 10$ n/2 $\times 20$ n $= .5$, the same as before.

Focus Questions

Name two factors that affect the force of friction between two materials.

How do the force vectors W and F_N illustrate Newton's third law?

Getting The Point.

Friction and Your Tires—Locked and Unlocked

The friction between the tires of your automobile and the road determine your maximum acceleration, and more importantly your minimum stopping distance. So the nature of that friction could actually be a matter of life and death. But like all applications of friction, it has frustrating ambiguities.

Many years of research and practice have led to tread designs for automobile tires that offer good traction in a wide variety of conditions. The tread designs channel water away from the bearing surfaces on wet roads to combat the tendency to hydroplane—a condition which allows your car to "ski" on the road surface because you have a layer of water lubricant under all parts of your tire.

Jones and Childers report coefficients of friction of about 0.7 for dry roads and 0.4 for wet roads. The tread design represents an "all weather" compromise. If you were an Indianapolis race driver, you would use "slick" racing tires with no tread. On dry surfaces you might get as high as 0.9 as a coefficient of friction, but driving them on wet roads would be dangerous since the wet road coefficient might be as low as 0.1.

Sooner or later, most people have to deal with the tricky judgment of how hard to put on the brakes in an emergency stop. It is a difficult issue, and no final answers are given here. In the best case scenario, you should keep your wheels rolling while braking because the bottom point of the tire is instantaneously at rest with respect to the roadway (not slipping), and if there is a significant difference between static and kinetic friction, you will get more braking force that way. But you generally don't have the luxury of time to make a delicate judgment about how hard to put on the brakes. For good tires on dry surfaces, there is not much difference between rolling and sliding friction, and if you back off the braking force very much, you will get less braking than if you just locked them down. The other issue is that in an extreme emergency, the braking is instinctive and you tend to hit the brakes as hard as you can before you can even think about it.

Maybe locking the brakes is not so bad in good conditions on the dry road, and you may not be able to keep from doing so in an extreme emergency. But if you lock the wheels on a wet road, the results could be disastrous! I don't have anything like reliable estimates of the effective coefficient of friction, but I am guessing that it could easily drop to less than half of the "wheels rolling" braking because you are sliding on a surface which is lubricated by water. It may be that even with wheels rolling you might have in the neighborhood of 0.4 as a coefficient compared to 0.7 on the dry road, and it might drop down to the 0.1 of the slick tire.

From HYPERPHYSICS, *"Friction and Automobile Tires,"* by Rod Nave, www.phy-astr.gsu.edu. Copyright © 2001 Carl R. Nave. Reprinted with permission. http://hyperphysics.ph-astr.gsu.edu/hbase/mechanics/frictire.html (June 10, 2003)

Focus Question

What factors determine the stopping distance of your automobile when you are driving?

Workplace Connection: Friction and Professional Cycle Racing

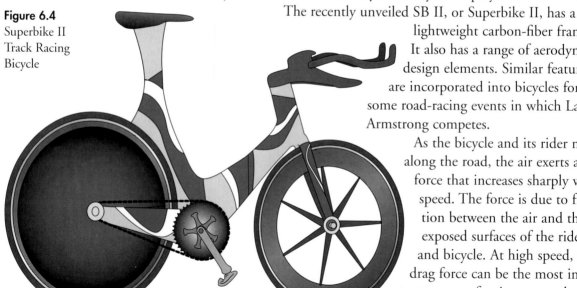

Figure 6.4
Superbike II
Track Racing
Bicycle

AERODYNAMICS have preoccupied bicycle designers since the early part of this century. The most advanced bicycles today are deployed in track racing. The recently unveiled SB II, or Superbike II, has a lightweight carbon-fiber frame. It also has a range of aerodynamic design elements. Similar features are incorporated into bicycles for some road-racing events in which Lance Armstrong competes.

As the bicycle and its rider move along the road, the air exerts a force that increases sharply with speed. The force is due to friction between the air and the exposed surfaces of the rider and bicycle. At high speed, this drag force can be the most important source of resistance, and with a wind blowing, it can also lead to significant side forces. The aerodynamic forces on a vehicle come primarily from differences in pressure and viscous shearing stresses. Pressure and viscosity are basic properties of fluids. There is an important connection between velocity and pressure and between velocity and cross-sectional area. The viscosity of air is very small, but it is not negligible. It is responsible for two types of drag: friction drag, and pressure drag. Frictional drag comes from friction between the air flow and the surfaces exposed to the air flow. This friction arises because air (and other fluids) has viscosity. Viscosity is associated with the ability of a fluid to flow freely. For example, honey has about 100 times the viscosity of water, and it is obvious that the two fluids flow differently, and that it takes much greater force to stir honey than water. Pressure drag comes from the eddying motions that are set up in air by the passage of the rider. This part of the flow is called the wake, and it is similar to the flow left behind a passing boat.

There are also two kinds of bodies: streamlined bodies and bluff bodies. A streamlined body looks like a fish, or an airfoil, and the streamlines go smoothly around the body. A bluff body looks like a brick, or a cylinder, and the streamlines break away whenever a sharp change in direction occurs. For streamlined bodies, the frictional drag is the dominant source of air resistance. For a bluff body, the dominant source of drag is the pressure drag. It is always true that, for a given frontal area and speed, a streamlined body will have a lower air resistance than a bluff body. The biggest difference between streamlined and bluff bodies is that in streamlined flow, the regions where losses occur are inside boundary layers and wakes that remain reasonably thin, whereas in bluff bodies, adverse pressure gradients cause the boundary layers to separate, which creates a large wake filled with energetic eddies which dissipate a great deal of mechanical energy and thereby increase the drag.

Parts of a rider and bicycle combination act like a streamlined body, whereas other parts behave like a bluff body. By understanding some basic aerodynamic principles, it becomes possible to identify these components, understand the magnitude of their different contributions to the overall drag, and see how we can reduce the overall drag by altering the shape of the component parts.

Reducing the friction allows for a higher constant velocity, which will give a shorter time, which can win races.

Adapted from *"Aerodynamics of Bicycles,"* by Alexander J. Smits and Barrie S. H. Royce, Department of Mechanical and Aerospace Engineering, Princeton University. Reprinted with permission. http://www.princeton.edu/~asmits/Bicycle_web/bicycle_aero.html (June 10, 2003)

Did You Know?

Teflon Is Like Dreadlocks!

Teflon has such a low coefficient of friction that it often peels off of pots and pans. (Use wooden or plastic utensils.) How do you get it to stick?

Dreadlocks analogy: Teflon is a polymer, individual strands of hair are slippery, but strands can tangle to the point where they can't be separated.

From *"Friction."* The Physics Hypertextbook, by Glenn Elert. http://hypertextbook.com/physics/matter/friction/index.shtml (June 10, 2003)

ACTIVITY 6.5

Conducting and Presenting the Performance Test of Tires

Getting In Gear

So how does all this work on frictional forces relate to ATV tires? How do different surfaces and different treads affect the coefficient of friction between the tires and the terrain? It's time to conduct your tire performance test and present your results to the class; use all of the information you have learned in the past 12 activities.

Getting To Work!

Job Sheet

To complete Project Milestone Three, you will

1. Obtain **Job Sheet 6.5** **Designing and Conducting the Tire Performance Test (and Revisit Officer Brown).** Address Parts 1 and 2 as you plan, conduct, and analyze the results of your performance test.

2. Participate in a class discussion about your presentation; then prepare it, practice it, and present it!

3. Revisit Officer Brown. Answer the questions on Part 3 of Job Sheet 6.5.

4. Check out Workplace Connection: *How Snow Tires Work* and the Did You Know? reading as time permits.

5. Review the concepts and answer the questions in What Have You Learned? for homework.

Ever wonder about the safety of car tires? Read Concept Connection: *The Safety of Tires.*

Concept Connection: The Safety of Tires

How do tires affect your safety when you drive your car along the highway? What factors help to prevent skidding and allow you to control your car when turning and stopping? What does friction have to do with this?

The tread pattern of rubber tires plays a major role in determining their friction, or skid resistance. Under dry conditions on paved roads, a smooth tire gives better traction than a grooved or patterned tread because a larger area of contact is available to develop the frictional forces. For this reason, the tires used for auto racing on the tracks at Darlington, Indianapolis, Talladega, and elsewhere have a smooth surface with no tread design. Unfortunately, a smooth tire develops very little traction under wet conditions because the frictional mechanism is reduced by a lubricating film of water between the tire and the road. A patterned tire provides grooves or channels into which the water can squeeze as the tire rolls along the road, thus again providing a region of direct contact between tire and road. A patterned tire gives typical dry and wet frictional coefficients of about 0.7 and 0.4, respectively. These values represent a compromise between the extreme values of about 0.9 (dry) and 0.1 (wet) obtained with a smooth tire.

Classical friction theory must be modified for tires because of their structural flexibility and the stretch of the tread rubber. Instead of depending solely on the coefficient of friction at the tire-road interface (which is determined by the nature of the road surface and the tread rubber compound), maximum stopping ability also depends on the resistance of the tread to tearing under the forces that occur during braking.

When a car is braked to a hard stop on a dry road, the maximum frictional force developed can be greater than the strength of the tread. The result is that instead of the tire merely sliding along the road, rubber is torn off the tread at the tire-road interface. Undoubtedly the tread resistance to this tearing is a combination of the rubber strength and the grooves and slots that make up the tread design.

The weight of the car is unevenly distributed over the tire-road contact area, creating areas of high and low pressure. (This is much like what you feel when you step on a pebble while walking in thin-soled shoes.) The resistance of the tread to tearing increases in the areas of higher pressure, where the tread is more compressed, causing an effective increase in traction.

Further, the size of the contact area is very important in car tires because the traction is dynamic rather than static; that is, it changes as the tire rolls along. The maximum coefficient of friction can occur anywhere in the contact area, so that the greater the area, the greater the likelihood of maximum traction. Thus, under identical load and on the same dry surface, the wider tire has a greater contact area and develops higher traction, resulting in greater stopping ability.

Next time you need to buy tires, think about what kind of climate you live in, what kind of roads you drive on, and what speeds you drive. If you live in a region with good paved roads, you may not need tires with extra tread. If you drive in areas with mud or snow, you need a tread designed for those conditions.

From *"The Friction of Automobile Tires."* CONTEMPORARY COLLEGE PHYSICS, 3rd ed., by Edwin Jones and Richard Childers. Copyright © 2001 McGraw-Hill Publishers. Reprinted with permission of The McGraw-Hill Companies.

Workplace Connection: How Snow Tires Work

In regions with little snow and moderate winter temperatures, all-season tires may be suitable throughout the year. However, as the temperature drops below −10 C, the rubber compound in all-season tires may cause them to lose their grip as the tires harden in the cold. Wherever cold or snowy winters are the rule, snow tires become a necessary safety precaution. In deep snow, winter

Did You Know?

In 1908, Harvey Firestone introduced the first "non-skid" tire. The words "Firestone Non-Skid" were actually vulcanized into the tire at an angle so the letters formed the tread pattern.

Adapted from *"Harvey S. Firestone and the Tractor Tire: Firestone Agricultural Tire Division Chronology."* Firestone Agricultural Tire Division. http://www.firestoneag.com/about/history_1900.asp (June 10, 2003)

treads improve traction by allowing the tire to rid itself of snow as it rolls, giving it a clear bite on the road.

Years ago, snow tires used to be knobby and noisy. They were made for driving in the snow, but had poor traction in the dry and wet. Today, winter tires are made of new rubber compounds that can handle not only ice and snow but also dry, wet or slushy driving conditions. With state-of-the-art road-clearing techniques, the roads can be clear and dry a few days after a major snow storm.

Adapted from *"Winter Tires,"* Canada Safety Council. Copyright © 2002 Canada Safety Council. http://www.safety-council.org/info/traffic/snowtires.html (June 10, 2003)

What Have You Learned?

KEY CONCEPTS

Friction. A force that is exerted between any two material surfaces that slows down a moving object. To move the object at constant speed, one must exert a force equal and opposite to the frictional force.

Sliding frictional force. When two objects slide past each other, the surface of each exerts a force on the other. This is called the sliding frictional force, and it depends on the nature of the two surfaces.

Static frictional force. When a force is applied that would tend to make one object slide past another, but no sliding occurs, the frictional force each surface exerts on the other is called the static frictional force. Static frictional force opposes the motion of two objects.

Normal or "pressing against" force. Frictional forces increase as the two surfaces in question press harder against each other. The "pressing against" force (usually the object's weight or a portion of the object's weight) that they exert on each other (sometimes called normal force) is perpendicular to the two surfaces.

Coefficient of friction. The magnitude of the frictional forces two objects exert on each other depends chiefly upon three factors:

1. the force with which the two objects press against each other;

2. the properties of the two surfaces (material, roughness, etc.) since different pairs of surfaces adhere to one another to different degrees; and

3. whether the two objects are sliding across each other or stationary with respect to each other, since the maximum static frictional force will be greater than the sliding frictional force. (If there is no sliding, the magnitude of the static frictional force will also depend on the other forces on the two objects.)

For a given pair of materials, the sliding frictional force is always the same fraction (usually expressed in decimal form) of the normal force. This fraction (which may in unusual instances be an improper fraction, that is, greater than one) is called the coefficient of sliding friction. In the same way, the coefficient of static friction for a pair of materials tells what fraction the critical, or threshold, frictional force is of the normal force.

CONCEPT QUESTIONS

1. What does the microscopic view of friction reveal about the surface nature of objects?

2. What are the three factors that determine the amount of frictional force exerted between an object and the surface the object is resting upon?

3. Why is the normal force called "normal"?

4. What is the coefficient of friction, and how is it related to finding the value of frictional forces?

5. How does static friction differ from sliding friction?

APPLYING WHAT YOU KNOW

1. If the force of kinetic friction on a mass is 40 newtons when the object weighs 80 newtons on a horizontal, wooden counter surface, what is the coefficient of friction?

2. The coefficient of friction between iron and a pine board is .4. If an iron block (mass 10 kilograms) slides on a horizontal pine board, what is the force of kinetic friction opposing the motion of the block?

What Makes a Vehicle Turn?

OVERVIEW

TURNING THE CORNER

The test was a success! The Wheelers and Dealers company is thrilled with the information you've given them about the performance of the test vehicle's tires in a straight line. This will help a lot in the production of their ATVs. They have one more big concern, however. They want to see how the tires should behave when the ATVs turn corners.

Changing direction involves forces in more than one direction, so you will learn something new as you develop a new tire performance test for cornering. Newton's laws of motion still apply, but you need to take into account forces in two dimensions. Put it all together and you'll have ATVs that can go anywhere!

Your last milestone:

Project Milestone 4 — **Evaluating a Tire's Performance during Cornering**

You will describe the desired behavior of an ATV's tires when the vehicle is turning a corner. You will design data collection procedures for a test during cornering, under the same terrain conditions you investigated in milestone three. You will implement the test, evaluate how well it works, and then report your findings to the other engineering groups.

Now your engineering team will explore the forces and motion involved when a wheeled vehicle corners. You will start by learning about the forces and motion involved in getting moving objects—yourself included—to change direction. You will investigate forces that produce changes of direction in wheeled vehicles and extend your understanding of velocity, speed, and Newton's second law to two dimensions. You will explore how and why different types of tire treads are important when an ATV changes direction in a variety of terrain conditions. By the end of the chapter, you will have designed and conducted a test of a tire tread's performance during cornering on a particular kind of terrain.

To help you accomplish Project Milestone Three, you will do the following activities:

Activity 7.1 Getting a Moving Object to Change Direction
You will experiment with different ways of making balls change direction, and start to discuss the forces and motion involved. While the answer to the question How does a car go in the direction that its wheels are pointing? may seem pretty obvious at first, you may be surprised at what's really going on. Down the road, your conclusions will help you to design your performance test of tires during cornering.

Activity 7.2 Thinking about Forces and Motion in Two Dimensions
You will now extend your understanding of velocity, speed, and Newton's second law to two dimensions. You will consider what forces are required for changing an object's direction in two different directions and what happens if two forces are exerted at once. You will be introduced to the idea of an equivalent force (equivalent to a combination of other forces), and to the idea that a force actually exerted on an object going around a corner is equivalent to a pair of component forces.

Activity 7.3 Why Does a Car Go in the Direction That Its Wheels Are Pointing?
You will explore what wheeled vehicles have in common with all moving objects and what aspects are specific to wheeled vehicles. When a car goes around a turn, why does a car (or other wheeled vehicle) go in the direction that its wheels are pointing? Does it always? What about when the car skids? To answer those questions, you will have to think about, and perhaps test, the following: Which of the approaches that you took to changing an object's direction works best for an object moving on wheels?

Activity 7.4   Examining Tire Treads

Now that you're ready to focus on your new assignment, you will check out the competition by examining various patterns of tire treads up close. You will analyze what tread features are important for different aspects of driving a car or bike (such as starting, stopping, and turning a corner). Then you will learn about the "connection" between forces and these features.

Activity 7.5   Testing a Tire's Performance during Cornering

Another deadline is fast approaching! Your engineering team will design, carry out, and make a presentation about its ATV tire performance test during cornering. Using a wagon, the test should show the differences in tire performance on particular terrain conditions between various types of tire tread.

ACTIVITY 7.1

Getting a Moving Object to Change Direction

Getting In Gear

Think about going around a corner in a car or a bus. If the driver turns sharply, which way does your body seem to move? What about an object that was resting on the dashboard or on a seat? Can you explain this behavior? (Hint: Remember Newton's First Law of Motion.)

You will work with a rolling heavy ball to make it turn a corner. You will use what you've learned about straight-line forces in earlier activities to figure out how to use forces in two dimensions to change the direction of an object.

Getting To Work!

To investigate how to get a rolling ball to change direction, you will

1. Read the overview scenario and project milestone for Chapter 7, and discuss the scenario with your class.

Job Sheet

2. Complete the activity in ⟨ **Job Sheet 7.1** ⟩ Getting a Moving Object to Change Direction.

3. Read Getting the Point: *How Does a Car Make a Turn?,* and answer the Focus Questions.

4. Check out the Workplace Connection: *Different Skates Lead to Faster Times on Short, Oval Tracks,* and the Did You Know? reading as time permits.

Wonder how airplanes change direction? Read Concept Connection: *How Airplanes Change Direction.*

Getting The Point.

How Does a Car Make a Turn?

A force is required for anything to change direction. Newton's first law states that an object will remain in straight-line motion, at a constant speed, unless acted upon by an outside force.

Therefore, for a vehicle to change direction, a force must be applied in the direction of that motion change. For a car to make a left turn, the force must be applied to the left. Where does this force come from? It is due to the friction between the wheels and the road. Think about it. Without friction, say on ice, the car would just continue moving in a straight line just as Newton said. The more friction, the greater the change in direction.

Figure 7.1
Force and Velocity Diagrams for the Moon and a Car

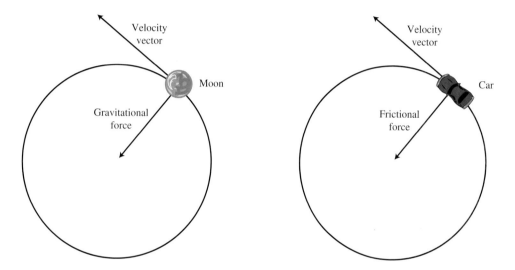

A large part of Sir Isaac Newton's genius was to convey these same earthly principles of motion to objects in space—that the same events and laws that occur here on Earth apply to objects in space. He often used the Moon to prove his ideas. First, he started with the idea of a falling apple. As the apple falls from the tree toward the Earth's surface, so the Moon falls toward the Earth. The difference is that the Moon is farther away so it falls a lot slower than the apple. Why? Because the force gets weaker as a function of the inverse square of the distance separating any two objects. The next part of the problem is, why doesn't the Moon get any closer? Why does it go in a circle (an ellipse, actually)? What makes it change direction? Unlike the car turning a corner, in space there is no friction. While the car has the frictional force of the road surface causing it to change direction, (due to the road pushing back on the tires), the Moon has a constant inward force from the gravitational force field between the Moon and Earth. This constant force is what causes the Moon to fall toward Earth.

However, just as the faster a car goes the wider the turn is, the Moon is moving really fast. So the Moon's turn is really wide!

Where does the force come from that enables a car to make a turn?

How is a car moving through a turn similar to the Moon traveling in its orbit around Earth?

Concept Connection: How Airplanes Change Direction

Force = Mass × Acceleration

Lift is a force. From Newton's Second Law of Motion, a force is produced when a mass is accelerated (F = m a). An acceleration is a change in velocity with a change in time. We have written a difference equation on this figure, but it is recognized that the relation is actually a differential (from calculus). The important fact is that a force will cause a change in velocity; and, likewise, a change in velocity will generate a force. The equation works both ways. A velocity has both a magnitude (called the speed) and a direction associated with it. Scientists and mathematicians call this a vector quantity (magnitude plus direction). So, to change either the speed or the direction of a flow, you must impose a force. And if either the speed or the direction of a flow is changed, a force will be generated.

Adapted from *"Lift from Flow Turning,"* by Tom Benson. Glenn Research Center. Courtesy of NASA. http://www.grc.nasa.gov/WWW/K-12/airplane/right2.html (June 10, 2003)

Figure 7.2
Correct Explanation of Lift from a Flow across an Airplane Wing

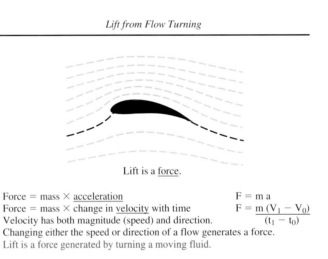

Lift from Flow Turning

Lift is a force.

Force = mass × acceleration   F = m a
Force = mass × change in velocity with time $F = \dfrac{m\,(V_1 - V_0)}{(t_1 - t_0)}$
Velocity has both magnitude (speed) and direction.
Changing either the speed or direction of a flow generates a force.
Lift is a force generated by turning a moving fluid.

There are many theories of how lift is generated. Unfortunately, many of the theories found in encyclopedias, on Web sites, and even in some textbooks are incorrect.

Figure 7.3

Incorrect Explanation of Lift from Flow across an Airplane Wing

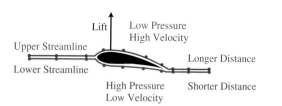

Incorrect Theory

Lift

Low Pressure
High Velocity

Upper Streamline

Longer Distance

Lower Streamline

High Pressure
Low Velocity

Shorter Distance

"Longer Path" or "Equal Transit" Theory
- Top of airfoil is shaped to provide longer path than bottom. Air molecules have farther to go over the top.
- Air molecules must move faster over the top to meet molecules at the trailing edge that have gone underneath.
- From Bernoulli's equation, higher velocity produces lower pressure on the top.
- Difference in pressure produces lift.

One of the most widely circulated, but incorrect, explanations can be labeled the "Longer Path" theory, or the "Equal Transit Time" theory. The theory states that airfoils are shaped with the upper surface longer than the bottom. The air molecules (the little colored balls on the figure) have farther to travel over the top of the airfoil than along the bottom in order to meet up at the trailing edge. Therefore, the molecules going over the top of the wing must travel faster than the molecules moving under the wing. On the basis of research done by Daniel Bernouli, an 18th century physicist and mathematician, one would predict that because the upper flow is faster, then the pressure is lower. The difference in pressure across the airfoil would produce the lift.

One problem with this theory: Lifting airfoils are designed to have the upper surface longer than the bottom. This is not always correct. The symmetric (same shape on both sides of wing) airfoil generates plenty of lift, and its upper surface is the same length as the lower surface. Think about a paper airplane. Its airfoil is a flat plate, top and bottom, exactly the same length and shape, and yet it flies just fine. This part of the theory probably got started because early airfoils were curved and shaped with a longer distance along the top. Such airfoils do produce a lot of lift and flow turning, but it is the *turning that's important,* not the distance. There are modern, low-drag airfoils that produce lift on which the bottom surface is actually longer than the top. This theory also does not explain how airplanes can fly upside down (the longer path would then be on the bottom!), which happens often at air shows and in air-to-air combat.

Another problem: Two molecules near each other at the leading edge will not end up next to each other at the trailing edge. The problem with the equal transit theory is that it attempts to provide us with the velocity based on a non-physical assumption as discussed above.

This example illustrates that even "experts" can get it wrong. Most physics ideas take a lot of thinking.

Adapted from *"Incorrect Theory #1,"* by Tom Benson. Glenn Research Center. Courtesy of NASA.
http://www.grc.nasa.gov/WWW/K-12/airplane/wrong1.html (June 10, 2003)

Workplace Connection: Different Skates Lead to Faster Times on Short, Oval Tracks

The following article was published in Popular Mechanics *just before the 1998 Winter Olympic Games.*

At this year's Winter Olympic Games in Nagano, Japan, speed skating will be a truly international competition. But the contest might be more technological than athletic. A new kind of skate is changing everything about the sport, from the way it's performed, to the standards of excellence, to the way it sounds. But the skates are so new and the manufacturers so overwhelmed that all skaters may not have access to the equipment. Some traditionalists wish no one did.

The new skates, known alternately as clap skates or slap skates, have a spring-loaded hinge on the toe that allows the heel to pull away from the blade at the end of the stride. This motion keeps the blade in contact with the ice longer and delivers more power per stride. As the blade snaps back into place, it creates the loud clap that led to the skate's name and forever eliminated the sport's gentle whooshing melody.

Skaters using the new skates have been dominating competition. At last year's World Single Distance Championships, 13 of the 16 men that qualified in the 5000 meters were on clap skates. Clap skate users also won first and third in the women's All-Around World Distance Championship. "We saw skaters medal this year who had never been a factor before," says U.S. skater Casey FitzRandolph, "and the difference was definitely the clap skate."

For the world's top skaters, the message is loud and clear: clap or be heard from no more!

The seeds of change were planted in the early '80s by a team of Dutch scientists. According to J.J. de Koning, a member of that team, the eureka moment came while comparing the differences between jumpers and skaters. Jumpers, it was noted, extend their ankles, flexing their calf muscles and pushing off their toes. Speed skaters keep their ankles locked and push off their heels, because pushing off their toes would cause the blade tip to dig into the ice and slow them down.

Based on these observations, the team theorized that a skate that allowed ankle flexion while keeping the blade parallel to the ice could produce faster times by creating a longer stride that included the calf muscles. The clap skate did just that.

Figure 7.4
A Traditional Speed Skate

A traditional speed skate comes off the ice long before the back leg is fully extended.

Figure 7.5
A Clap Skate

The clap skate allows a longer stride.

Although the skate showed great promise, during the subsequent 10 years the team had a hard time selling it to the skeptical and tradition-bound skating world. The mechanism itself proved delicate and tuning it was a challenge. But the team continued making improvements and testing the skate. Skaters who used the new skates showed improvement, but top-level international skaters were still reluctant to try them.

Finally, in the '94-'95 season, 11 Dutch junior skaters agreed to use the clap skates. The group improved their times by an average of 6.2%, compared with 2.5% for normal skaters.

CLAP ON?

But a haunting reality looms for athletes who have dedicated their lives to the sport: the race for Olympic gold may have been won on the drawing board, not the ice. de Koning, who helped develop the skates, disputes that outlook. "The slap is meant to enable the skater to 'slap on' an extra amount of work per stroke," he says. "Note, however, that this extra work is not free. One has to have the physical capacity to increase the work per stroke and the mean power output in order to skate faster." In other words, it still comes down to who's the best skater.

But one question remains. Isn't introducing a mechanical device into a sport that never required anything but sharpened steel, frozen water and painstaking effort a little like painting a mustache on the Mona Lisa?

Now that the Nagano Olympics are over, every winner wore clap skates and so the controversy may be over; until the next invention comes along.

Did You Know?

Leonardo da Vinci studied speed skating. In 1488, Leonardo da Vinci, the Renaissance visionary who foresaw the coming of the military tank, the parachute and the water turbine, studied speed skating. But like one of his artworks, Leonardo finally dropped the subject when he could find no way to improve it. In fact, the sport of speed skating did not undergo a significant technological alteration until the 1980's!

ACTIVITY 7.2

Thinking about Forces and Motion in Two Dimensions

Do you ever feel like everyone is pulling you in different directions? Your friends, your family, your teachers—all trying to lead you in their direction. How do you choose a path of your own? When forces act on an object from multiple directions, the object's path is a result of all of the forces pushing or pulling on it. You will learn how to analyze forces in two dimensions using vectors. Vectors allow you to find the net force that is the result of all of the forces acting on the object. It is this net force that determines the motion of the object.

Getting To Work!

Job Sheet

To explore forces and motion in two dimensions, you will

1. Complete the activity in | **Job Sheet 7.2** | Testing Forces in Two Dimensions.

2. Read Getting the Point: *Analyzing Two-Dimensional Motion,* and answer the Focus Questions.

3. Discuss the analysis of two-dimensional motion.

4. Check out the Did You Know? reading as time permits.

Ever wonder why racetracks have banked curves? Read Concept Connection: *The Normal Force and Curves.*

Getting The Point.

Analyzing Two-Dimensional Motion

Many of the motions you have studied so far have been linear, that is, objects, cars, and tires have been moving in a straight line due to a single unbalanced force. But many forces are applied in several directions at the same time. The resulting force, and the motion of the object that the force is acting upon, can be determined through a special kind of analysis using vectors. Vectors are quantities with both a magnitude and a direction. They can be added together in scale diagrams to find a sum of a number of forces, or conversely, the components of a single force or any other vector quantity, such as velocity, acceleration, or displacement.

Two perpendicular force vectors can be added to find the resultant force. By drawing the vectors to scale, you can find the resultant, or answer to the problem. For instance, if you apply a force of 10 newtons due north on a mass, and also a force of 10 newtons due east on it, what is the net force acting on the mass?

In your mind, you can imagine that two such forces would move the mass in a northeasterly direction. But what would the magnitude of this force be, and in what exact direction would the mass move?

A step-by-step procedure for adding vectors follows:

1. Select a scale and accurately draw the first vector to scale in the indicated direction. Vectors are drawn to scale as arrows, with the head of the arrow pointing in the vector's specified direction.

2. Draw the second vector to scale, and place its tail on the head of the first.

3. Draw the answer (called the resultant) from the tail of the first vector you drew to the head of the last vector. This will be the hypotenuse of the triangle.

4. Using a ruler and a protractor, measure the length of the resultant (magnitude), and measure the number of degrees from the north toward the east (direction).

5. In our example, the magnitude of the resultant is approximately 14 newtons, and the direction of the force is N45°E.

In addition, a single force, velocity, or any other vector quantity can be resolved into its horizontal and vertical components. In this case, the single force is drawn to scale. Then the horizontal and vertical components can be drawn and measured with a ruler. Here is an example:

What is the horizontal and vertical velocity components of a force pulling up on a wagon with a force of 50 newtons at an angle of 40° to the horizontal?

Solution:

Figure 7.6
Vector Analysis of Forces Pulling a Wagon

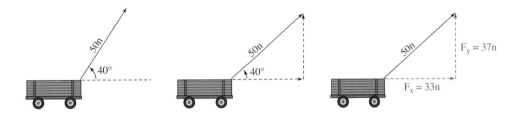

Focus Questions

What is a vector quantity?

Why is mass not considered a vector quantity?

If a man walks his dog 100 feet down the street, then turns left for an additional 100 feet, what is the dog's actual distance from its starting point?

Concept Connection: The Normal Force and Curves

The <u>normal</u> force is the reaction force from a surface, usually due to the weight of an object and perpendicular (at a right angle) to the surface. Newton's third law describes this as an action-reaction pair. The action is the weight of the car pushing down due to gravity ($F = mg$), the reaction is the road pushing back ($N = mg$). They are equal and opposite.

FLAT CURVES VERSUS BANKED CURVES

A flat curve is when a vehicle turns right or left on a flat surface. In the diagrams in Figure 7.7, the car is traveling toward the reader and making a left turn.

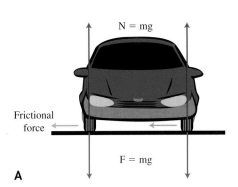

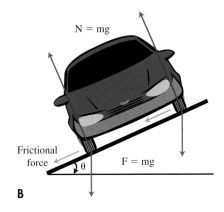

On the flat turn the friction of the road has to be such that it will hold the car to the road's surface. If the car's velocity is too high the car will slide to the right.

Likewise when you are in the car you feel "pulled" to the right because you are trying to maintain straight line motion as in Newton's first law. It is your inertia.

On the banked curve the normal force from the road has a horizontal component that acts in the direction of the turn. So the road itself assists the car's turning, and its vertical component helps keep you in your seat. In fact, if the car's velocity is just right, the car will turn left without your turning the steering wheel at all, even if the road has ice on it!

Did You Know?

Have you ever traveled through a curve in a car and felt as if you were about to slide toward the outside of the curve? If you have, your car was traveling too fast for the speed the curve was engineered for. If you travel exactly at the design speed, centripetal and frictional forces are balanced and you feel a steady pull on the wheel toward the center of the curve and a steady force pushing you across the seat of the car. The equation for calculating the safe design speed of a curve is

$$v^2 = rg \tan \theta$$

where *v* is the velocity (speed) of your car through the curve, *r* is the radius of the curve, *g* is the acceleration due to gravity (9.8 m/sec^2), and θ is the angle that the curve is banked.

Figure 7.8
Components of Force Vector while Car Is Banking

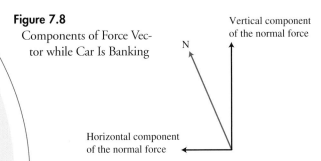

To help think about this, think of a curved bank of ice and a hockey puck. If the puck has just the right velocity it will travel smoothly through the curve; if it is going too fast it will move up the bank; if it is traveling too slowly it will travel down the bank.

An airplane uses the same principal to make a turn. It "banks" through the turn.

HIGH SPEED BANK	MEDIUM SPEED BANK	LOW SPEED BANK
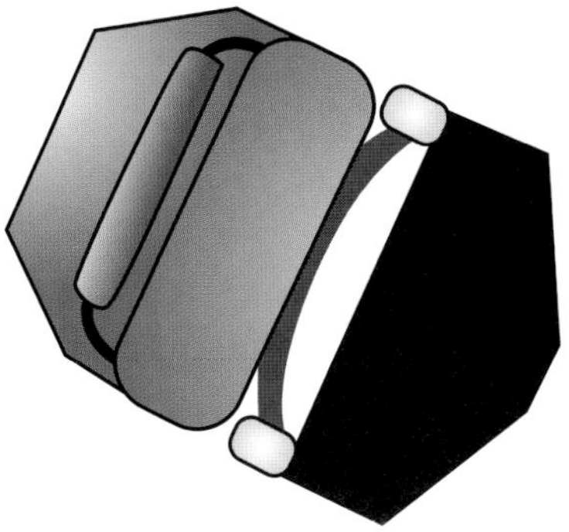	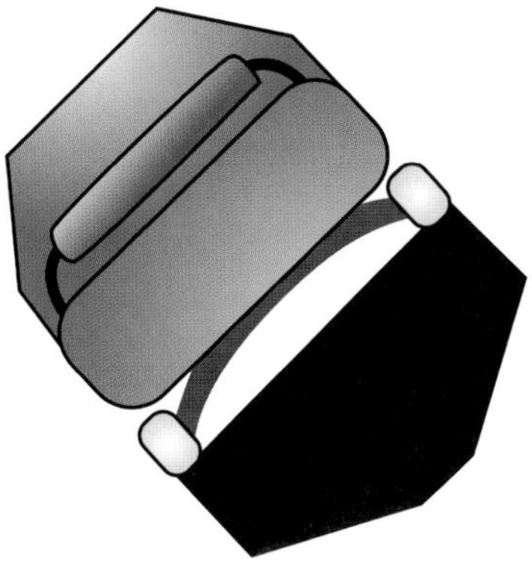	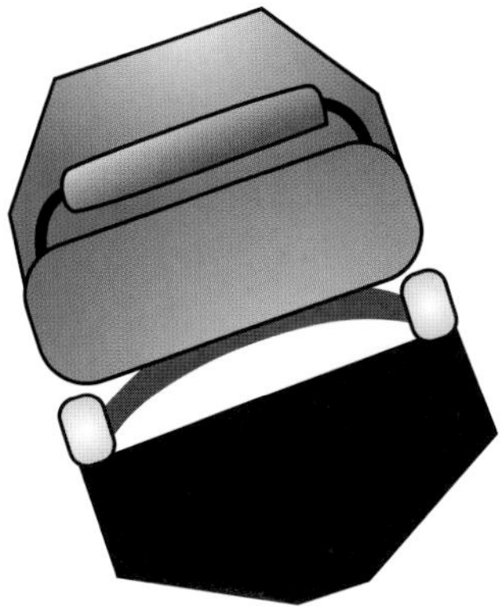
Too much bank for the car's velocity, the car could tip to the inside. The undercarriage wheels are holding the car on. The rider feels a force pushing himself down. Friction is needed to keep the car on the track.	At just the right bank for the car's velocity, the car does not need any type of undercarriage to stay on the track. The rider feels a force pushing his bottom into the seat. This is the optimum position where no friction is needed to keep the car on the track.	Not enough bank for the car's velocity. The car could tip to the outside. The undercarriage wheels are holding the car on. The rider feels a force pushing himself to the outside of the curve—sideways. Friction is needed to keep the car on the track.

Figure 7.9
Roller Coaster Cars on Speed Banks

ROLLER COASTERS

A flat curve gives a rider the sensation of being thrown sideways. If the roller coaster car's velocity is fast enough and the radius small enough, the stresses on the car's under carriage can be tremendous. For a flat curve the inward net acceleration felt by the rider is calculated from the equation.

A banked curve reduces the rider's sensation of being thrown sideways by turning the car sideways. The car is tilted. The trick is to tilt the track just the right amount.

Adapted from Roller Coaster Physics, *"Curves,"* by Tony Wayne. Reprinted with permission. http://www.vast.org/vip/book/CURVES/HOME.htm (June 10, 2003)

ACTIVITY 7.3

Why Does a Car Go in the Direction That Its Wheels Are Pointing?

When a car or a bus goes around a turn, why does it go in the direction that its wheels are pointing? Does it always? What about on an icy or rainy street? You will investigate how best to make a moving wheeled object change direction. This will help you understand how different types of tires are important when you want to make a vehicle such as an ATV change direction in a variety of terrain conditions.

Getting To Work!

Job Sheet

To investigate the two-dimensional motion of wheeled vehicles, you will

1. Follow the instructions on **Job Sheet 7.3** Making Cars Go in Circles.

2. Participate in a class discussion about why a car does or doesn't go in the direction that its wheels are pointing.

3. Read Getting the Point: *Force and Direction,* and answer the Focus Questions.

4. Check out Workplace Connection: *Dizzy in the Curves of Texas Motor Speedway* and the Did You Know? reading as time permits.

Were you ever curious about how trains turn on straight tracks? Read Concept Connection: *Superelevation Turns Trains.*

Getting The Point.

Force and Direction

All objects will travel in a straight line or remain at rest unless an external force acts upon them. Car wheels are always experiencing an opposing force to the direction the car is moving—friction from the surface of the road or other terrain. So if a car is going to change direction, say go left, it needs to encounter a force in that direction.

The force that acts on your car can be exerted when you move the steering wheel, or if the angle of the road changes. In either case, your car will change direction. If your car changes direction (an aspect of changing the velocity vector), it must be undergoing acceleration. The acceleration is toward the center of the curve you are turning through and is called the *centripetal* or "center-seeking" acceleration. From a vector diagram (not shown here), the value for centripetal acceleration can be derived as follows:

$$a_c = v^2/r$$

It follows that the force that is producing the acceleration, called centripetal force, is the inward pulling force that keeps you traveling in a circular or curved path. Newton's second law derives its value as follows:

$$F = ma \quad a_c = \frac{v^2}{r} \quad \text{so: } F = m\frac{v^2}{r}$$

where r is the radius of the turn, and the force is directed toward the center, the direction the object will move.

So when the wheels on your car change direction, they require a new force. Until a new one acts on the car, it will continue to travel in a straight line according to Newton's first law. If you have had the experience of riding in a car when the driver attempted to turn—only to have the car keep traveling in a straight line—you will appreciate how important friction is in supplying the centripetal force your car wheels need!

Focus Questions

What is centripetal acceleration? What causes it?

What is the origin of the centripetal force required to keep your car turning through a curve with radius _r_?

Concept Connection: Superelevation Turns Trains

Trains usually travel straight but when they change directions it is caused by a reaction force opposing the inside rim of the train's wheels from the track pushing back.

RAILROAD OPERATIONS

The secret to a train's great efficiency is its road of rails. There is very little resistance to moving anything on rails. The steel wheel on a steel rail takes up very little room. For example, a train wheel on a rail occupies the space of a dime, whereas a truck tire occupies the space of a paper dollar! An eighteen-wheel truck takes up eighteen paper dollars worth of road space. The eight-wheel rail car takes up only the space of eight dimes. And the rail car can carry many times more weight than the truck. Tracks are often "superelevated" on curves. Superelevation is the making of the outside rail on a curve higher than the inside one. The superelevation permits trains to negotiate the curve more safely at a higher speed.

Adapted from *"Railroad Curriculum."* Federal Railroad Administration.
http://www.fra.dot.gov/public/edu/school/curriculum/8-12/activities8-12.html (June 10, 2003)

Workplace Connection: Dizzy in the Curves of Texas Motor Speedway

RACE CAR DRIVERS DIZZY OVER PHYSICS

College Park, MD (May 24, 2001) The drivers competing in the Indianapolis 500 race this weekend will have to contend with more that just the other drivers—they'll have to battle the gravitational forces of physics.

In April, the Firestone Firehawk 600 Championship Auto Racing Teams (CART) race at Texas Motor Speedway was cancelled because most of the drivers became dizzy while practicing at speeds over 230 mph. Physicists say this is unlikely to happen during the Indianapolis 500 race. "Speed isn't the reason drivers get dizzy," says Dr. Richard Hewko, a professor of physics at East Kootenay Community College in British Columbia. "It's the speed and the driver's head position combined with the total forces acting on the driver."

These forces called G-forces (Gs) describe the amount of push or pull on an object, with 1 G equal to the gravitational force on an object at sea level. For example, 5Gs would equal 5 times the effect of gravity. G-forces can be front-to-back (Gx), side-to-side (Gy), and head-to-toe (Gz). When Gx forces increase, your body is pulled forward or pinned to the seat like an astronaut during liftoff. Gy forces push your body up against the side of the car like someone riding a rollercoaster, but when Gz forces increase on your body, it will feel heavier. "The blood that normally goes up to the arteries of the brain is pulled down by G-forces towards your feet," says Dr. Paul Werchan, a research physiologist at Brooks Air Force Base's Air Force Research Laboratory. "People can experience a wide variety of symptoms at 3Gs including dizziness and can loose consciousness at 5Gs." Werchan has been contacted by CART's medical team to help analyze the G-forces on the drivers practicing for the race in Texas.

To determine the total G-forces acting on a driver it is necessary to take into account the speed, and the position of the driver. Other crucial factors include the radius, length, and banking angle of the turns of the speedway. The Texas Motor Speedway's track has longer turns with higher banks at each corner than the Indianapolis 500 track. This affects the G-forces on the driver and how long they are acting on them. According to Beckman, at 230 mph drivers at Texas Motor Speedway would feel G-forces of almost 5Gs for about 6 seconds, but in Indianapolis the drivers would only feel G-forces of about 3Gs for about 4 seconds.

"Drivers feel the G-forces longer in the turns at Texas Motor Speedway than at the Indianapolis 500 track," says Brian Beckman, physicist and member of the No Bucks Racing Club. "This might explain why the drivers had a harder time handling the turns even though their speeds were comparable to what they would drive at Indianapolis."

According to Hewko, the drivers head position also plays a role in how drivers handle turns. "The banking of the turns confuses the relationship between your eye, brain, and inner ear," says Hewko. "The inner ear tells the driver which way the G-forces are acting, but the force is not the typical down force of gravity—that's what makes drivers feel dizzy."

With the help of physics, drivers in this weekend's Indianapolis 500 race will be able to maintain their fast speeds without the threat of getting dizzy like the drivers at Texas Motor Speedway, but they still have to be driven to defy gravity.

From *"Race Car Drivers Dizzy Over Physics."* Inside Science News Service (ISNS), American Institute of Physics. Reprinted with permission. http://www.aip.org/isns/reports/2001/015.html (June 10, 2003)

ACTIVITY 7.4

Examining Tire Treads

Getting In Gear

What is the difference between the tires on race cars and the tires on ATVs? Well, the size might be different, but also the secret is in the tread? Do you think you'd want smoother or bumpier treads for your ATV?

Why? What about a race car? Does the pattern of the tread make a difference? You will examine tire treads up close and think about what makes the best tire for different types of terrain and for different types of motion such as stopping, starting, and turning corners.

Getting To Work!

To explore the treads of different tires, you will

1. Engage in a class discussion with your teacher.

2. Obtain Job Sheet 7.4 Tire Treads Up Close, and answer Questions 1–3.

3. Check out the Did You Know? reading as time permits.

Were you ever curious about the physics of your bicycle tires? Read Concept Connection: *Physics of Bicycle Tires*.

Job Sheet

Concept Connection: Physics of Bicycle Tires

TENSION NOT COMPRESSION

It's easy to think of the spokes as columns supporting the wheel and helping it retain its shape. But, the "support" that the wheel receives is created by pulling the spokes towards the center of the wheel (tension) rather than pushing out from the center (compression). If you've had the occasion to hold a spoke that was removed from a wheel, you've probably noticed how flimsy it is. You could bend one in half without too much effort. However, if you tried to pull one apart you would not be able to. The "pulling" of the spokes toward the center of the hub is what gives the bicycle wheel its strength.

So just how strong are bicycle wheels? "Wheels, from what I remember, can hold about 400 times their own weight on a regular basis and they won't collapse until roughly 700 times their own weight, which makes them one of the strongest man-made structures on the planet," explained bicycle maker Paolo Salvagione.

PNEUMATIC TIRES

The pneumatic (or air-filled) rubber tire is something we take for granted today. Almost every type of bicycle wheel has a pneumatic tire on its rim. The development of the pneumatic tire was an important landmark in the development of the modern bicycle. Prior to its invention in 1888 by John Boyd Dunlop, bicycling was a bumpy and somewhat uncomfortable experience. Tires were made out of leather (and later solid rubber) attached to a wood or metal rim. The air-filled tire brought with it a smooth, comfortable, and stable ride. It's no surprise that it also helped make bicycling more popular.

ARE YOUR TIRES FAT OR THIN?

Depending on the type, your bicycle has either fat tires or thin tires. Most road bikes and touring bikes have thinner tires, while mountain bikes have big fat tires. Each

Did You Know?

Tire Facts

- The first "tire deal" was cut in 1901 by Goodyear's co-founder and sales manager, Charles Seiberling, when he wrote young Henry Ford regarding Ford's new race car: "I am willing to throw away the profit on this set of tires in order to get you started and give you a chance to test them."

- The first notable race tire development was a switch from square-woven fabric to cord fabric when a number of "side flange detachable" tires suffered cord failure in a major race in England in 1902.

- Some race tires are inflated with air treated by a special dryer to remove excess moisture, which results in better tire pressure control.

- Almost 85 percent of the many, many hours of testing that go into a new Goodyear race tire is done on the computers and in the laboratories of the Akron Technical Center. Only 15 percent of the testing is actually done on the track.

Adapted from *"Did You Know?–Goodyear Fast Facts for Those Trivia Lovers."* The Goodyear Tire & Rubber Company. http://www.racegoodyear.com/fastfacts.html (June 10, 2003)

type of tire has been adapted for the surfaces they ride on. The road tires are inflated to 100 or even 120 PSI (pounds per square inch). A firm thin tire on the asphalt surface won't flatten much. The less the tire flattens out on the bottom, the less surface area is in contact with the road. Less contact in this case means less friction, and more speed. This is why keeping tires properly inflated is so important.

Wide and fat mountain bike tires flatten out more on a hard asphalt surface. However, on a dirt trail, a mountain bike tire "floats" on top of the rough surface. A thinner road tire would cut deep into the dirt, forcing the cyclist to pedal her way out of a hole.

It is easy to imagine a pneumatic tire "flattening out" on the bottom as it rotates. But surprisingly, steel train wheels on a steel rail experience the same effect. The temporary flattening-out of the wheel, as well as sinkage on the contacting surface, is what leads to "rolling resistance." This term is used to describe how much energy is "lost to the road" as a wheel moves forward. Tires with low pressure traveling on soft ground tend to have higher rolling resistance. This is one of the major reasons why road racing is a faster sport then mountain biking.

TIRE TREADS

The treads of mountain bike tires can affect performance. Rough or "knobby" treads grip dirt trails better, but create greater friction on smooth roads. Smooth tires grip smooth roads better, with less resistance, but slip on dirt trails. Mountain bike tires manufacturers produce a variety of different patterned nobby treads. While cyclists have different preferences, there has been little scientific support for one tread performing better than another.

From *"The Wheel."* Science of Cycling. © Exploratorium, www.exploratorium.edu. Reprinted with permission. http://www.exploratorium.edu/cycling/wheel3.html (June 10, 2003)

ACTIVITY 7.5

Testing a Tire's Performance during Cornering

Getting In Gear

Now that you have some familiarity with forces in two dimensions and of various types of tire treads, how are you going to use all this knowledge to test your tire's performance? This time the test requires deciding how to measure which types of tires are best for cornering. Drivers, start your engines!

Getting To Work!

To complete Project Milestone Four, you will

1. Complete ⎢ **Job Sheet 7.5** ⎢ **Testing a Tire's Performance during Cornering.**

2. Follow your teacher's directions for preparing your presentation.

3. Check out Workplace Connection: *Why Bobsleighs and Toys Need Banked Curves* and the Did You Know? reading as time permits.

4. Review the concepts and answer the questions in What Have You Learned? for homework.

Job Sheet

Ever wonder how astronauts create their own gravity? Read Concept Connection: *Circular Motion Can Simulate Gravity.*

Concept Connection: Circular Motion Can Simulate Gravity

An artist's conception of a rotating space colony in the form of a giant wheel. A person living in this noninertial frame of reference has an illusion of a force pulling her outward, toward the deck, for the same reason that a person in a pickup truck has the illusion of a force pulling the bowling ball toward the door when making a turn. By adjusting the speed of rotation, the designers can make an acceleration (v^2/r) equal to the usual acceleration of gravity on earth. On earth, your acceleration standing on the ground is zero, and a falling rock heads for your feet with an acceleration of 9.8 m/s^2. A person standing on the deck of the space colony has an upward acceleration of 9.8 m/s^2, and when she lets go of a rock, her feet head up at the nonaccelerating rock. To her, it seems the same as true gravity.

Figure 7.10
A Rotating Space Colony
Image from http://www.jsc.nasa.gov/er/seh/settle86.GIF (June 10, 2003).
Courtesy of NASA.

Adapted from NEWTONIAN PHYSICS, by Benjamin Crowell.
© Copyright 1998 Benjamin Crowell. http://www.lightandmatter.com/htmlbook/bk1ch09.html (June 10, 2003)

How important is friction in the real world?

Did you know that an Indianapolis style racecar could just as easily drive upside down due to the incredible downward pressure (Force (weight)/Area (tires)) created by controlling the airflow? At high speed the lifting force is many times it's resting weight. With this much pressure the tires must be able to handle not only a lot of force, in all directions, but at the same time last as long as possible. Not an easy task for the design team.

In 1985, race winner Danny Sullivan became the first driver to complete the full 500-mile distance with a final lap speed faster than 200 mph. Sullivan's time for the white-flag lap was 44.302 seconds, and his speed was 203.151 mph. Coming across the finish line right behind Sullivan was runner-up Mario Andretti, with an even-faster speed of 203.422 mph.

From *"Jewels of the 500,"* Saturday, May 25, 2002. Compiled by Bob Wilson. My Brickyard. http://my.brickyard.com/500/jewels/archives.php (June 10, 2003)

One of the most interesting characters in the field of human occupation of space was Princeton Professor of physics, Gerard K. O'Neill. During the course of this work he wrote several books, including the award-winning The High Frontier; served as an adviser to NASA, the Congress and as a member of the President's National Commission on Space.

"... I think there is reason to hope that the opening of a new, high frontier will challenge the best that is in us, that the new lands waiting to be built in space will give us new freedom to search for better governments, social systems, and ways of life, and that our children may thereby find a world richer in opportunity by our efforts during the decades ahead."

From THE HIGH FRONTIER: HUMAN COLONIES IN SPACE, by Gerald K. O'Neill. Space Studies Institute Press 1989, Princeton NJ.

Workplace Connection: Why Bobsleighs and Toys Need Banked Curves

Bobsleigh was invented by a group of Englishmen on holiday in Switzerland in 1890. Their aim was to create a sled that could carry two or more people down a snow-covered road between St. Moritz and Cerlina. The new sport immediately caught on

Figure 7.11
Race Car

Courtesy of Corel

Figure 7.12
Bobsleigh

Courtesy of Corel

and a special track, complete with banked curves, made of ice, was constructed next to the road in 1902.

Bobsleigh has evolved over the years into a dramatically exciting and demanding sport. Competitions are run down ice tracks that are at least 1500 m long with at least 15 banked curves. Speeds of over 90 mph are reached. The bobsleighs themselves are extremely expensive, high technology, machines made from steel, aluminum and composites. The slider of today is a highly trained athlete and a good start at the beginning of the run (lauf) is vital. It is the pilot's responsibility to steer the bobsleigh down the track in the most efficient way possible. Bobsleigh is a team sport and teamwork is the essential ingredient in order to create the perfect harmony necessary to complete a successful run.

Adapted from *"The History of Bobsleigh"* and "The Sport Today." Calgary Bobsled Club. http://www.telusplanet.net/public/oaneale/history.htm (June 20, 2002)

What Have You Learned?

KEY CONCEPTS

Force and acceleration during a change in direction. Turning is inescapably a two-dimensional motion. Because there is a change in direction, the velocity changes, and the turning object is therefore accelerating. The net force on the object must be in the direction of the acceleration.

Vector quantity. A variable in physics that has both a magnitude (number value) and a specified direction (i.e., distance, velocity, acceleration, and force).

Vector analysis. A method of adding two vector quantities together to obtain a sum (resultant), or a method of finding two components of a single vector.

Centripetal acceleration. The acceleration of anything moving in a circular path directed toward the center of the circle.

Centripetal force. The force that is required to keep an object moving in a circular path. Always directed toward the center of the circle. In the absence of this force, the object would move in a straight line, obeying Newton's First Law of Motion.

CONCEPT QUESTIONS

1. Why is it easier to drive faster through a curve if it is banked?

2. What is the role of frictional forces as a car goes through a tight turn (small radius)?

3. Why do most car tires have treads?

APPLYING WHAT YOU KNOW

1. Two high school softball teams play a seven-inning game. List four examples of two-dimensional motion that occur during the contest.

2. A teacher fills a bucket with water and begins to swing the bucket in a vertical circle. Surprisingly, the water stays in the bucket and does not spill out even when upside down. Explain how that can happen using Newton's laws and centripetal acceleration principles.

3. Given $F_c = mv^2/R$, explain what happens to the force exerted on a car when
   a. the car doubles in velocity in the curve.
   b. the car reduces its speed from 60 miles/hour to 20 miles/hour.
   c. the radius of the curve is suddenly half its original value.
   d. the radius of the curve is three times larger.
   e. the car is hauling a trailer equal to half its mass.

Electricity and Simple Circuits | Restoring a Heartbeat

OVERVIEW

This unit focuses on a medical device called a defibrillator. A defibrillator is a battery-run device that restores a normal heartbeat when a heart is beating erratically. This life-threatening erratic heartbeat, called ventricular fibrillation, is caused by an electric malfunction within the heart.

Someday you may operate a defibrillator. Medical technicians, nurses, and doctors all use defibrillators during medical emergencies that involve cardiac arrest and heart fibrillation. Because fibrillation is a common life-threatening problem, airplanes today carry a defibrillator on board, and airplane personnel are trained to use the device. There are even plans to place defibrillators in government buildings and other public places, with instructions on how to use them.

Like all electric devices, a defibrillator contains a circuit and specific kinds of circuit parts, called components. By the end of this unit, you will have designed and built an electric circuit similar to the circuit that controls a defibrillator. This assignment is your unit project, and the work on this project is divided into four project milestones.

When you read through the milestones, you'll notice that the milestones involve many facets of what is known as the design process. From your initial design of the simplest circuit to your ultimate designing, building, and testing of the final defibrillator circuit, you will be practicing the work of engineers.

PROJECT MILESTONES

Your unit project is to design and build an electric circuit similar to the circuit that controls a defibrillator. This assignment is divided into four project milestones.

Project Milestone 1   Describing the Operation and Function of a Defibrillator

You will study the general design of the defibrillator, and describe its operation and function. You will list possible parts of the defibrillator circuit.

Project Milestone 2   Choosing the Best Battery for the Defibrillator

You will determine the best battery for your model emergency defibrillator circuit.

Project Milestone 3   Designing the Emergency Defibrillator Circuit

You will determine a safe level of current for the model defibrillator circuit, calculate voltage, and evaluate information about defibrillators. Then you will design the first version of your model defibrillator circuit.

Project Milestone 4   Building and Presenting the Emergency Defibrillator Circuit

You will build a model defibrillator circuit, test and label your circuit, and present your results.

ACTIVITES AND ASSIGNMENTS

Your work on this unit project requires an understanding of electricity and circuits. As you progress through the unit, you will complete a number of activities and assignments that will help you accomplish each of the project milestones.

Just as there are four project milestones, the activities and assignments in the unit are organized into four chapters. Each chapter focuses on a different aspect of circuits.

1. In Chapter 8, you will take apart simple devices and see what's inside. You will describe how a device works, how its circuit is designed, and how the circuit transfers energy. You will also build and diagram your own circuits.

2. In Chapter 9, you will observe the process that takes place inside a battery, leading to an understanding of a battery as an energy source. You will build your own battery and read about commercial batteries. You will measure and describe the electric quantity of voltage.

3. In Chapter 10, you will describe and quantify the flow of electricity through wires and see how this flow relates to the transfer of energy in a circuit. You will measure and describe the electric quantities of current and resistance. You will then determine how voltage, current, and resistance relate to each other mathematically. You will also learn how different levels of current can affect the heart under different conditions.

4. In Chapter 11, you will learn about capacitors and how they act in a circuit. Capacitors are charged and discharged during defibrillator operation. You will see how they form the core of the defibrillator circuit by transferring the right amount of energy to the heart.

Examining Devices and Their Circuits

OVERVIEW

IT'S IN YOUR HANDS

Having graduated from high school, you're eager to start your training program in the field of biomedical equipment technology. And you can't wait for the day when you will be working in a hospital—repairing, troubleshooting, and using medical equipment.

In walks the instructor, Ms. Lacy.

"This course is about electricity and simple circuits. I believe the best way to learn is by *doing*. You'll be working on a project. There will be lots of hands-on work, exploring science concepts and principles and learning how they apply to the project. You will undertake cycles of designing, building, testing, and communicating your results.

"You won't be memorizing facts from a textbook, but you will do some reading, which will help you to execute your project successfully. I will do some lecturing and demonstrations, but mostly I'm here as a resource to facilitate your work. The responsibility for learning is in your hands. Here's your project for the course:

Working in teams, design and build a simple but working model of a defibrillator circuit from easily available electric components."

"Build a what?," you wonder.

You quickly learn that cardiac fibrillation is a potentially life-threatening event. A defibrillator is a battery-run device that restores a normal heartbeat when a heart is beating erratically (fibrillating). The defibrillator delivers a measured amount of electricity to the heart, allowing it to "reset" and begin beating normally again.

Fascinating, but this project is a tall order. . . .

You're not so sure where to start. You have a bunch of questions and not too many answers. After all, designing, building, and testing a model defibrillator circuit is complex stuff. So the instructor asks you to decide what you think you need to know at this point. For starters, the class comes up with some basic questions: What is a circuit? What are defibrillators? Who works with, and on, them in hospitals? Your exploration of these questions begins.

Your first milestone:

Project Milestone 1

Describing the Operation and Function of a Defibrillator

You will study the general design of the defibrillator, and describe its operation and function. You will list possible parts of the defibrillator circuit.

By the end of this chapter, you will be on your way to designing a model defibrillator circuit. You will have a chance to hear from experts in a hospital about defibrillators and how they work. You will learn how to recognize, build, and diagram circuits, and you will list rules that make circuits work. You will also reflect on the use of circuits. Circuits usually transfer energy from one place to another. This energy is used in our homes, schools, business, and in many other places. The defibrillator also works by transferring energy from the defibrillator's battery to the patient.

To help you accomplish Project Milestone One, you will need to understand how a defibrillator is used when a heart is fibrillating, and you will need to learn a little about how a heart works. To reach this first milestone, you will complete the following six activities.

Activity 8.1   Examining Devices
What is in an electric device? What is its purpose? You will disassemble a battery-run device and examine the components of the electric circuit.

Activity 8.2   How Does a Circuit Work?
You will build simple circuits using batteries, wire, and lightbulbs. You will learn to diagram circuits and compile a list of "circuit rules."

Activity 8.3   Building a Model Circuit
You will build a circuit for a household device, test it, diagram it, and mount it for display.

Activity 8.4   Tracing Circuit Paths
You will learn more about circuits by tracing the circuit path and examining the electric components of an electric light. You will learn how a wall outlet, cord, and bulb make a complete circuit.

Activity 8.5   A Visit to a Hospital
The class will visit a hospital and learn about medical equipment and careers in hospital equipment maintenance. You will find out what a defibrillator does and how it is used.

Activity 8.6   Learning about Defibrillators
You will complete Project Milestone One by describing the operation and function of a defibrillator. You will list possible parts of the defibrillator circuit.

ACTIVITY 8.1

Examining Devices

Getting In Gear

Y̶ou are about to begin a study of electricity, circuits, and electric devices. Because this is the beginning of a new unit, you will want to know more about your responsibilities and the topics you will be studying. You may ask, What project will I be working on? What is electricity? Why do people use electricity? Why is electricity important to study? More specific questions may include, What is in an electric device? What is its purpose? What is a circuit? How are electric devices and circuits connected?

This first activity will help answer some of those questions. You will have opportunities to ask questions about the unit project and to discuss what you already know about some of the topics found in this unit. You will also take apart some household devices and find out what's inside.

Although taking apart devices will help you begin to understand circuits, it is especially important in this first activity for you to take the time to understand the outline of the unit project and of the day-to-day activities throughout the unit. This knowledge will help you see how the work in the unit is connected, will help you gauge your own progress, and will give meaning to the activities in the unit.

Getting To Work!

T̶o understand your unit project and the material you will cover in Chapter 8 (what circuits are and the role of circuits), you will

1. Read the overview for Unit Three, and discuss as a class the unit project and the outline of work throughout the unit.

2. Read the overview scenario and project milestone for Chapter 8, and discuss the scenario with your class.

3. Brainstorm as a class everything you know about electricity, and create a list of everyone's ideas.

4. Work in groups and use **Job Sheet 8.1** How Does This Thing Work? to investigate what's inside a simple battery-run household device, such as a flashlight.

    Job Sheet

   a. Take your device apart and list the components.

   b. Participate in a class discussion about the components found inside the devices.

   c. Describe in words the *purpose* and *operation* of your group's device.

   d. Participate in a class discussion about energy.

   e. Identify the energy source and energy transfer in your device.

5. Read Getting the Point: *Energy and Work,* and answer the Focus Questions.

6. Read Concept Connection: *Systems* as time permits.

Energy and Work

Several concepts are defined here that will help you to understand electric devices. To complete Activity 8.1, you describe the flow of energy in the device you examine. As you work on activities throughout this unit, think about how energy flows through the circuits.

Electric circuits involve the transfer of *energy*. For example, electric energy is transformed into light, heat, and movement by electric devices such as light bulbs, heaters, and fans. Energy is one of the most important ideas in science and technology.

Energy is a property of an object that is related to its movement or position. A moving object is said to have *kinetic energy*. If a moving object hits you, the object's energy is transferred to your body. A baseball that has just been hit by a bat has kinetic energy.

An object that could move because of its position is said to have *potential energy*. An example is a ball held in one's hand. If released, the ball could move and then transfer its energy to what it hits. Another example of potential energy is a jack-in-the-box, where an object has been pushed down and the lid closed. By pushing the "jack" in the box down, you transferred energy to the jack-in-the-box. The jack-in-the box stores this energy as potential energy. The potential energy of the compressed spring becomes the kinetic energy of the moving spring when jack pops out of the box.

Energy can change from one form to another, but it is never created or destroyed. The total amount of energy is always the same. This is the Law of Conservation of Energy. Electric circuits provide a way to transfer electric energy to light energy, heat energy, and mechanical energy.

For example, when an electric circuit lights a bulb, it changes electric energy to light and heat energy. The light and heat energy is further transformed. Light is transformed to heat when the air and objects in the room absorb it. Both the direct and indirect heat from the bulb is absorbed by air, which in turn rises. The rising air then warms other things that are cooler than it is. As can be seen from these examples, the chain of transformations is almost infinite; only when all things in the universe have the same amount of energy will transformations cease.

Energy is measured in units of *joules*. Energy use over time is counted in units of joules per second, which are also called *watts*. For example, a 60-watt lightbulb uses 60 joules of energy every second.

Focus Questions

List three appliances that transfer electric energy to mechanical energy.

What is the Law of Conservation of Energy?

What is a joule?

Concept Connection: Systems

You can view the defibrillator or any other device as a system. As you disassemble the device, you identify the components of the system. In this unit, we talk about the operation and function of the device. Instead, you could talk about the *input* and *output* of a system using the language of a *system* in technology. The Universal System Model is diagrammed below. The *input* starts some *process* in the device that in turn produces some *output*. *Input* is the operation that turns a device, or part of a device, on or off. Often, the input is the flicking of a switch. For example, you push or flip a light switch to turn on a light. *Output* is what is produced by the device or its function, for example, light, heat, or sound. Some outputs are *intended*, such as the motion generated by a car engine. Others are *incidental*, like the heat generated by the car engine as it powers the car. It is the *process* that creates the output, and it is the process of a defibrillator that you will design in this unit.

Figure 8.1
System Model

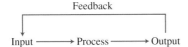

ACTIVITY 8.2

How Does a Circuit Work?

Getting In Gear

Could you build a working circuit? In Activity 8.1, you disassembled simple battery-run devices and became familiar with their components. You know that these components make up the circuit that is inside the device, but the arrangement of the components isn't that easy to see.

In this activity, you connect batteries, wires, and lightbulbs together to make a working circuit. As you do so, you will consider what constraints or rules govern circuits. Think about watching a soccer game; even without much knowledge of the sport, you would be able to guess most of the important rules. Your observations of circuits will lead to a set of "circuit rules."

When you design your defibrillator at the end of this unit, you will use the circuit rules you develop now. They should apply to every circuit. You may want to modify your list as you learn more about circuits.

Getting To Work!

To understand how to build and draw simple circuits, you will

1. Share with your class any experiences you've had building circuits.

2. Follow │ **Job Sheet 8.2** │ **How Do You Build a Circuit That Lights a Bulb?** to build and document circuits.
   a. Study batteries, battery holders, lightbulbs, bulb holders, wires, and their electric symbols.
   b. Build different arrangements using your components; keep track of your work with drawings. (Refer to Getting the Point: *Electric Symbols* in this

Job Sheet

activity as you sketch the circuits that you design. Throughout this unit, you will draw and read technical circuit diagrams that use these symbols.)

    c. Identify circuit rules that state which arrangements of components succeed in lighting the bulb.

3. Read Getting the Point: *Circuits,* and answer the Focus Questions.

4. Read Concept Connection: *Preventing Death from Sudden Cardiac Arrest* as time permits.

**Getting
The Point.**

Circuits

L et's meet three common circuit structures: series circuit, parallel circuit, and short circuit. You'll recognize these circuits from your work in Activity 8.1. Throughout this unit, you will work with series circuits.

    An electric device produces the desired output only when the connections form a pathway that closes back on itself without any breaks. Such a closed path is called a circuit. Since the devices operate electrically, you can call the circuit an electric circuit. The circuit provides a path for electricity to flow. The flow of electricity in circuits is useful because it transfers *energy* from one place to another.

SERIES AND PARALLEL CIRCUITS

The various parts of a battery-powered device can be connected in different ways. When there is more than one of a given part connected in a circuit, the circuit may be connected in series or in parallel. Series and parallel circuits are shown in the figure below. Bulbs, batteries, and other circuit elements can be connected in series or in parallel or in circuits that combine both types of connections.

Figure 8.2
Ways That Circuit Elements Can Be Connected

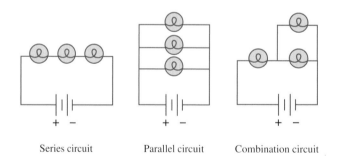

Series circuit   Parallel circuit   Combination circuit

SHORT CIRCUIT

A short circuit is a complete circuit that includes a battery and wire but no other components. A short circuit can start a fire.

**Focus
Questions**

What is an electric circuit?

How could you tell if a circuit is a short circuit?

Getting The Point.

Electric Symbols

To work on circuits, people make circuit diagrams that show the parts of the circuit and how they are arranged. To make drawing and reading such diagrams easier, there is a system of commonly used electric symbols. For every kind of circuit component, there is a corresponding symbol. Some standard circuit symbols are shown below.

Figure 8.3
Electric Symbols

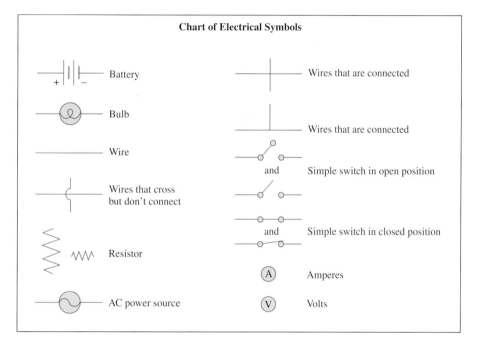

Concept Connection: Preventing Death from Sudden Cardiac Arrest

Muscles in the heart are controlled by electrical signals and form a circuit within the body. Sudden cardiac arrest is usually caused because of a disruption of those electrical signals. A defibrillator allows the signals to start working properly again.

Before you start working on a defibrillator, you should know when it is used. This reading shows how defibrillators can save the lives of people with sudden cardiac arrest.

Facts about Sudden Cardiac Arrest

Sudden Cardiac Arrest
- One of the leading causes of death in the United States, sudden cardiac arrest strikes an estimated 350,000 Americans yearly and less than 5% survive
- Usually caused by an electrical malfunction of the heart called ventricular fibrillation
- Strikes men and women, young and old, though prevalence increases with age
- Difficult to predict; many victims have no prior symptoms
- Symptoms of sudden cardiac arrest include immediate loss of consciousness and death within a matter of minutes without prompt medical intervention

Defibrillation
- Stops ventricular fibrillation with an electrical pulse that allows a normal heart rhythm to resume
- Highly effective when administered within the first few minutes following sudden cardiac arrest

Response Time and Survival Rates

- The likelihood of successful resuscitation decreases by approximately 10 percent with each minute following the onset of sudden cardiac arrest. In New York City, the average paramedic response time is 12 minutes and only 1 percent of victims survive. In Seattle, the average response time is 4–6 minutes and approximately 30 percent of victims survive.
- Patients who survive sudden cardiac arrest have an excellent long-term prognosis; 57 percent of survivors survive for five years or longer.
- The American Heart Association estimates that as many as 100,000 deaths could be prevented each year through the widespread deployment of defibrillators.

Television programs featuring emergency rooms and rescue settings have familiarized the public with external defibrillators—the devices used to shock victims whose hearts are beating erratically (fibrillating). Defibrillation, the treatment delivered by these external defibrillators, is highly effective in real life for restoring a normal heartbeat to victims of sudden cardiac arrest. The problem is that defibrillators often reach the scene too late—or not at all.

The American Heart Association developed the "Chain of Survival" in 1990 to educate the public as to the four crucial "links" toward resuscitation.
- Link One: Recognize an Emergency and Call 911
- Link Two: Begin Cardiopulmonary Resuscitation (CPR)
- Link Three: Use the Automated External Defibrillator (AED) to Treat Ventricular Fibrillation
- Link Four: Early Advanced Care

A break in any of the four links in the chain can compromise the victim's chance for survival; however, early defibrillation is recognized as most important for victims of sudden cardiac arrest. While CPR is effective for temporarily maintaining oxygenation of the blood and blood flow to the brain, it is only a stop-gap measure, buying time for the victim until a defibrillator is available. Defibrillation is the only effective method of restoring normal cardiac rhythm and resuscitating the victim following sudden cardiac arrest from ventricular fibrillation. Defibrillation should be administered as quickly as possible following cardiac arrest, ideally by the first responder, i.e., the first appropriately trained person to arrive on the scene.

Adapted from "Preventing Death from Sudden Cardiac Arrest." Philips Medical Systems. http://www3.medical. philips.com/resources/hsg/docs/en-us/custom/scaissues_textgeneric.asp (June 25, 2002)

ACTIVITY 8.3

Building a Model Circuit

Getting In Gear

You learned in Activity 8.1 that you will build a model defibrillator circuit for your unit project. But what exactly is a model circuit? In this activity, you learn about model circuits by building one of the battery-run household devices you examined in Activity 8.1. Your circuit may look crude, but it is the circuit that forms the heart of every electric device.

Your circuit may use a bulb, buzzer, or motor. You will learn how to wire these components into your circuit and how to draw their electric symbols. Since most household devices contain a switch, you will probably also use a switch in your model circuit.

This is your first design job in this unit. As you progress through the unit, you will work on more complicated design tasks. Your final design task will be the design of the model defibrillator circuit. As you work, think about the different aspects of the design.

Getting To Work!

To check your understanding of circuits and to build models, you will

1. Work by yourself to answer the first question on **Job Sheet 8.3** Building a Model Circuit. Then share your answer with your group, and build the two circuits shown in Question 1 to check your answer.

Job Sheet

2. View a model circuit made by your teacher.

3. Continue in groups with Job Sheet 8.3.

   a. Reread your analysis of the household device you examined in Activity 8.1, recorded on Job Sheet 8.1: *How Does This Thing Work?*

   b. Choose the components you need for your model circuit of a household device; then build the circuit and test it. Draw a diagram of the circuit.

   c. Mount your circuit on cardboard and label it. If time and materials allow, create an outside frame and make cutouts for your switch and major component.

   d. Demonstrate and explain your circuit and circuit diagram to the class.

4. Read Getting the Point: *The Design Process,* and answer the Focus Question.

Getting The Point.

The Design Process

Together with understanding the science necessary to design a defibrillator, you learn about the process of engineering design. You develop skills in engineering design in many activities in this unit, from your design of the simplest circuit to the final design of the defibrillator. As you work, keep in mind the steps in the design process.

1. Identify a problem, or develop and identify design constraints.

2. Design possible solutions, and choose the alternative that best conforms to the design constraints.

3. Develop the proposed solution.

4. Evaluate the solution and its consequences.

5. Communicate the problem, that is, how you thought about the design problem and possible solutions.

Focus Question

Identify the activities in making the model circuit that correspond to the five steps in the design process.

ACTIVITY 8.4

Tracing Circuit Paths

Getting In Gear

In Activity 8.2, you created a list of circuit rules for battery-run circuits. You noticed then that electricity appears to travel in closed paths. Consider the following questions: Does the circuit rule of closed paths apply inside components, such as inside lightbulbs? Does this circuit rule apply to devices plugged into electric outlets? In this activity, you have an opportunity to answer those questions by examining lightbulbs and electric plugs in more detail.

This experience will prepare you to work with more complicated circuits later in this unit. A strong understanding of circuit paths will help you build your model defibrillator circuit.

Getting To Work!

To gain a better understanding of circuit paths through bulbs and household circuits, you will

1. Work in groups and follow Job Sheet 8.4 | Where Is the Electric Circuit?
    a. Examine a clear glass bulb that has been broken at the base. Draw the bulb and label its parts.
    b. Discuss the bulb's circuit path. Redraw the bulb to show the circuit path in as much detail as possible.
    c. Examine an ordinary plug-in lamp closely; then brainstorm where the electric circuit is in the lamp. Record your ideas.
    d. Inspect a lamp with the insulation on the cord removed. Use your observations to describe the circuit paths of household devices and appliances.
    e. Get a bulb from your teacher. Predict whether the bulb will work.

2. Read Getting the Point: *A Defibrillator Shocks the Heart,* which will provide helpful background for your visit to the hospital, and answer the Focus Questions.

3. Read Workplace Connection: *Biomedical Equipment Repair Technician* as time permits.

Job Sheet

Getting The Point.

A Defibrillator Shocks the Heart

A defibrillator is a medical device that applies an electric shock to restore the rhythm of a heart that is not beating properly. To understand how it works, you need to know something about the normal action of the heart.

The heart is a collection of muscle cells. Normally, the action of those cells is coordinated, and the heart contracts in a very definite rhythm. This synchronized beating of the heart pumps blood through the circulatory system and produces the sound you hear when you listen to a heartbeat.

Figure 8.4
Diagram of a Human Heart

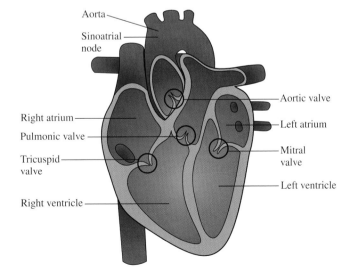

Heart cells work together in response to electric signals generated by a cluster of special cells located in the right atrial wall of the heart. This cluster is called the *sinoatrial node.* It acts as a kind of bandleader, directing the signals that set the normal rhythm. It is the heart's natural pacemaker.

But sometimes the bandleader cells "misfire"; they get "out of sync" and no longer work together. The signals are no longer coordinated, and in response, heart cells no longer beat together. The uncoordinated beating is called fibrillation.

Ventricular fibrillation (V-fib) is fibrillation in the lower chambers of the heart, called the *ventricles.* When V-fib occurs, emergency actions must be taken because the heart is no longer pumping blood effectively throughout the body. The electric shock delivered by a defibrillator, when successful, stops the uncoordinated muscle contractions. The sinoatrial node regains control of the rhythm, and the heart restarts itself with a normal heartbeat (normal sinus rhythm).

An *electrocardiogram* (EKG) records the electric signals of the heart. The EKG pattern below records the wild, rapid signaling associated with fibrillation, followed by a stoppage, followed by the resumption of the signals driving a normal heartbeat.

Figure 8.5
EKG Patterns Associated with Fibrillation, Total Polarization, and Resumption of Normal Activity

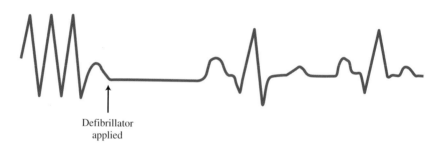

Defibrillator
applied

Focus Questions

What is a defibrillator used for?

How does the heart normally function?

What is ventricular fibrillation?

Workplace Connection: Biomedical Equipment Repair Technician

You are training to become a biomedical equipment repair technician. So what exactly does a biomedical equipment repair technician do? This is a job description adapted with permission from the U.S. Department of Labor for its Biomedical Equipment Technician Apprenticeship Program.

Biomedical equipment technicians are skilled health-care industry service and repair workers who are employed by equipment manufacturers, specialized medical equipment servicing companies, and in some cases directly by hospitals and medical laboratories in order to perform critical maintenance and repairs on sensitive medical machines and equipment. Although this trade does not require formal postsecondary coursework or degrees, biomedical equipment technicians require an understanding—and practical skill—in such areas as electricity, mechanics, pneumatics, hydraulics, instrumentation, and working with radio-active materials. They also require the personality, and interpersonal relations skills, to work in fast-paced, high pressure environments—such as hospitals and laboratories—where extremely accurate yet timely repairs and adjustments are often required.

Biomedical Equipment Technicians:

- Install, inspect, calibrate, service, repair, and maintain medical and related technical equipment used in the health-care delivery field. This equipment includes patient monitors, electrocardiographs, x-ray machines, anesthesia apparatus, defibrillators, electro-surgical units, sterilizers, and a wide-range of similar machines, equipment, and apparatus.
- Safety-test medical equipment, as well as the physical environment of health-care facilities.
- May consult with medical or research staff, and/or scientific or engineering personnel to determine if specialized medical and research equipment is functioning as required.
- Some also have managerial and supervisory responsibilities.
- Use various power tools; hand tools; and measuring and calibration instruments in their work.

Biomedical equipment technicians may learn this specialized installation, service, and repair trade through:
- Training provided by medical equipment manufacturers.
- On-the-job training provided by hospital or medical laboratory engineering or senior biomedical equipment personnel.
- Training programs offered by specialized medical equipment service and repair companies.
- Coursework provided by public or private postsecondary vocational schools or technical institutes.
- Community colleges.
- Correspondence courses.
- A formal apprenticeship program, such as the registered apprenticeship program for biomedical equipment technicians offered by the U.S. Department of Labor, Bureau of Apprenticeship and Training.

ACTIVITY 8.5

A Visit to a Hospital

Getting In Gear

How are defibrillators used, and who uses them? In this activity, you visit a hospital to meet with a clinical engineer or medical equipment repair technician who demonstrates a defibrillator and explains its medical uses. You will also learn about medical equipment and careers in medical equipment maintenance.

Visiting a hospital workplace is a rare privilege for high school students. Please be courteous and respectful to everyone you encounter, and remember that patients and their families are always nearby.

Getting To Work!

Before, during, and after your hospital visit, you will

Job Sheet

1. Participate in a class discussion about the visit to the hospital. At this time, you will also review the questions on ⏐**Job Sheet 8.5**⏐ **A Visit with a Hospital Clinical Engineer.**

2. Work in groups to develop questions about medical equipment and about the work engineers and biomedical equipment technicians do in the hospital. Practice asking your questions.

3. Make sure that you hand in all permission forms, and that you understand the transportation arrangements, what can and cannot be taken into the hospital, and how you will make up missed classes.

4. View some videos your teacher may show about biomedical equipment or careers.

5. Meet with your tour leader at the hospital. Your guide will show you several pieces of medical equipment, including a defibrillator, and will talk about his or her work at the hospital.

6. Listen to the tour leader during the tour, and answer the questions on Job Sheet 8.5. Ask questions if you need more information from the tour leader about items on the job sheet or for any other reason.

7. Read Getting the Point: *Technical Information about the Defibrillator* after the hospital visit, and answer the Focus Questions.

8. Write a thank-you letter to your tour leader.

Technical Information about the Defibrillator

Read these paragraphs to help you build your defibrillator circuit later in this unit. Although some of the terminology is new, you will understand these terms as you go through the unit.

Scope. A cardiac defibrillator is an electronic apparatus used to terminate ventricular fibrillation by the application of brief electroshock to the heart by means of electrodes.

Charge Indicator. Because of the unique function and operation environment of defibrillators, the committee deemed it essential that the operator be aware of device status at all times. For this purpose, a positive visual indication must be provided when the defibrillator is charged and ready to fire, and when it has been discharged.

Battery Charge Indicator. The basis for this requirement is that it is necessary for the user to be able to determine when the battery will no longer provide sufficient power for the defibrillator to be operable. Since many commonly used batteries exhibit a sudden rapid fall in power output when they reach the failing point, advance prediction of failure is difficult. A continuous battery charge indication, a "push to test" mechanism, or other more sophisticated methods may be used.

From *Cardiac Defibrillator Devices,* 3rd edition (ANSI/AAMI DF2: 1996 American Association for the Advancement of Medical Instrumentation/American National Standard).

Summary of the Use of the Defibrillator

A defibrillator is used to stop ventricular fibrillation of the heart in order to restore a normal heartbeat. The defibrillator's charging circuit must first be turned on until the *capacitor* (a common circuit component) is fully charged. When the capacitor is fully charged, the device must signal the user that the charging is complete, using either a visual or an audio signal. At this point, the user turns off the charging circuit. With the paddles attached to the patient, the user turns on the discharging circuit by pressing two switches, one on each paddle. Electricity then goes through the patient's heart and stops the fibrillation.

Focus Questions

What is defibrillation?

What is a charge indicator?

What is a battery charge indicator?

What circuit component is vital for the operation of the defibrillator?

ACTIVITY 8.6

Learning about Defibrillators

Getting In Gear

The defibrillator is a battery-run electric device like those you have been studying in this chapter. In Activity 8.1, you specified the function and operation of a simple battery-run household device. In this activity, you create a similar description for a defibrillator. With the information about function and operation, you then create a list of components that might be in the defibrillator circuit.

Although it may not seem so now, this work will form the heart of your design process. A description of the defibrillator's function and operation is the first step in design—it is a summary of the tasks a successful model defibrillator circuit must be able to do.

Getting To Work!

To complete Project Milestone One, you will

Job Sheet

1. Work in groups to answer the questions on | **Job Sheet 8.6** | How Does a **Defibrillator Work?** You may need to review Getting the Point: *Technical Information about the Defibrillator* in Activity 8.5.

   a. Explain a defibrillator's use and function; list its main parts and safety features.
   b. Explain how the defibrillator is operated.
   c. List possible components inside the defibrillator.
   d. Describe energy transfer in a working defibrillator.

2. Share your answers in a class discussion.

3. Revise your answer to Question 4 after the responses on Job Sheet 8.6 have been checked. If necessary, make changes directly on your job sheet.

4. Review the concepts and answer the questions in What Have You Learned? for homework.

5. Read Workplace Connection: *The History of the Defibrillator* as time permits.

Workplace Connection: The History of the Defibrillator

The following information is from the Institute of Electrical and Electronic Engineers (IEEE), a professional association of more than 350,000 individual members in 150 countries. Through its members, the IEEE is a leading authority in technical areas ranging from computer engineering to biomedical technology and consumer electronics.

Some early researchers recognized that an electric shock could "reanimate" the heart. As early as 1918, Albert Hyman suggested that small electrical pulses supplied directly to the heart might keep an ill heart beating, and coined the term "artificial pacemaker." Then, in 1933, William Kouwenhoven, an electrical engineer working with a team of physiologists, demonstrated scientifically that an electric shock can restore a fibrillating heart to normal rhythm. One of the doctors, Paul Zoll, demonstrated that such shocks could be applied to the exterior of the chest without opening it surgically. During the winer of 1957–58, Earl E. Bakken developed the first wearable transistorized pacemaker.

This work led to two parallel engineering pursuits: for a defibrillator that medical and paramedical personnel could use quickly, easily, safely and reliably to resuscitate a stopped heart; and for a pacemaker that could keep an imperfect heart going indefinitely with minimal impact on the patient's quality of life.

In 1961, Karl Edmark first tested a battery-powered direct current defibrillator, and soon defibrillators were ready to leave the operating room and become part of mobile care units. In parallel, as cited above, Bakken and his team were able to produce a battery-powered dc pacemaker that, while not fully implanted, allowed the patient to be mobile.

Both these technological streams have continued to be refined to this day. Defibrillators are now hand-carried, easily used with minimal training, and can detect the signals from the heart and compute whether or not a shock is even needed. Today's pacemakers can sense electric activity in both the atria and ventricles of the heart, and simulate those chambers independently. Sophisticated algorithms are available for interpreting the sensed signals and delivering an appropriate sequence of pulses to achieve proper functioning of the heart.

Adapted from "History: Nominating Milestones." Courtesy of the IEEE History Center. Institute of Electrical and Electronics Engineers. Copyright © 1999 by IEEE. Reprinted with permission. http://www.spectrum.ieee.org/INST/oct99/history.html (June 4, 2002)

What Have You Learned?

Circuits. A device works only when the connections form a pathway that closes back on itself without any breaks. Such a closed path is called a circuit. The circuit provides a path for electricity to flow. The flow of electricity in circuits is useful because it transfers energy from one place to another.

Energy. Energy is a property of an object that is related to movement. A moving body is said to have kinetic energy. A body that could move because of its position (a ball held in one's hand would move if released) is said to have potential energy. Energy is continually being transferred from one object to another. Energy is measured in units of joules.

Law of Conservation of Energy. The total amount of energy is always the same. Energy can change from one form to another, but it is never created or destroyed.

Defibrillation. Defibrillation is an electric pulse that allows a normal heart rhythm to resume.

CONCEPT QUESTIONS

1. List 10 different types of electric devices in your house.

2. Determine the operation and function of the devices listed below. Find another electric device at home or at school and determine its operation and function.
   a. smoke detector
   b. burglar alarm
   c. fire alarm
   d. other electric device (your choice)

3. Which is the first step in the design process?
   a. Propose a solution.
   b. Evaluate your design.
   c. Identify possible solutions.
   d. Identify the problem.

4. Does a flashlight work if you turn over the batteries? Try it. Why or why not?

5. Which of the diagrams in Figure A illustrate short circuits?

Figure A

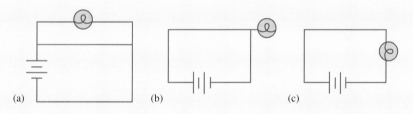

(a)   (b)   (c)

6. Name the medical condition that is treated by a defibrillator.

7. Use the chart of electric symbols (Figure 8.3) to draw a schematic illustration of the following circuits (Figure B):
   a. two batteries, one bulb, and one switch
   b. one battery, two switches, and one bulb

Figure B

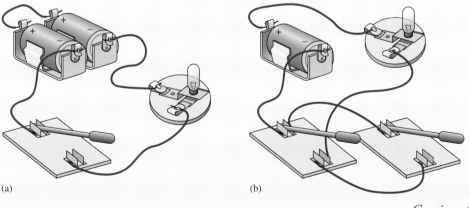

(a)   (b)

Continued

8. The batttery charge indicator on a defibrillator tells you that the
    a. battery has enough power to operate the machine.
    b. battery is recharging.
    c. defibrillator capacitor has been charged.
    d. defibrillator capacitor has been discharged.

9. A defibrillator operator knows when the defibrillator is charged or discharged because
    a. the defibrillator will respond to the patient's condition.
    b. the defibrillator will automatically charge and discharge when it is turned on.
    c. two visual signals confirm whether the defibrillator has been charged or discharged.
    d. charging occurs because the defibrillator becomes hot.

APPLYING WHAT YOU KNOW

1. In each of the schematic illustrations in Figure C, will the circuit light the bulb? If not, explain how you could fix the circuit so that the bulb will light.

Figure C

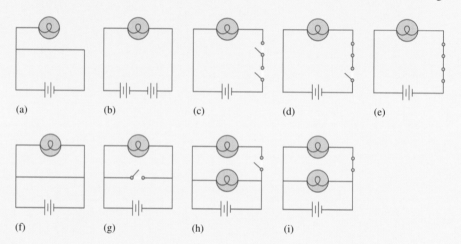

(a)   (b)   (c)   (d)   (e)

(f)   (g)   (h)   (i)

2. There are many different kinds of switches, such as push buttons, dimmers, and on-off switches. Find five switches in your home, and describe each one and its purpose.

3. Find out about the electricity in your home.
    • Where does the electricity enter your home?
    • Do you have fuses or circuit breakers?
    • Explain why fuses and circuit breakers are important.

4. Where is the defibrillator closest to your home? Who is trained to use it?

5. You can view the model circuit you built in Activity 8.3 as a system with the following parts: input, process, and output. Explain how your system works in terms of input, process, and output.

Choosing the Best Battery

OVERVIEW

BAFFLED BY BATTERIES

Having learned about circuits, you know that you will need a battery for the defibrillator circuit. Looking in the storeroom, you find it is chock full of batteries: alkaline batteries, lithium batteries, 9-volt batteries, D batteries, nickel-cadmium batteries, little AAA batteries—even a car battery. Which battery should you use?

You realize that before you can choose the proper battery, you need to understand what is going on inside the circuit and how batteries work. This is complicated, but you need to learn it if you want to design, build, and fix circuits. So your teacher wants you to build some homemade batteries—not to use with patients, of course—but because she believes that there's no better way to learn something than by doing it.

Your next milestone:

Project Milestone ②

Choosing the Best Battery for the Defibrillator

You will determine the best battery for your emergency defibrillator circuits.

The defibrillator works because it transfers electric energy to the patient. Like the battery-run devices you studied in Chapter 8, the source of the defibrillator's energy is the *battery*.

By the end of this chapter, you will have learned a great deal about batteries-how they are made, how they are measured, how they create and maintain electricity, and their important characteristics. By building some batteries yourself, you will see that different kinds of batteries can be made from different combinations of reactive metals and metal compounds.

To help you accomplish Project Milestone Two, you will do the following activities:

Activity 9.1   Exploring Charge
To learn about electric charge and electric force, you will make an electroscope with pieces of Scotch tape.

Activity 9.2   Observing the Reactivity of Metals
By putting strips of metal into acid, you will see which metal corrodes the fastest. Use these results to make a chart of metal reactivity.

Activity 9.3   Building Batteries and Measuring Voltage
You will build a battery using metal strips and solutions of metallic ions, and measure its voltage. Try to determine how voltage is related to metal reactivity.

Activity 9.4   Measuring Voltage Discharge Rate
To understand how voltage, charge, and energy are related, you will measure the rate at which voltage discharges for different batteries.

Activity 9.5   Choosing the Best Battery
In conclusion, you will determine the best battery for your model defibrillator circuit.

ACTIVITY 9.1

Exploring Charge

Getting In Gear

Although this chapter focuses on batteries, it starts with an activity that will help you refine your understanding of electricity. You will create static electricity (seen in situations that cause a small shock, spark, or static cling), and measure it using an instrument called an *electroscope*. It may surprise you how easy this will be; you can create static electricity with Scotch tape, and build an electroscope out of clay and straws.

Using the electroscope, you can transfer your own energy to the Scotch tape by ripping it quickly from various surfaces. You will then observe the effect of the energy transfer on the pieces of tape. Analyzing these observations will likely give you new insights into electricity.

Figure 9.1
An Electroscope Made of Clay and Straws

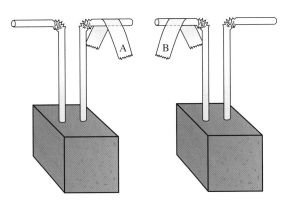

Getting To Work!

To begin your investigation of batteries, you will

1. Read the overview scenario and project milestone for Chapter 9, and discuss the scenario with your class.

2. Watch a demonstration by your teacher on how to use an electroscope.

3. Work in groups and follow | **Job Sheet 9.1** | **What Can We Learn from Scotch Tape?** to investigate static electricity.
   a. Build a simple electroscope, and do the experiments outlined.
   b. Share your observations from the experiments with your class.
   c. Determine how many kinds of tape there are, and all the possible interactions between them.

Job Sheet

4. Participate in class discussions about the data and important concepts of electric charge.

5. Read Getting the Point: *The Electroscope Experiment,* and answer the Focus Questions.

6. Read Concept Connection: *Observing Static Electricity,* and check out the Did You Know? readings as time permits.

Getting The Point.

The Electroscope Experiment

In the Scotch tape experiment you did using Job Sheet 9.1, the tape you pulled off the roll had no ability to push or pull, but the tape you attached to the straws did. How did that happen? *You* did it. In fact, you transferred energy to the tape in a way that is similar to the energy transferred to a circuit by a battery. You created static electricity and even observed static cling when two of the pieces of tapes stuck together.

Although it is pretty easy to create electricity, it's a bit harder to understand what is happening. You only saw the tapes attracting or repelling each other, depending on how they were prepared. If you think about this observation and what you have already learned in physics, you might remember that a force causes this kind of movement. This particular force is called *electric force.*

You know about gravity. Most things fall down because two masses attract each other, which is gravitational force. What is it that makes the pieces of tape move toward and away from each other? When you pulled the pieces of tape off the table or off each other, you actually moved an invisible thing called *charge* from one tape to another.

Charge is responsible for electric force. Since there are two kinds of electric force, there are also two kinds of charge, called *negative charge* and *positive charge.* One of the reasons we can't see charge is that charge can be carried by particles that are even smaller than an atom. In fact, charges exist on particles that are *within* an atom. *Protons,* at the center of the atom, carry positive charge. *Electrons,* at the outer edges of the atom, carry negative charge (Figure 9.2).

Figure 9.2
Protons and Electrons in a Helium Atom

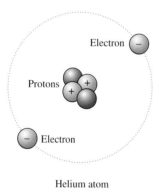

Helium atom

Most atoms have the same number of protons and electrons. These *neutral* atoms can't exert electric force because equal amounts of the two kinds of charge add up to zero, electrically speaking. (Now you see why the two forms of charge are called positive and negative!) However, atoms can lose or gain electrons under certain circumstances, and then they become *charged.*

With this new information, review the electroscope experiment again. When you pulled the two pieces of tape apart from each other, some electrons moved from one piece to the other, making one tape negative and the other positive. These tapes attracted each other. When you pulled both tapes from the table both lost? gained? electrons, making each positive? negative? These two pieces of tape repelled each other. A summary of the relationship between charge and electric force is *unlike charges attract and like charges repel.*

Sophisticated electroscopes not only indicate the kind of charge, but the exact amount of charge. Charge is measured in *coulombs.* One coulomb has the same amount of charge as 6.25×10^{18} electrons.

How did electricity get its name?

Amber is preserved plant resin that is used in jewelry. Ancient Greeks found that when they rubbed amber, it pulled and pushed other objects. Rubbing amber is much like pulling the pieces of tape. In both cases, energy of motion moves electrons. Electricity, electrons, and related words come from amber, because its name in Greek is *elektron.*

Benjamin Franklin and charge

Two thousand years after the Greeks observed electric effects with amber, Benjamin Franklin gave the two forms of electric charge their names: positive and negative. Even though Franklin thought wrongly that electricity was caused by two kinds of fluids, we still use his names today.

Focus Questions

What are the particles in an atom that carry charge?

How do atoms become charged?

The history of charge

In sixteenth century England, Queen Elizabeth I had a doctor called William Gilbert. Gilbert found that rubbing semiprecious stones would cause them to attract light objects. Like others of his time, Gilbert thought that static attraction was caused by magnetism. In his experiments, he found that some stones attracted better than others. To measure just how well these objects worked, he invented the first electrical instrument—the Versorium, the first version of today's electroscope.

Objects like paper and straw that were attracted to the versorium were called electrics. Those that were not attracted, he called non-electrics. From these two words, Gilbert gets credit for making up the word ELECTRICITY.

Adapted from "Making an Electroscope." http://www.schoolnet.ca/general/electric-club/e/page4.html (June 10, 2002)

Concept Connection: Observing Static Electricity

The energy of your feet moving against the carpet separates electrons from the atoms in the rug. You become negatively charged. These electrons "jump" to a more positive surface, such as a metal doorknob, when you touch it.

When clothes tumble in a dryer, the energy of the moving clothes separates electrons from atoms of different fabrics. Some fabrics will be more negatively charged and some more positively charged. Just like the tape, pieces of fabric with the same charge will push each other away when they come out of the dryer. Fabrics with two different kinds of charge will stick together, causing static cling.

The energy of moving storm clouds can separate huge amounts of electrons from atoms in the clouds. The result is lightning.

ACTIVITY 9.2

Observing the Reactivity of Metals

Getting In Gear

How are charge and batteries connected? In Activity 9.3, you will build a battery, but first you will observe one of the things that takes place inside of a battery. This is corrosion—the wearing away of metal. In fact, when a battery no longer works, it is because a piece of metal inside the battery has corroded.

Corrosion occurs when metal atoms lose electrons. As you see in this activity, when you place metals in acid some of the metals corrode faster than others. This property of metals is called *reactivity*. Metals that corrode faster (lose electrons faster) are more reactive. You will observe bubbling during the acid-metal reaction when gas is formed.

Getting To Work!

To explore reactivity of metals, you will

1. Work in groups to observe an alkaline battery and find a connection between batteries and charge.

2. Listen to a lecture on batteries and learn about the materials they are made of and the chemical reactions that take place inside of them.

3. Work in groups and follow the instructions on | **Job Sheet 9.2** | Observing the Reactivity of Metals. Be sure to follow all the rules for the safe use of acids.
   a. React different metals with the same amount of hydrochloric acid, and carefully time each reaction until the bubbling stops.
   b. Enter the data in Table 1 on the job sheet.
   c. Clean up as directed by your teacher. Acid solutions require special disposal techniques.
   d. Construct a metal reactivity chart using chart paper and markers.
   e. Discuss what changes occur to the metal and the acid as the corrosion occurs, and work out the chemical reaction that takes place between the metal and the acid.

4. Watch a demonstration of a zinc-copper battery by your teacher, and identify which metal is the negative terminal and which metal is the positive terminal.

5. Read Getting the Point: *Understanding Metal Reactivity,* and answer the Focus Questions.

6. Check out the Did You Know? readings as time permits.

7. Read Workplace Connection: *Implantable Defibrillators* as time allows.

Job Sheet

Getting The Point.

Understanding Metal Reactivity

In the metal and acid experiment, you watched four kinds of metal corrode. What happens when metals corrode? Where does charge fit into this picture?

When you put the metal in acid, you saw bubbles form and the metal disappear. Both the metal and the acid changed. These changes occurred because metal atoms gave some of their electrons to atoms in the acid. The metal atom went from neutral charge to positive charge. To describe this process specifically, we say that the metal atom became a positive metal *ion.* An ion is what an atom or group of atoms is called when it carries positive or negative charge.

In this activity, you were introduced to the word *reactivity,* which describes how quickly the metal corrodes. More reactive metals corrode faster. Metals can be ranked, as in the table below.

Table 9.1
Reactivity of common metals.

Symbol	Name	Reactivity
Li	Lithium	Most reactive
Na	Sodium	
Mg	Magnesium	
Al	Aluminum	
Mn	Manganese	
Zn	Zinc	
Cr	Chromium	
Fe	Iron	
Ni	Nickel	
Sn	Tin	
Pb	Lead	
Cu	Copper	
Ag	Silver	
Au	Gold	Least reactive

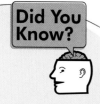
The change you observed during corrosion is part of the science of chemistry. When something changes from one thing to another, a chemical change or a *chemical reaction* has occurred. (The electric properties of atoms are the basis of all chemical reactions, which involve the rearrangement, transfer, or sharing of electrons between different atoms.)

What is the exact chemical reaction that takes place between the metal and the acid? Let's look at zinc. Place zinc in contact with hydrochloric acid, which is made up of neutral water molecules (a molecule is a group of connected atoms), a positive hydrogen ion, and a negative chlorine ion. You may have deduced that hydrogen gas is produced during the reaction. It turns out that the zinc gives up electrons to the hydrogen ions, which grab the electrons because they are already short of an electron. The addition of electrons to hydrogen ions causes hydrogen gas to form.

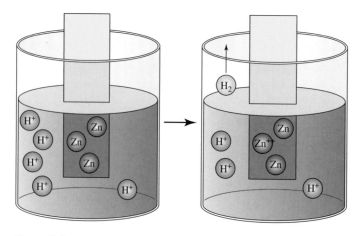

Figure 9.3
Reaction between Zinc and Hydrochloric Acid

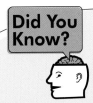

Focus Questions

What is an ion?

How do ion solutions cause metal corrosion?

Workplace Connection: Implantable Defibrillators

WHAT IS AN IMPLANTABLE CARDIOVERTER-DEFIBRILLATOR?

An implantable cardioverter-defibrillator (often called an ICD) is a device that briefly passes an electric current through the heart. It is "implanted," or put in your body surgically. It includes a pulse generator and one or more leads. The pulse generator constantly watches your heartbeat. It is like a small computer that runs on a battery. The lead (pronounced: "leed") is a wire from the pulse generator to the inside of your heart. The lead takes signals from your heart to the ICD and then takes an electric current from the pulse generator to your heart.

WHY MIGHT I NEED AN ICD?

Normally, your heart has a natural pacemaker that helps your heart beat steadily. An electrical current starts in one of the upper chambers (called the atria) of the heart and goes through the heart to the bottom chambers (called the ventricles).

You may need an ICD if you have had, or are at high risk of having, certain heart rhythm problems (ventricular tachycardia or ventricular fibrillation).

WHAT IS VENTRICULAR FIBRILLATION?

When a ventricular arrhythmia (irregular heartbeat) becomes very fast and irregular, it's called ventricular fibrillation. The heart just quivers, and no blood is pumped to the body or the brain. A person with ventricular fibrillation usually passes out very quickly. Unless treatment is given in 5 to 10 minutes, ventricular fibrillation causes death.

In people who don't have an ICD, ventricular fibrillation is treated with an external defibrillator. Paddles are put on the outside of the chest, and an electrical shock is given through the paddles. This shock goes through the heart and stops the irregular beat. The heart then goes back to a more regular rhythm.

Unfortunately, ventricular fibrillation can occur without warning—often, treatment can't be given in time. An ICD may be recommended for you because your doctor thinks you're at high risk for having ventricular fibrillation. The ICD can quickly recognize and stop ventricular fibrillation.

HOW DOES THE ICD WORK?

The ICD constantly watches your heart rhythm. If it sees that your heart is beating fast, it delivers the treatment programmed by your doctor. The ICD can do several things:

Pacing. If you have ventricular tachycardia that isn't too fast, the ICD can deliver several pacing signals in a row. When those signals stop, the heart may go back to a normal rhythm.

Cardioversion. If the pacing doesn't work, cardioversion can be used. In cardioversion, a mild shock is sent to the heart to stop the fast heartbeat.

Defibrillation. If ventricular fibrillation is detected, a stronger shock is sent. This stronger shock can stop the fast rhythm and help the heartbeat go back to normal.

Pacemaker. The ICD can also see when your heart beats too slowly. It can act like a pacemaker and bring your heart rate up to normal.

WHAT DOES TREATMENT WITH AN ICD FEEL LIKE?

When the ICD delivers pacing therapy, you may not feel anything. Some people feel a fluttering in their chest. They usually say that it doesn't feel uncomfortable or painful.

Cardioversion is stronger than a pacing pulse. It feels like being thumped in the chest.

The defibrillator shock is the strongest treatment. Many people say it feels like being kicked in the chest. It usually comes suddenly and lasts only a second. Although you may feel upset for a short time after a defibrillator shock, it is good to know that the ICD is treating the heart rhythm problem.

Pacing a slow heart rate uses very little energy. You may not feel it at all.

HOW IS AN ICD IMPLANTED?

The pulse generator may be implanted either under your collarbone on the left or right side of your chest, or in your abdomen (stomach area). In either place, the generator can be put in a "pocket" the doctor makes under your skin or, sometimes, in a muscle. One end of the lead wire is put into a vein that goes to your heart. The wire is moved through the vein until it reaches the heart. The other end of the wire is attached to the pulse generator. Once it is implanted, the doctor will program the ICD to treat your specific heart rhythm problem.

HOW WILL AN ICD AFFECT MY LIFESTYLE?

You'll need to stay away from machines that could interfere with your ICD. You shouldn't work near strong magnetic fields or strong electric fields. The ICD is built to be protected from most home shop tools and electric appliances, including microwave ovens. However, you need to be certain that all electric items are properly grounded and in good repair. Your doctor will help you understand what to avoid when you have an ICD.

Adapted with permission from "The Implanted Cardioverter-Defibrillator," *American Family Physician,* January 1998. Copyright © American Academy of Family Physicians. All rights reserved.

ACTIVITY 9.3

Building Batteries and Measuring Voltage

Getting In Gear

What is inside a battery? Like the reactions you just observed in Activity 9.2, batteries use metals, metal compounds, and solutions. In this activity, you will build a battery using two of the metals you tested in Activity 9.2.

If you build a battery, how do you know that it *is* a battery? Batteries are rated primarily by *voltage.* In this activity, each group will build batteries made of different combinations of metals. When you look at the data from each battery at the end of the activity, you will find that each combination gives a different voltage. Look for a relationship between metal reactivity and voltage when you discuss the results at the end of class.

As you build your battery, observe how electric energy is created. In a defibrillator, it is the chemical reactions in the battery that provide the energy it needs to stop fibrillation in a heart.

Getting To Work!

To learn more about batteries, you will

1. Work in groups and use **Job Sheet 9.3** **How Do You Build a Battery?** to learn about voltage and battery construction.
   a. Measure the voltage of an alkaline battery with a meter.
   b. Record your two metals, and use your reactivity chart from Activity 9.2 to determine which metal should be the negative terminal and which metal should be the positive terminal.

Job Sheet

c. Build a battery with two kinds of metals and two kinds of electrolytic (ion) solutions.

d. Describe the relationship between the voltage of the class batteries and the placement of their metals on the reactivity chart.

2. Read Getting the Point: *What Happens Inside a Battery?*, and answer the Focus Questions.

3. Read Concept Connection: *Battery Electrodes, Battery Terminals, and Circuits* and Workplace Connection: *What Pairs of Metals Are Used in Batteries?* as time permits.

4. Check out the Did You Know? readings as time permits.

Getting The Point

What Happens Inside a Battery?

Now that you have built a battery, you can understand how it works. A reactive metal releases electrons in the presence of an ion solution. The metal is used up as it reacts because its positive ions go into solution. A less reactive metal accepts the electrons in the presence of an ion solution and more metal is created as it reacts. You also learned the vocabulary used in describing parts of a battery: the metals are called *electrodes* and the ion solutions are called *electrolytes*.

Batteries can be made because metals differ in reactivity. Reactivity applies to both the release and the acceptance of electrons. A more reactive metal atom is *more* likely to release electrons, and its ion is *less* likely to accept electrons. The reactivity chart helps you predict what will happen when atoms from two metals react with an ion solution. Electrons will flow mostly in one direction, from the atoms of the more reactive metal to the ions of the less reactive metal.

The batteries you built had metals and metal ions. In the zinc-copper battery, the zinc electrode was placed in a solution containing zinc ions. The copper electrode was placed in a solution containing copper ions. The flowerpot allowed electrons to move from one ion solution to the other. The very reactive zinc atoms broke down into ions and electrons. Some of these electrons made their way through the flowerpot and into the solution containing copper ions. The electrons combined with the copper ion to create a copper atom.

Using the reactivity chart, we see why zinc corrodes and copper builds up. Zinc *atoms* are more likely to lose electrons and become positive ions, when compared to the copper atoms. At the same time, the copper *ions* are more likely to combine with free electrons, when compared to the zinc ions.

Did You Know?

Ions in the body are often referred to as electrolytes. There are electrolytes in the human body that are responsible for such diverse functions as transmitting nerve signals, stabilizing the normal heart rhythm, maintaining cell size, and contracting muscles. Sodium and potassium are two important electrolytes in your body. A decrease in sodium concentration in body fluids is known as hyponatremia, and can result in seizures or other complications.

The large numbers of batteries in use today have sophisticated design and materials. The negative electrode, a reactive metal, is arranged to increase the area exposed to the electrolyte (Figure 9.4). Instead of metal, solid materials that contain positive metal ions are used for the positive electrode. The positive metal ions are good acceptors of the electrons released by a reactive metal. In this case, battery designers compare the reactivity of a metal atom with the reactivity of a metal ion, using a longer reactivity chart. One advantage of this design is that both the negative electrode and the positive electrode are used up in a way that is often reversible, making rechargeable batteries possible.

Did You Know?

*T*he history of the battery

In 1780 an Italian anatomist, Luigi Galvani, noticed that the severed leg of a dead frog could be made to twitch when touched by pieces of metal. Galvani concluded rightly that electricity was producing the reaction, but it was another Italian, Alessandro Volta, who found that the electricity came not from the frog, as Galvani had thought, but from the metals. Eventually Volta found that copper and zinc together produce a strong charge and that if he built a pile of metal disks, alternately copper and zinc separated by pads soaked in salty water, he could produce a continuous electric current. Perfected in 1800, the Voltaic pile, as it is called, was the first electric battery. Since then, a great range of different types of battery has been developed.

Adapted from THE WAY THINGS WORK, by David Macaulay, 1988. Houghton Mifflin Company: Boston, MA.

Figure 9.4
Cut-Away to See Inside of a Battery

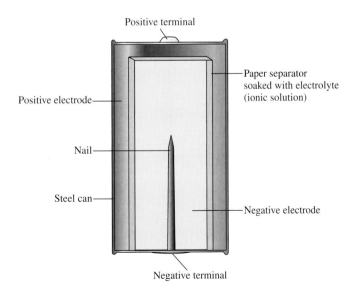

Focus Questions

What is an electrode?

What is an electrolyte?

Why does zinc corrode when it is placed in a solution containing zinc ions?

Why are two different metals used for a battery's electrodes?

Concept Connection: Battery Electrodes, Battery Terminals, and Circuits

What's the difference between a battery electrode and a battery terminal? In this activity, you learned that electrodes are the part of the battery that reacts with an electrolyte. The terminals are the two parts of the battery (or any circuit component) that connect it to the circuit. Terminals are made of materials, usually metals, which carry electricity easily.

The battery positive electrode is connected to the positive terminal, and the battery negative electrode is connected to the negative terminal. When placed in a circuit, the battery design ensures that most of the electrons released at the negative electrode will move toward the positive terminal by moving into the circuit and not through the battery.

Workplace Connection: What Pairs of Metals Are Used in Batteries?

You might wonder which metals are actually used in batteries. Here is a list of 11 different kinds of batteries and their uses.

1. **Zinc-carbon battery**–Also known as a **standard carbon** battery. Zinc-carbon chemistry is used in all inexpensive AA, C and D dry-cell batteries. The electrodes are zinc and carbon, with an acidic paste between them that serves as the electrolyte.

2. **Alkaline battery**–Used in common Duracell and Energizer batteries. The electrodes are zinc and manganese-oxide, with an alkaline electrolyte.

3. **Lithium photo battery**–Lithium, lithium-iodide and lead-iodide, used in cameras because of its ability to supply power surges.

4. **Lead-acid battery**–Used in automobiles. The electrodes are made of lead and lead-oxide with a strong acidic electrolyte. Rechargeable.

5. **Nickel-cadmium battery**–Uses nickel-hydroxide and cadmium electrodes, with potassium-hydroxide as the electrolyte. Rechargeable.

6. **Nickel-metal hydride battery**–Rapidly replacing nickel-cadmium because it does not suffer from the memory effect that nickel-cadmiums do. Rechargeable.

7. **Lithium-ion battery**–Very good power-to-weight ratio, often found in high-end laptop computers and cell phones. Rechargeable.

8. **Zinc-air battery**–Lightweight, rechargeable.

9. **Zinc-mercury oxide battery**–Often used in hearing-aid batteries.

10. **Silver-zinc battery**–Used in aeronautical applications because the power-to-weight ratio is good.

11. **Metal Chloride battery**–Used in electric vehicles.

Adapted from "How Batteries Work," by Marshall Brain. Copyright © 1998–2002 HowStuffWorks, Inc. All rights reserved. http://www.howstuffworks.com/battery3.htm (June 24, 2002)

ACTIVITY 9.4

Measuring Voltage Discharge Rate

Getting In Gear

If you go to a store that sells batteries, you see many different kinds of batteries. How do these batteries differ? They differ in their composition, which determines voltage or strength. Batteries also differ in size, which is the amount of reactive metal they contain. The labels DC, AA, and AAA refer to the size.

The strength and size of a battery are important battery characteristics. Another important battery characteristic is how steady its voltage remains when in use. The graph of voltage over time for a battery is called its *voltage discharge rate*. In this activity, you and your classmates find this rate for three kinds of batteries. Begin thinking which battery characteristics are important in a defibrillator.

Getting To Work!

To learn more about battery characteristics, you will

1. Participate in a class discussion about the important characteristics of batteries: strength (voltage), size, and voltage discharge rate.

2. Work in groups and use | **Job Sheet 9.4** | **How Does Battery Voltage Vary over Time?** to investigate voltage discharge rate.
   a. Collect voltage-over-time data for one kind of battery.
   b. Graph the voltage to show voltage discharge.
   c. Describe and compare graphs of three kinds of batteries.

Job Sheet

3. Participate in a class discussion about how voltage discharge of each battery will affect device performance and energy transfer.

4. Read Getting the Point: *Batteries and Voltage,* and answer the Focus Questions.

5. Read Workplace Connection: *The Best Battery for a Flight Defibrillator* and Concept Connection: *Power Surges,* and check out the Did You Know? reading as time permits.

Getting The Point.

Batteries and Voltage

We can describe *voltage* in several ways. It is related to the reactivity of metals. When you made different kinds of batteries and measured voltage, you saw that voltage increased when metals were farther apart on the reactivity chart. Voltage is also related to battery strength. Batteries connected end-to-end (in series) will have their voltages added together. For example, assume that a large radio needs six alkaline batteries and that a small radio uses two. The combined batteries in the large radio have 9 volts, and the combined batteries in the small radio have 3 volts.

Both of these descriptions refer to energy. There is a greater difference in energy released between metals far apart on the reactivity chart. You need more energy to produce the louder sound from the speakers of the larger radio. In fact, voltage is defined as energy per unit of charge. But this definition may raise as many questions as it answers. What does energy per unit of charge mean in a battery?

Let's first consider the kind of energy. Voltage refers to the stored or *potential energy* of charges. Potential energy means "energy of position." Remember that an example of potential energy is a ball held in one's hand. If released, it could move and then transfer its energy to what it hits.

Figure 9.5
Charge Carriers

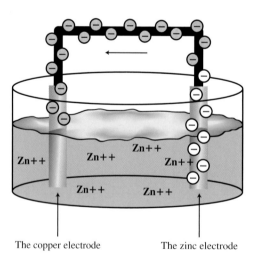

The copper electrode   The zinc electrode

Charge carriers flow from the zinc electrode toward the copper electrode. The shaded electrons are charge carriers provided by the metal.

In the zinc-copper battery, negative electrons released by zinc atoms have potential energy because they are attracted to positive ions. Some positive ions have greater attracting force than other ions. The stronger the attraction, the greater energy the electrons will have. This is why different combinations of metals have different voltages. In a way, the distance between metals in the reactivity chart is like height; the greater the distance the more energy is stored.

The common unit of voltage is the volt (V), which is equal to 1 joule of energy per 1 coulomb of charge.

Focus Questions

What are two ways to describe voltage?

What is voltage?

Why do different combinations of metals in a battery have different voltages?

Concept Connection: Power Surges

SURGE BASICS

The main job of a surge protector system is to protect electronic devices from "surges." If you're wondering what a surge protector does, the first question is what are surges anyway? And why do electronics need to be protected from them?

A power surge, or transient voltage, is an increase in voltage significantly above the designated level in a flow of electricity. In normal household and office wiring in the U.S., the standard voltage is 120 volts. If the voltage rises above 120 volts, there is a problem, and a surge protector helps to prevent that problem from destroying your computer.

To understand the problem, it is helpful to understand something about voltage. Voltage is a measure of a difference in electric potential energy. Electric current travels from point to point because there is a greater electric potential energy on one end of the wire than there is on the other end. This is the same sort of principle that makes water under pressure flow out of a hose—higher pressure on one end of the hose pushes water toward an area of low pressure.

You can think of voltage as a measure of electrical pressure.

As we'll see later on, various factors can cause a brief increase in voltage.

When the increase lasts three nanoseconds (billionth of a second) or more, this is called a surge. When it only lasts for one or two nanoseconds, it's called a spike.

If the surge or spike is high enough, it can inflict some heavy damage on a machine. The effect is very similar to applying too much water pressure to a hose. If there is too much water pressure, a hose will burst. Approximately the same thing happens when too much electrical pressure runs through a wire—the wire "bursts." Actually, it heats up like the filament in a light bulb and burns, but it's the same idea. Even if increased voltage doesn't immediately break your machine, it may put extra strain on the components, wearing them down over time.

SURGE SOURCES

Power surges occur when something boosts the electrical charge at some point in the power lines. This causes an increase in the electrical potential energy, which can increase the current flowing to your wall outlet. A number of different things can cause this to happen.

The most familiar source is probably lightning, though it's actually one of the least common causes. When lightning strikes near a power line, whether it's underground, in a building or running along poles, the electrical energy can boost electrical pressure by millions of volts. This causes an extremely large power surge, which will overpower most any surge protector. In a lightning storm, you should never rely on your surge protector to save your computer. The best protection is to unplug your computer.

A more common cause of power surges is the operation of high-power electrical devices, such as elevators, air conditioners and refrigerators. These high-powered pieces of equipment require a lot of energy to switch on and turn off components like compressors and motors. This switching creates sudden, brief demands for power, which upset the steady voltage flow in the electrical system. While these surges are nowhere near the intensity of a lightning surge, they can be severe enough to damage components, immediately or gradually, and they occur regularly in most building's electrical systems.

Other sources of power surges include faulty wiring, problems with the utility company's equipment, and downed power lines. The system of transformers and lines that bring electricity from a power generator to the outlets in our homes or offices is extraordinarily complex. There are dozens of possible points of failure, and many potential errors that can cause an uneven power flow. In today's system of electricity distribution, power surges are an unavoidable occurrence.

Workplace Connection: The Best Battery for a Flight Defibrillator

LITHIUM BATTERIES VITAL IN FLIGHT DEFIBRILLATORS

Automated external defibrillators (AEDs), are designed to enable people without extensive medical expertise to treat ventricular fibrillation (V-fib).

British Airways carries the LIFEPAK 500 AED, manufactured by Medtronic Physio-Control. This rugged, compact and portable device weighs in at only seven pounds (3.2 kg). Its low maintenance requirements and intuitive operation, aided by concise voice prompting, audio warnings and instructions displayed on an LED screen, makes it ideal for use by infrequent AED users such as cabin staff.

The LIFEPAK 500 AED is powered by a long-life, high power Saft lithium sulfur dioxide battery pack. This battery pack provides the 500 with the longest battery life rating of any AED—a minimum of 230 full discharges and typically over 300. This reduces the cost of ownership and maintenance since the battery needs to be changed less frequently. In addition, this feature combines with the extremely long shelf life (four years in aircraft use) to eliminate one of the most common problems reported with defibrillators: depleted batteries.

Lithium sulfur dioxide cells also lend themselves to the design of simple and reliable circuits for low-battery detection. This eliminates the need for extra sensing cells or complicated detection techniques.

Adapted from "Lithium Batteries Vital in Flight Defibrillators." ElectronicsTalk.com. http://www.electronicstalk.com/news/saf/saf100.html (June 2, 2002)

ACTIVITY 9.5

Choosing the Best Battery

Getting In Gear

To complete Project Milestone Two, you will choose the best battery for a defibrillator depending on its intended use, such as in a hospital, rescue vehicle, or on an airplane. Choosing a battery is the first design decision you will make for your model defibrillator circuit.

In design, you make thoughtful decisions based on needs and choices. You will need to discuss and determine which battery characteristics are important for your defibrillator's intended use. After deciding on important battery characteristics, you will make your final decision from a list of available batteries.

Getting To Work!

To complete Project Milestone Two, you will

1. Work in groups and follow the instructions on | **Job Sheet 9.5** | What Is the **Best Battery for Our Defibrillator?**
   a. Choose a specific kind of defibrillator for the unit design project.
   b. Develop design criteria for the defibrillator.
   c. Select the best battery for the defibrillator.

Job Sheet

2. Review the concepts and answer the questions in What Have You Learned? for homework.

3. Read Workplace Connection: *Engineering Technician* as time permits.

4. Check out the Did You Know? reading as time permits.

Workplace Connection: Engineering Technician

Engineering technicians use the principles and theories of science, engineering, and mathematics to solve technical problems in research and development, manufacturing, sales, construction, inspection, and maintenance. Their work is more limited in scope and more practically oriented than that of scientists and engineers. Many engineering technicians assist engineers and scientists, especially in research and development. Others work in quality control-inspecting products and processes, conducting tests, or collecting data. In manufacturing, they may assist in product design, development, or production.

Engineering technicians who work in research and development build or set up equipment, prepare and conduct experiments, collect data, calculate or record the results, and help engineers or scientists in other ways, such as making prototype versions of newly designed equipment. They also assist in design work, often using computer-aided design equipment.

Electrical and electronics engineering technicians help design, develop, test, and manufacture electrical and electronic equipment such as communication equipment, radar, industrial and medical measuring or control devices, navigational equipment, and computers. They may work in product evaluation and testing, using measuring and diagnostic devices to adjust, test, and repair equipment.

Electrical and electronic engineering technology is also applied to a wide variety of systems such as communications and process controls. Electromechanical engineering technicians combine fundamental principles of mechanical engineering technology with knowledge of electrical and electronic circuits to design, develop, test, and manufacture electrical and computer-controlled mechanical systems.

Although it may be possible to qualify for a few engineering technician jobs without formal training, most employers prefer to hire someone with at least a 2-year associate degree in engineering technology. Training is available at technical institutes, community colleges, extension divisions of colleges and universities, public and private vocational-technical schools, and the Armed Forces. Persons with college courses in science, engineering, and mathematics may qualify for some positions but may need additional specialized training and experience. Although employers usually do not require engineering technicians to be certified, such certification may provide jobseekers a competitive advantage.

Because many engineering technicians may assist in design work, creativity is desirable. Good communication skills and the ability to work well with others also is important because these workers often are part of a team of engineers and other technicians.

Did You Know?

You might save a life with a portable defibrillator?

Defibrillator manufacturers are always working to design new, useful defibrillators. Some are designed for use by people without medical training. In addition to defibrillating, portable defibrillators can record and analyze EKGs, and then recommend whether to proceed with defibrillation. These types of defibrillators are being placed in public spaces such as airports and public buildings.

Adapted from OCCUPATIONAL OUTLOOK HANDBOOK. "Engineering Technicians." U.S. Department of Labor, Bureau of Labor Statistics. http://www.bls.gov/oco/ocos112.htm (June 4, 2002)

KEY CONCEPTS

Electric force. When certain kinds of objects are rubbed together, they begin to attract *or* repel each other. This type of force is called electric force.

Charge. The property of matter responsible for electric force is charge. Because there are two kinds of electric forces observed, there are also two forms of charge. The forms of charge are called negative and positive. A positive charge will repel another positive charge. Likewise, two negative charges repel each other. A positive and a negative charge will attract each other.

Different parts within an atom carry the two forms of charge. Protons, which are located at the center of the atom, carry positive charge. Electrons, which are located at the outer edges of the atom, carry an equal amount of negative charge. Atoms have equal amounts of protons and electrons. Since the total charge of an electron and a proton taken together is zero, ordinary matter made of atoms has no charge, or is neutral. If energy is used to move charge from one place to another, then matter can acquire more of one kind of charge and is described as charged.

Charge is measured in units of coulombs. One coulomb has the same amount of charge as 6.25×10^{18} billion electrons.

Ions. Some atoms can gain electrons, and other atoms can lose electrons. These atoms become ions. If an atom gains electrons, it has more electrons than protons, and becomes a negative ion. If an atom loses electrons, it has more protons than electrons, and becomes a positive ion.

Reactivity of metals. One of the properties of metals is that they easily lose electrons to become positive ions. Each metal differs in how easily it loses electrons. This property is described as the reactivity of the metal. A metal that gives up electrons more easily is said to be more reactive.

Electrolytes. An electrolyte is solution that can act like a circuit. Electricity occurs when there is movement of charged particles, and an electrolyte contains charged ions that can move throughout the solution. An electrolyte is used in a battery to facilitate the separation of electrons from a reactive metal.

Batteries. A battery contains two kinds of reactive materials and an electrolyte. The two kinds of reactive materials form the positive and negative ends of the battery, called electrodes. The negative electrode is made of a reactive metal that gives up its electrons easily, giving them energy. The positive electrode usually contains a chemical compound that includes positive metal ions. Although the positive terminal's positive ions attract the electrons at the negative electrode, the battery design prevents this direct transfer of electrons. Only when the battery is connected to a circuit can the energetic electrons move toward the positive electrode by traveling into the wire.

Because energy is released by the chemical reactions at the two battery terminals, the electrons at the battery's negative electrode contain potential (stored) energy. It is useful to think of a battery as an electron mover or pump driven by chemical reactions. There are many different kinds of batteries, composed of different kinds of metals and metal compounds.

Voltage. Voltage is a measurement of the level of the stored energy for a set amount of charge. It can also be described as a measure of how hard a battery pumps or moves charge. With more voltage, a battery can move electrons more quickly through the same circuit. Voltage is measured in volts:

1 volt is equal to 1 joule of energy per 1 coulomb of charge (1 volt = 1 joule/coulomb). You can measure the voltage of a battery with a voltmeter connected between the battery's two terminals.

1. Name the two kinds of charge.

2. When you built your electroscope, you saw that the pieces of tape both attracted and repelled each other. Explain why.

3. You have two metals. They both react safely with acid. How would you determine which one is more reactive?

4. When zinc tranfers two electrons to hydrogen ions in solution, a zinc ion and hydrogen gas are formed. This change is called a chemical _____.

5. You have two alkaline batteries, each 1.5 volts. One battery is large (D), and one small (AA) (Figure A). The large battery contains more reactive metal. For the two batteries, compare the amount of (a) energy per charge, and (b) total energy output over the lifetime of the battery.

Figure A

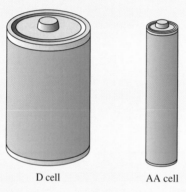

D cell   AA cell

6. The graphs in Figure B show how two batteries hold their charge. Each graph shows 8 hours of data.

Figure B

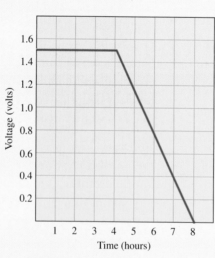

Battery A

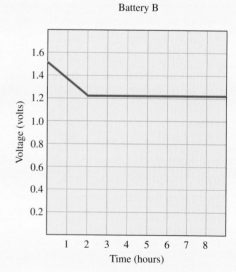

Battery B

a. What do you notice about Battery A?
b. What do you notice about Battery B?

Continued

c. You want to buy a battery for a portable tape cassette player. The store only carries Battery A and Battery B. Which battery would you pick? Explain the reason for your choice.

7. You are designing a camera that requires 6 volts. You will choose a battery from the list in Figure C.

Figure C

	Battery Characteristics		
Battery Brands	Size/Volume (cubic cm)	Voltage (volts)	Price (dollars)
Charger	0.5	1.5	2.00
Power Blast	12.0	1.5	1.00
Serve-Cell	8.0	1.5	0.75
Live-Long	0.5	6.0	12.00
Electro-Belt	1.0	3.0	3.00

a. For each battery, list how many you would need if used in your camera.
b. For each battery, list the total volume and cost if used in your camera.
c. Choose a battery to use in your camera. Explain the reasons for your choice.

APPLYING WHAT YOU KNOW

1. Find several battery-run devices in your home, such as a flashlight, a smoke detector, a portable phone, a camera, and a cell phone. With the help of an adult, look at the battery in each device. What kind of battery does each device contain?

2. Visit a store that sells many kinds of batteries. Look over the different kinds of batteries, and ask the salesperson about their uses. Record each kind of battery, and list its voltage, type, and uses.

3. Research voltage of the electric outlets in homes, and answer the following questions:
a. What is the standard voltage output of an outlet?
b. What is the voltage output of outlets in several other parts of the world?

4. Different kinds of batteries are suitable for different kinds of devices. Under what conditions would you recommend using the following batteries? Be sure to consider cost.

a. rechargeable battery
b. long-lasting battery
c. light-weight battery
d. nontoxic battery
e. solar battery
f. inexpensive, short-lasting, nonrechargeable battery

Specifying Current and Voltage in the Model Defibrillator Circuit

OVERVIEW

THE JOLT OF LIFE OR THE KISS OF DEATH?

The training team has selected the defibrillator battery.

You're almost ready to start building the model defibrillator circuit, but there is something you need to know first. As medical equipment technicians, you will service and operate some very powerful lifesaving equipment. But that same equipment can also take lives. If a defibrillator has faulty wiring or is improperly calibrated, the jolt of electricity delivered to the heart can stop it permanently.

You need to worry about the amount of electricity reaching the patient's heart. You need to worry about current.

Your next milestone:

Project Milestone 3 — Designing the Emergency Defibrillator Circuit

You will determine a safe level of current for the model defibrillator circuit, calculate voltage, and evaluate information about defibrillators. Then you will design the first version of your model defibrillator circuits.

It is *current* that matters in a defibrillator. Too little current and the defibrillator won't do its job; too much current and the patient can die. You will learn more about current in this chapter, beginning with how to measure current and regulate it.

How do a battery's energetic electrons light a bulb or charge a defibrillator? Current is the movement of these energetic electrons through a circuit. In this chapter, you will measure current and observe how well different objects carry current, a property of objects known as *resistance*. You will also learn how voltage, current, and resistance are related. This information is vital for anyone whose work involves the testing or repair of equipment using direct-current circuits, including defibrillators. You learn when current is dangerous, and determine a safe current for your model defibrillator circuit. You learn more about defibrillators from an emergency medical technician or firefighter. Finally, you design a circuit for your model.

You're moving ahead in the design process. Given the problem to design a model defibrillator circuit, you've learned about defibrillators and identified some of the constraints for their design. As you proceed, you are learning the science necessary to complete the design.

By the end of this chapter, you will have created an initial circuit design for the discharging part of the defibrillator circuit. In the next and last chapter of this unit, you will develop your proposed defibrillator circuit, evaluate that solution, and present it to the class.

To help you accomplish Project Milestone Three, you will do the following activities:

Activity 10.1 Understanding and Measuring Electric Current
How does a battery light a bulb? You will learn that energetic electrons in a battery circulate a flow of charge, called current, through a circuit. You will observe that current transfers energy to a bulb and measure current in battery-and-bulb circuits.

Activity 10.2 Exploring Conductivity and Measuring Resistance
Find out how well different objects carry current by seeing if they can conduct enough current to light a bulb. You will measure current through circuits, and measure resistance across objects in the circuit. You will see what happens to current when an object's resistance increases.

Activity 10.3 Describing How Resistance, Voltage, and Current Are Related
You will learn about resistors—circuit components that are used to control current—by measuring resistance across individual resistors and combinations of resistors. You will

increase voltage in a circuit with known resistance, and measure current. You will analyze data relating voltage, resistance, and current, and learn Ohm's law.

Activity 10.4 Specifying Current in a Defibrillator Model

How much current can safely pass through your model defibrillator circuit? Given a value for average patient resistance, you will use Ohm's law to calculate the amount of voltage you need to produce a safe current in your model defibrillator circuit. You will meet an emergency medical technician or firefighter, and learn uses for a portable defibrillator.

Activity 10.5 Designing the Emergency Defibrillator Circuit

You will consult your resources, explore various circuits, and complete the first iteration of your emergency defibrillator. You will make a schematic diagram and a rough model for one part of the circuit.

ACTIVITY 10.1

Understanding and Measuring Electric Current

Getting In Gear

In a defibrillator, the amount of *current* the patient receives is carefully regulated to ensure that the heart restarts properly. What is current? How do you measure it? Why is it important to regulate in a defibrillator? These are the questions you will address in this activity.

As you study current, you will gain a more complete picture of how a circuit works. Previously, you learned that voltage describes the energy of electrons. In this activity, you learn that current is the movement of energetic electrons through a circuit. This movement results in energy transfer in a circuit. As you investigate current, think about how your observations will apply to a defibrillator-and-patient circuit, and also consider what safeguards are needed to limit the amount of energy delivered to the heart.

Getting To Work!

To begin to understand current and its importance in the design of a defibrillator circuit, you will

1. Read the overview scenario and project milestone for Chapter 10, and discuss the scenario with your class.

2. Review the major ideas of Chapter 9 with your teacher.

3. Work by yourself and use 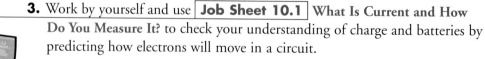 **Job Sheet 10.1** What Is Current and How Do You Measure It? to check your understanding of charge and batteries by predicting how electrons will move in a circuit.

Job Sheet

4. Watch your teacher demonstrate a model of the movement of electrons through a wire.

5. Discuss the definition of current and its units with your teacher.

6. Work in groups and use Job Sheet 10.1 to explore current in circuits.
   a. Learn how to use a meter to measure the current through a circuit.
   b. Observe what happens to the value of current when voltage is increased in a circuit.

7. Read Getting the Point: *How Do Charges Move in a Circuit?,* and answer the Focus Questions.

8. Read Concept Connection: *Power,* and check out the Did You Know? readings as time permits.

Getting The Point.

How Do Charges Move in a Circuit?

When you build a circuit, you connect the two terminals of a battery to metal wires and components. The battery has done work separating negative electrons from the positive ions, giving the electrons potential energy. When the wire is connected to a battery, "energetic electrons" move very slowly away from the negative terminal of the battery toward the positive terminal. The metal wire contains a "sea" of free electrons. The energetic electrons from the battery repel these electrons at one end of the wire. At the other end of the wire, the sea of electrons is attracted by the positive charges at the battery's positive terminal. This simultaneous push and pull gets the sea of electrons moving through the wire. This moving mass of electrons is called *current.*

Figure 10.1
A Battery in a Circuit

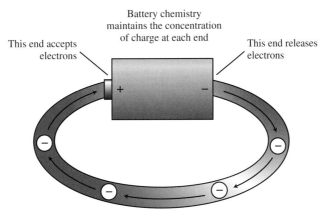

Battery chemistry maintains the concentration of charge at each end

This end accepts electrons

This end releases electrons

A "sea" of electrons drifts through the wire from the "−" to the "+" end of the battery

There are 40,000,000,000,000,000,000,000 free electrons in an all-copper penny. A piece of wire can contain that many electrons or more, depending on its length and thickness.

Current (*I*) is usually expressed in amperes (A); it is measured by an ammeter. The number of amperes tells us how many coulombs of charge pass a given point each second, for example, 1 ampere means 1 coulomb per second. In the case of a metal wire, the charge carriers are electrons, which carry a negative charge. In the human body, which also has electric current running through it (for instance, in the brain and muscles), the charge carriers are usually positive ions.

Current refers to the *rate* of flow. Think of it this way: If you are standing beside a road and carrying a stopwatch, you could count cars and calculate how many cars pass by, on average, each minute. The result would be a rate called the *traffic flow*, for example, 14 cars per minute. Now picture a person smaller than an atom standing inside a wire counting the passing electrons and figuring out the charge flow in the same way. This rate of charge flow is the current.

Figure 10.2
Measuring the Rate of Traffic Flow

You have probably heard about or seen fuses or circuit breakers. These devices open or break a circuit if too much current is flowing through it. Different kinds of wires carry different amounts of current. A fuse or circuit breaker in a circuit only opens (or breaks) when too much current for that size wire tries to flow through the circuit.

Your teacher can show you how a fuse works by adding a strand of wire from a stainless steel wool cleaning ball to a battery-and-bulb circuit.

Circuit designers use metal wires in their circuits because metal atoms do not hold tightly to their electrons. This is why metal wires contain a sea of free electrons. When pushed and pulled by charges at the battery terminals, the electrons in the wire gain energy, which is in turn transferred to components in the circuit. As these energetic electrons travel through the wire from the negative electrode and toward the positive electrode, they experience many collision-like interactions with the latticelike structure of the metal of the wire. These little collisions slow down the electrons until they travel at a constant rate called the *drift speed*. In fact, electrons drift through circuits very slowly, typically traveling only a few inches per day.

It is the collisions of electrons as they travel through a circuit with other materials that make current useful to us. In a wire, electrons have few collisions. In a lightbulb, electrons collide with the atoms of the filament more frequently because the wire is very thin. These collisions cause the filament to heat up, because all collisions create heat. If the filament gets hot enough, it glows. In all circuits, the potential energy of the electrons is transferred from the electrons to the circuit because of collisions.

What Does the Ammeter Read?

The *ammeter* measures current in *amperes* (amps). One ampere means 1 coulomb per second. A coulomb is equal to 6.25×10^{18} electrons. Therefore, a current reading of 1 amp means that 6,250,000,000,000,000,000 electrons move past any point along the wire every second. Of course, electrons are very small, and they can travel side by side, so they don't have to go very far, or very fast, for a lot of them to move past a point.

Figure 10.3

Measuring Current in a Circuit with an Ammeter

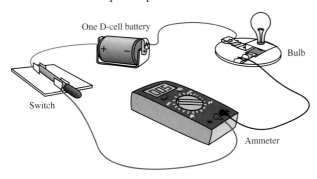

You will often see abbreviations for milliamps (mA), each valued at one one-thousandth of an amp, and sometimes for microamps (µA), each valued at one one-millionth of an amp.

Focus Questions

How do electrons in current transfer their energy to circuit components?

What is the source of the electrons that make up current?

Concept Connection: Power

The energy a lightbulb uses over time is the power used by the bulb. This is measured in units called *watts*. To find the power consumption, multiply the voltage measurement across the bulb and the current measurement across the bulb.

$$V \text{ (volts)} = \frac{\text{joules of energy}}{\text{coulombs of charge}}$$

$$I \text{ (current)} = \frac{\text{coulombs of charge}}{\text{second}}$$

$$P \text{ (power or energy used per second)} = \frac{\text{joules}}{\text{coulombs}} \times \frac{\text{coulombs}}{\text{second}}$$

$$= \frac{\text{joules}}{\text{second}} = \text{watts of power}$$

$$P = V \times I$$

ACTIVITY 10.2

Exploring Conductivity and Measuring Resistance

Getting In Gear

In Activity 10.1, you learned that metal wires provide a sea of electrons. Now consider these questions: If you change the material of a component in a given circuit, does the amount of charge flowing change? Can you expect your defibrillator to send current through the human body?

You probably concluded that not all materials would carry the same amount of current in a circuit. For example, current does not pass easily through air, which is why an open switch breaks a circuit. You may also have noticed that wires in your home are wrapped in plastic, which prevent you from receiving a shock.

Air and plastic are two examples of materials that do not have free electrons. Very little current travels through them. This property of materials is called conductivity, and it varies from material to material. In a circuit, we want to know about a related quantity—the extent to which any object (even one made out of mixed materials) will allow current flow. This electric quantity is called resistance. As you work on this activity, start thinking about how you can use resistance to control the flow of current through the defibrillator.

Getting To Work!

To explore conductivity and measure resistance, you will

1. Contribute to class predictions about what happens to the flow of charge if the materials in a component of a circuit are changed.

Job Sheet

2. Work in groups and use 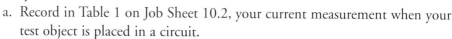 **Job Sheet 10.2** What Is Resistance and How Do You Measure It? to investigate how well objects made of different materials carry current.

   a. Record in Table 1 on Job Sheet 10.2, your current measurement when your test object is placed in a circuit.

   b. Work with your teacher to classify the data from Table 1 posted on the board.

   c. Participate in a class discussion about the nature of resistance.

   d. Learn how to measure resistance of objects.

   e. Record your data about resistance in Table 2.

3. Theorize with the class the relationship between resistance and energy transfer in a circuit.

4. Read Getting the Point: *Conductivity and Resistance,* and answer the Focus Questions.

5. Read Workplace Connection: *Wire* and Concept Connection: *The Resistance of a Patient* as time permits.

6. Check out the Did You Know? readings as time permits.

Getting The Point.

Conductivity and Resistance

The ability of a material to carry current when a difference in voltage exists is called *conductivity*. If current flows easily through a material, that material is called a *conductor*. Metals are good conductors. If current flows slowly through a material, that material is called an *insulator*. Plastic, glass, and air are good insulators.

Some materials are rated between conductors and insulators in their ability to carry current. These materials are called *semiconductors*. Metals are conductors, carbon is a semiconductor, and plastic is an insulator.

One of the important understandings in electricity is that the charges that make up current must come from the material used in the circuit. In solids, the conductivity of a material is related to its ability to lose electrons easily, which is why metals are good conductors.

Even if free electrons are available to flow through an object, the internal arrangement of atoms and molecules will still impede the flow of electrons to some extent. This property of objects is called *resistance*. Resistance varies with several factors, including both the conductivity and shape of an object, and temperature. Resistance *(R)* is measured in ohms (Ω). Under many conditions, the resistance of an object can be treated as a constant, not dependent on voltage or current.

A good conductor has low resistance. The most common way to assess the conductivity of an object, therefore, is to measure its resistance. Like voltage and current, how well an object carries current is a useful quantity to know when working with circuits. In fact, you will need to understand and use resistance when you build your defibrillator model circuit.

Resistance is measured in units of *ohms;* Ω is the symbol for ohms. A meter measures resistance by sending a small amount of current through an object. If you need to measure the resistance of a component in a circuit, disconnect the component from the voltage source first. **There must be no current going through the circuit.** Otherwise you may damage the meter. The circuit must **always** be broken (or switch turned off) to measure resistance with a meter. The following table contains sample data of resistance:

Table 10.1
Resistance of test objects.

Object	Resistance (Ohms Ω)
paper clip	0.1 Ω
penny	0.0 Ω
nickel	0.2 Ω
quarter	0.2 Ω
pencil lead insert	11.0 Ω
plastic spoon	OL (very high)

Focus Questions

What is the difference between a conductor and an insulator?

Why are metals good conductors?

How do you find out the resistance of your object, or of a circuit component?

Workplace Connection: Wire

HOW DO I CHOOSE THE BEST KIND OF WIRE FOR A PARTICULAR USE?
Here are some basic facts that will help you make a selection:

1. The conductor is the metal part of the wire or cable that carries electricity. Just as a large pipe can carry more water than a small one, a large wire conductor can carry more electrical current.

2. The gauge number indicates the size of the conductor. A lower gauge number means larger wire. A 12-gauge conductor is larger and can carry more current than an 18-gauge conductor.

Figure 10.4
Gauge Sizes of Wire

12   16   18   20   22   24

3. Stranded-conductor wire is useful in speaker and audio hookups as well as connections where wire flexibility is desired.

4. Solid-conductor wire is used in hookups or circuits where flexibility is not needed.

Figure 10.5
Solid-Conductor
Wires of Different
Gauge

24-gauge uninsulated
copper wire

18-gauge stranded wire.
Hookup wire is priced
by the spool.

High-amperage 8-gauge
megacable Power Cable Rope-
Strand copper conductor covered
by rugged PVC insulation,
rated 105° C.

Adapted from RadioShack Product Catalog. Copyright © RadioShack Corporation 2002. Reprinted with permission. http:///www.radioshack.com/

Concept Connection: The Resistance of a Patient

The following reading is taken from the *Textbook of Advanced Cardiac Life Support,* published by the American Heart Association. Doctors, nurses, medical students, respiratory therapists, emergency technicians and paramedics use this textbook when trained in advanced cardiac life support, or ACLS.

Defibrillation is accomplished by passage of sufficient electrical current (amperes) through the heart for a brief period of time. Current flow is determined by the energy chosen (joules) and the transthoraic impedance (ohms), or resistance to current flow. Many factors determine transthoracic impedance. These include energy selected, electrode size, electrode-skin coupling material, number and time interval of previous shocks, phase of ventilation, distance between electrodes (size of the chest), and electrode-to-chest contact pressure. Human transthoracic impedance has been reported to range from 15 to 150 ohms, with the average adult human impedance about 70 to 80 ohms. If transthoracic impedance is high, a low-energy shock may fail to pass enough current through the heart to achieve defibrillation. Clinicians should not expect a sudden "jump" of the patient with every defibrillation attempt. Defibrillation "failures" are sometimes reported by mistake because the operator failed to see dramatic muscular jerks by the patient. Skeletal muscle response can be affected by sedation, anesthesia, drug overdoses, the patient's muscle mass and general condition, body temperature, and the interval without spontaneous circulation.

To reduce impedance when using hand-held defibrillation paddles, the defibrillator operator should always apply a defibrillation electrode gel or paste made specifically for defibrillation. Adhesive defibrillation electrodes connected directly to the defibrillator ("remote" or "hands-off" defibrillation) as well as gelled pads permeated with electrode paste are also acceptable. Use of bare paddles without a coupling material between the electrodes and the chest wall results in very high transthoracic impedance. Although the phase of respiration influences impedance, most arrested patients will be in end-expiration, especially those with firm paddle-to-chest contact pressure, and this will give a lower impedance. It is important to use an appropriate

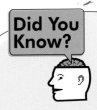

Did You Know?

Direct current (DC). Batteries produce direct current. The electrons flow in one direction from the negative terminal to the positive terminal of the battery.

Alternating current (AC). Your electric power company supplies alternating current. In AC, the electrons move back and forth 60 times a second so that the terminals of the supply repeatedly change from positive to negative and vice versa.

Did You Know?

Nikola Tesla, who was born in Croatia in 1856, developed the AC generator for Westinghouse in order to generate current at high voltages and over long distances. It was not possible to do this with the direct-current generators that Thomas Edison developed at the beginning of the 20th century.

conductive material between the paddles and the chest to maximize current flow. Use of improper gels or pastes can cause burns or sparks and can pose a serious risk of fire in an oxygen-enriched environment.

Figure 10.6
Automated External Defibrillator and Its Attachments to a Patient

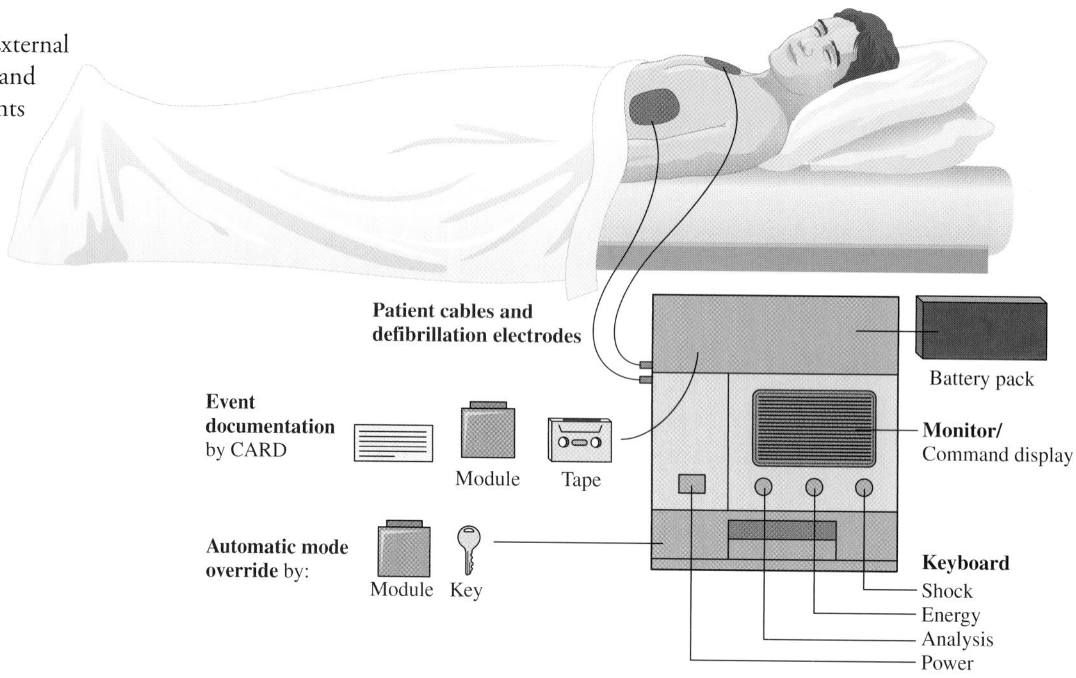

Patient cables and defibrillation electrodes

Battery pack

Event documentation by CARD

Module   Tape

Monitor/ Command display

Automatic mode override by:

Module   Key

Keyboard
Shock
Energy
Analysis
Power

Reproduced with permission. *Advanced Cardiac Life Support.* © 1997, Copyright American Heart Association.

ACTIVITY 10.3

Describing How Resistance, Voltage, and Current Are Related

As you discovered in Activity 10.2, you can measure the resistance of different materials. Everything has some resistance. That includes lightbulbs, buzzers, even the wire the current flows through in a circuit—and, of course, human bodies. If you increase the resistance in a circuit that includes a lightbulb, how does the resistance affect the functioning of the bulb? If you know the voltage and the resistance in a circuit, exactly how much current will flow in the circuit?

To answer these questions, you will use *resistors,* which are circuit components of known resistance. With these resistors, you will test what happens to current when you increase voltage while keeping resistance constant. You will graph this data and find the slope of the line. This calculation will help you find the equation that relates voltage to current and resistance, which is expressed in a formula known as *Ohm's law.*

Because voltage, current, and resistance are related, it is possible to predict current in a given circuit and to control current in circuits by changing the resistance. You will use Ohm's law in Activity 10.4 to determine the number of batteries and which resistors you will use in your model defibrillator circuit.

Getting To Work!

To understand resistors and the relationships among voltage, current, and resistance, you will

1. Observe resistors and see how they act in a circuit.

2. Work in your group and follow ⏐ **Job Sheet 10.3** ⏐ **How Are Voltage and Resistance Related to Current?** to investigate what happens to the value of current when you keep resistance constant and increase voltage.

   a. Build a circuit with a resistor and see how current changes when the number of batteries is increased.

   b. Record in Table 1 on Job Sheet 10.3 your resistance, current, and voltage measurements.

   c. Graph the data you collected.

   d. Calculate the slope of your graph. (If necessary, refer to Concept Connection: *Finding the Slope of a Graph.*)

   e. Use your findings and the equation of the line to discover how voltage, current, and resistance are related mathematically.

3. Read Getting the Point: *Ohm's Law and Resistors* for homework, and answer the Focus Questions. If your teacher assigns several Ohm's law problems, solve them as well.

4. Read Workplace Connection: *The Resistor Color Code* and Concept Connection: *Finding the Slope of a Graph* as time permits.

Job Sheet

Getting The Point.

Ohm's Law and Resistors

In this activity, you discovered Ohm's law, which explains the relationship between voltage *(V),* current *(I),* and resistance *(R).* It is most often expressed as

$$V = R \times I$$

The equation can be expressed in two other ways to help find a missing value:

$$I = V/R \quad \text{and} \quad R = V/I$$

Ohm's law is used every day to identify the correct wiring and components for circuits in homes, business, and within electric devices. Most of these circuits have a constant voltage source—the voltage is always the same. This leaves two variables, current and resistance. We control the amount of current in a circuit by changing the resistance of a circuit.

Resistors are one of the major circuit components that are used to control current by changing the amount of resistance in a circuit. The symbol for a resistor in a circuit is

Figure 10.7
Symbol for Resistor
in a Circuit

The unit of resistance is the ohm; its symbol is Ω (the Greek letter omega). When more than one resistor is used in series in a circuit, the total ohm value is the sum of the individual values. For example, a circuit with two 100-ohm resistors has a total of 200 ohms of resistance.

Focus Questions

In Ohm's law, what do V, I, and R stand for?

When do you use Ohm's law?

Why do you put a resistor in a circuit?

What is the symbol for a resistor in a circuit?

Concept Connection: Finding the Slope of a Graph

After you plot the points on your graph, the first step is to draw a straight line that best fits the data on the graph. Usually, it is impossible to draw a straight line that goes through all the data points. You will have to guess where to draw a straight line that comes closest to representing the pattern in the data. There are ways to calculate the best-fit line using mathematical formulas, and some graphing calculators and software packages will do this for you. If you have access to such a tool, use it and move on to the next step.

Sometimes, people will connect the data point that is closest to the origin and the data point that is farthest from the origin, but that does not make sense. Those two data points are not any more important or accurate than the others. In fact, the best-fit line may not pass right through any data point at all! You will need to "average out" the locations of the points by eye, trying to leave about as many points above the line as below the line.

Figure 10.8
Finding the "Best-fit" Line on a Voltage versus Current Graph

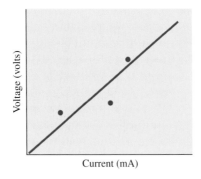

The second step is to find the coordinates of two points on the line that are far apart. You do not need to pick two data points; rather, pick two points that are on the line. It is better to pick two points near the ends of the line in order to get the most accurate value for the slope. If you can find points whose coordinates are round numbers, your calculations will be easier, but that is not always possible.

Call the point closer to the origin point 1, and the farther point 2. On your own paper, write out the coordinates of the points as follows:

$$x_1 = \text{\_\_\_\_\_} \qquad y_1 = \text{\_\_\_\_\_}$$

$$x_2 = \text{\_\_\_\_\_} \qquad y_2 = \text{\_\_\_\_\_}$$

Calculate the slope. The slope of a line is the rate at which the line rises or falls as it goes from left to right, or the steepness of the line. This can be found by determining how much the y coordinate changes as the x coordinate changes by a certain amount.

$$\text{slope} = (\text{change in } y)/(\text{change in } x)$$

$$= (y_2 - y_1)/(x_2 - x_1)$$

Example:

$$x_1 = \underline{\ 0.32 \text{ A}\ } \qquad y_1 = \underline{\ 1.48 \text{ V}\ }$$

$$x_2 = \underline{\ 0.59 \text{ A}\ } \qquad y_2 = \underline{\ 2.89 \text{ V}\ }$$

$$\text{slope} = (y_2 - y_1)/(x_2 - x_1)$$

$$= (2.89 \text{ V} - 1.48 \text{ V})/(0.59 \text{ A} - 0.32 \text{ A})$$

$$= (1.41 \text{ V})/(0.27 \text{ A})$$

$$= 5.22 \text{ V/A}$$

Figure 10.9
Finding the Slope of a Straight Line

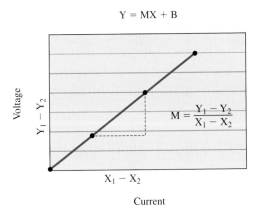

Workplace Connection: The Resistor Color Code

The color bands on the body of the resistor show the value of its resistance. The Resistor Colors Code table below shows the numerical values assigned to the colors. For instance, two red bands followed by an orange band indicate a resistance of $22 \times 1{,}000$ ohms and a tolerance of 20 percent. The color of the first band tells the first significant figure of the resistance. The color of the second band tells the second significant figure. The color of the third band tells the multiplier. A fourth color band is used to designate tolerance. The absence of the fourth color bands means 20 percent tolerance. Tolerance is the maximum amount by which the resistance *may* vary. Note that depending on their position, colors can represent either "values" or "multipliers."

Table 10.2
Resistor color code.

Color	Value	Multiplier
Black	0	1
Brown	1	10
Red	2	100
Orange	3	1,000
Yellow	4	10,000
Green	5	100,000
Blue	6	1,000,000
Violet	7	10,000,000
Gray	8	100,000,000
White	9	1,000,000,000
Color	Tolerance	Multiplier
No color	±20%	
Silver	±10%	0.01
Gold	±5%	0.1

Figure 10.10
Resistors

RadioShack Product Catalog. Copyright © RadioShack Corporation 2002. Reprinted with permission.
http://www.radioshack.com

ACTIVITY 10.4

Specifying Current in a Defibrillator Model

Getting In Gear

In this activity, you finally move away from lightbulbs and apply what you know about circuits to current flowing through the human body. You will begin making decisions about your model. You will apply what you have learned about circuits and use Ohm's law to determine the current, voltage, and resistance in your model defibrillator circuit.

This is your first design work on the layout of the defibrillator circuit. In Activity 10.5, you will use this analysis to make a preliminary design for a defibrillator circuit.

Getting To Work!

To determine the current, voltage, and resistance in your model defibrillator circuit, you will

1. Review any assigned Ohm's law problems with the class.

2. Discuss models and their advantages of use in the design process with the class.

3. Work in groups and use $\boxed{\textbf{Job Sheet 10.4}}$ **How Much Current and Voltage Do We Need?** to assign the electric values for your defibrillator model circuit.
   a. Determine how much current can safely pass through your model circuit after reading Getting the Point: *How Current Affects the Human Body.*
   b. Use Ohm's law together with a value for average patient resistance to calculate the minimum amount of voltage you need in your model defibrillator circuit.
   c. Determine exactly how many batteries and how much total resistance you need in your model defibrillator circuit.

4. Have the opportunity to visit with an emergency medical technician or firefighter who will describe uses for a portable defibrillator.

5. Review Getting the Point: *How Current Affects the Human Body,* and answer the Focus Questions.

6. Read Workplace Connection: *Emergency Medical Technicians and Paramedics* as time permits.

Job Sheet

Getting The Point.

How Current Affects the Human Body

A critical factor in designing a defibrillator is to determine how much current the defibrillator will provide. A paramount consideration in defibrillator design is the safety of the patient, who in essence becomes a component in the electric circuit. Also critical is the safety of the person using the defibrillator, who should *not* become a component in the defibrillator circuit!

Shock occurs when a person is part of a complete electric circuit. Macroshock is defined as shock that occurs when current is introduced to the surface of the body. Lightning striking a human, or accidental electrocution are examples of macroshock. About 1000 people die every year from electrocution, excluding lightning strikes.

External defibrillation is a controlled macroshock. During defibrillation, paddles are placed on the patient so that the chest is part of the circuit and maximum current density will pass through the heart. The challenge is to deliver a sufficiently high current for an extremely short period of time, in order to restore the heartbeat while minimizing damage to tissue. Typically, a current of 34 amps is delivered for just 5 milliseconds. This amount of current is extremely dangerous, so defibrillator design and operation require tight control of exactly the amount and duration of current delivered.

You are building a model that works like a defibrillator, but does not serve to actually defibrillate. Like an actual defibrillator, your models must be able to deliver a tightly controlled amount of current. For your models, you need to build a circuit that delivers exactly the amount of current that you calculate. Your model defibrillator should not be dangerous, even if for some unforeseen reason you become a part of the model defibrillator circuit for an extended period of time.

The table below displays the different effects for different ranges of current passing through the body.

Table 10.3
Effects of current across and through the body.

Current		Effect
0-1	Milliamps	No sensation
0.5-2	Milliamps	Threshhold of sensation—'Let go' point
2-10	Milliamps	Muscular contractions mild to strong
5-25	Milliamps	Painful unable to let go
>25	Milliamps	Violent muscular contractions
>100	Milliamps	Paralysis of breathing
20-200	Milliamps	Ventricular fibrillation
>200	Milliamps	Paralysis of breath without fibrillation

You will select a current that is below the "unable-to-let-go" range. When the human body is part of a circuit with a current of 5–25 milliamps, the person in the circuit feels pain and is unable to let go or disengage themselves from the circuit.

Given the desired current and the known patient resistance, you must determine the necessary voltage to achieve this current.

We recommend a current of 5 milliamps through the discharging circuit. This is the threshold of the unable-to-let-go range.

Focus Questions

What is macroshock?

What is meant by "let-go" current?

Workplace Connection: Emergency Medical Technicians and Paramedics

The following job description for emergency medical technicians and paramedics is excerpted from the Occupational Outlook Handbook *published by the Bureau of Labor Statistics, an agency within the U.S. Department of Labor.*

People's lives often depend on the quick reaction and competent care of emergency medical technicians (EMTs) and paramedics. Incidents as varied as automobile accidents, heart attacks, drownings, childbirth, and gunshot wounds all require immediate medical attention. EMTs and paramedics provide this vital attention as they care for and transport the sick or injured to a medical facility.

The specific responsibilities of EMTs and paramedics depend on their level of qualification and training. To determine this, the National Registry of Emergency Medical Technicians (NREMT) registers emergency medical service (EMS) providers at four levels: First Responder, EMT-Basic, EMT-Intermediate, and EMT-Paramedic. Some States, however, do their own certification and use numeric ratings from 1 to 4 to distinguish levels of proficiency.

The lowest level—First Responders—are trained to provide basic emergency medical care because they tend to be the first persons to arrive at the scene of an incident. Many firefighters, police officers, and other emergency workers have this level of training. The EMT-Basic, also known as EMT-1, represents the first component of the emergency medical technician system. An EMT-1 is trained to care for patients on accident scenes and on transport by ambulance to the hospital under medical direction. The EMT-1 has the emergency skills to assess a patient's condition and manage respiratory, cardiac, and trauma emergencies.

The EMT-Intermediate (EMT-2 and EMT-3) has more advanced training that allows administration of intravenous fluids, use of manual defibrillators to give lifesaving shocks to a stopped heart, and use of advanced airway techniques and equipment to assist patients experiencing respiratory emergencies. EMT-Paramedics (EMT-4) provide the most extensive pre-hospital care. In addition to the procedures already described, paramedics may administer drugs orally and intravenously, interpret electrocardiograms (EKGs), perform endotracheal intubations, and use monitors and other complex equipment.

* State requirements vary, but formal training and certification are required.
* Employment is projected to grow rapidly as paid emergency medical technician positions replace unpaid volunteers.
* Irregular hours and treating patients in life-or-death situations lead to job stress in this occupation.

Adapted from OCCUPATIONAL OUTLOOK HAND-BOOK. "Emergency Medical Technicians and Paramedics." U.S. Department of Labor. Bureau of Labor Statistics. http://www.bls.gov/oco/ocos101.htm (June 11, 2002)

ACTIVITY 10.5

Designing the Emergency Defibrillator Circuit

In Activity 10.4, you recorded the average resistance of a person and the level of current for your prototype circuit. You used this information to determine the number of batteries and the resistance needed for the discharging circuit within the defibrillator. Now you will apply this information as you design and build the discharging circuit as it will appear in your model defibrillator circuit.

You will need to develop several iterations of the circuit design. (An iteration is

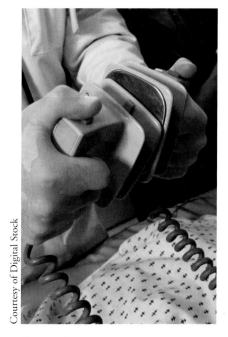

Figure 10.11
Defibrillator Paddles

like a draft or a working version.) With each iteration, you will probably encounter some problem that you can't solve without further research. Most problem solving in workplaces follows this pattern. You will work on several versions of your circuit design before you build your final circuit. The design work you do in this activity is your first "rough draft."

Getting To Work!

Job Sheet

To complete Project Milestone Three, you will

1. Work in groups and use ☐ **Job Sheet 10.5** ☐ What Will Our Defibrillator Circuit Look Like? to begin to design and build your model emergency defibrillator circuit.
   a. Work with your teacher to review what you have already learned about defibrillators.
   b. Design the discharging circuit, working backward from the model defibrillator current, voltage, and resistance you determined in Activity 10.4.
   c. Determine how to arrange the paddle on/off switches in the discharging circuit. (The discharging circuit has two switches. You may wish to read Getting the Point: *AND and OR Switches* to help you choose the correct switch logic.)
   d. Draw a final schematic diagram of your design showing the electric components and electric values of the discharging circuit.
   e. Build the discharging circuit, and measure current to confirm that you have the correct current output.

2. Read Getting the Point: *AND and OR Switches* if you have not done so, and answer the Focus Questions.

3. Review the concepts and answer the questions in What Have You Learned? for homework.

Getting The Point.

AND and OR Switches

You will use two switches in your discharging circuit. Two switches can be arranged in AND or OR gates. You'll need to check that the switches are placed so that the circuit goes on when both switches are turned on. This is an AND gate.

AND and OR gates are two-switch arrangements used everywhere in electric and electronic devices. They represent an important way to control how circuits behave. These arrangements are called gates, because they determine if a device is turned on. Just as a gate controls whether people can pass through, electric gates control whether a signal can get through.

If a circuit is built with an AND gate, you get the desired outcome only if you activate both the first and the second switch. With an OR gate, activating either switch will produce the desired outcome.

Complicated circuits will have many AND and OR gates. The result is that different combinations of incoming signals will produce different outcomes. In this way, gate technology allows engineers to build sophisticated circuits, such as those used in computers.

Circuit diagrams of an AND and an OR gate are shown below. You can build these gates yourself using one battery, one bulb, two switches, and wires.

Figure 10.12
Diagrams of AND Gate and OR Gate

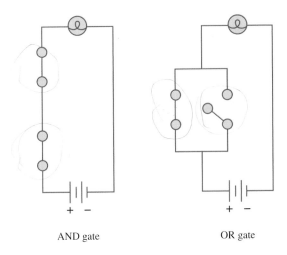

AND gate   OR gate

Focus Questions

Explain the differences between an AND gate and an OR gate.

The two switches in the discharging circuit of the defibrillator are an example of which kind of gate?

What Have You Learned?

KEY CONCEPTS

Current. Current is the rate of flow of electric charge through a circuit or other pathway. Current *(I)* is usually expressed in amperes (A); it is measured by an ammeter. The number of amperes tells us how many coulombs of charge pass a given point each second—1 ampere means 1 coulomb per second.

Conductivity. Conductivity is the ability of a material to carry current when a voltage difference exists.

Resistance. Resistance is the ability of objects to impede the flow of electrons. Resistance varies with several factors, including both the conductivity and shape of an object, and temperature. Resistance *(R)* is measured in ohms (Ω).

Resistors. Resistors are circuit components of a specific resistance that are used to control current.

Ohm's law. Ohm's law is the mathematical relationship relating voltage *(V)* and resistance *(R)* to current *(I)*: $V = R \times I$.

CONCEPT QUESTIONS

1. Which of the following statements best describes current in an electric circuit?
   a. the number of electrons in the circuit
   b. the speed at which an electron passes a point in the circuit
   c. the number of electrons that pass a point in the circuit in a given amount of time
   d. the amount of energy pushing electrons through the circuit

2. In a simple circuit with a battery, wire, and a lightbulb, compare the current going into the lightbulb and the current coming out of the lightbulb.

3. Suppose you have two pieces of wire that are identical except that one is twice the diameter of the other (in other words, it is twice as thick). If you connect these two wires, one at a time, between the ends of a battery, which circuit will give you more current? Why? Which wire has the greater resistance?

4. Table A shows voltage and current for four circuits. The voltage increases while the current stays the same. Calculate the resistance for each circuit. What is happening to the resistance? (Use Table A on your handout; do not write in this book.)

Continued

Number of Batteries	Total Voltage (volts)	Resistance (ohms)	Current (amps)
1	1.5		0.5
2	3.0		0.5
3	4.5		0.5
4	6.0		0.5

Table A

5. Ahmed needs a 4-volt battery to run his CD player. A friend gives him a battery of unknown voltage. Ahmed decides to determine the voltage of the battery by testing it with a 4-ohm resistor. He measures 0.8 amps through the resistor. Does the battery have enough voltage to run Ahmed's CD player? Explain why.

6. What is the current flowing through the circuit represented by the schematic diagram in Figure A?

Figure A

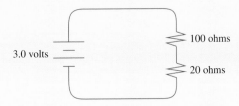

3.0 volts

100 ohms

20 ohms

7. You measure 0.7 amps through a circuit run by a 12-volt battery. Which of the following might be the resistance of the circuit?
   a. 8 ohms
   b. 18 ohms
   c. 28 ohms
   d. 128 ohms

8. Andrew measures 12 amps through a 10-ohm resistor in the circuit in Figure B. Which of the following might he measure through a 100-ohm resistor.
   a. 1.2 amps
   b. 120 amps
   c. 0.2 amps
   d. 9.9 amps

Figure B

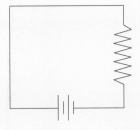

Continued

9. Suppose you measure 8 amps with the ammeter shown in the circuit in Figure C. What is the resistance of the mystery element?

Figure C

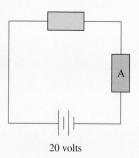

20 volts

10. In testing a battery, Liz discovers that it can put 1.6 amps through a 15-ohm resistor. Which of the following is a possible voltage for the battery?
a. 5 volts
b. 10 volts
c. 25 volts
d. 50 volts

11. You measure 0.15 amp through a circuit run by a 6-volt battery. Which of the following might be the resistance of the circuit?
a. 0.9 ohms
b. 9 ohms
c. 90 ohms
d. none of the above

12. Suppose you are in charge of training technicians to monitor the performance of a defibrillator. Explain why it is important to have proper current through the defibrillator.

APPLYING WHAT YOU KNOW

1. Semiconductors are often found in devices that use electric signals to transmit information. Explain why semiconductors are a good choice for this application of electric current.

2. Variable resistors are called potentiometers, and they can continuously change the resistance in a circuit over a certain range. Potentiometers are usually made in the form of a dial to turn easily. Identify three possible potentiometers in electric devices, appliances, or home wiring circuits.

3. Cathy would like to figure out the voltage of a battery she found in a drawer, but she doesn't have a voltmeter. However, she does have a toolbox containing a lightbulb, motor, ammeter, 10-ohm resistor, screwdriver, and copper wire. How might she be able to determine the voltage of the battery?

Continued

4. Suppose that you want to run a 0.5-amp current through the buzzer in the circuit in Figure D. The resistance of the buzzer is 10 ohms. You don't have any extra resistors. Is it possible to run the current? If so, how? Draw the new circuit.

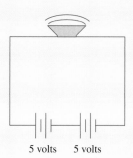

Figure D

5 volts   5 volts

5. In a defibrillator, both the amount of current and the length of time the current flows must be controlled. Identify another device that needs these two kinds of controls.

6. The circuit in Figure E has been proposed as the controller for a light outside the garage of a new home.

Figure E

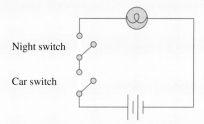

Night switch

Car switch

The designer claims that the light will go on when a car drives into the driveway, thereby closing the "car switch." Also, to avoid wasting electricity, the light only goes on at night, when the "night switch" is closed. Do you agree or disagree with the designer's claims? To evaluate this question, fill in Table B on your handout. (Do not write in this book.)

Table B

Night Switch	Car Switch	Status of Light (on/off)	
		What the Designer Claims	What the Circuit Does
ON	ON		
ON	OFF		
OFF	ON		

The Best Circuit Design

OVERVIEW

A WHAT?

You've adjusted the voltage and current in the first iteration of your discharging circuit. It seems to work, but the defibrillators you have seen are more complicated than your preliminary design. There is a charging circuit as well as a discharging circuit. Now your instructor tells you that you have to put a capacitor in the circuit. What is a capacitor anyway? How does a capacitor work in a circuit, and how is it different from a battery?

Ms. Lacy tells you to find out how a capacitor charges and discharges and take some time to investigate whether the capacitor will give your circuit an advantage. Then you can make your final circuit design.

Your last milestone:

Project Milestone 4

Building and Presenting
the Emergency Defibrillator Circuit

You will build a model defibrillator circuit, test and label your circuits, and present your results.

You are now ready to complete your defibrillator circuit design. You have learned what defibrillators do and how they are used. You have learned about circuits, batteries, and resistors. By the end of this chapter, you will have used that information to design and build your final defibrillator circuit.

But first you investigate one more circuit component: the capacitor. You will experiment with capacitors in circuits and observe charging and discharging. Once you understand capacitors, you can complete your model emergency defibrillator circuit. You test it, and if necessary, adjust the design. Then to complete the design process, you document your work and present your final project with supporting arguments to the class and invited guests.

To help you accomplish Project Milestone Four, you will do the following activities:

Activity 11.1 Observing Capacitors in Simple Circuits
What is a capacitor? You will build circuits that charge and discharge a capacitor. You will compare high-current bulbs and low-current bulbs in these circuits.

Activity 11.2 Charging and Discharging a Capacitor in a Circuit
Why is a capacitor useful in a defibrillator? You will build a single circuit that both charges and discharges a capacitor. Then you will modify the design of your model defibrillator to include this circuit.

Activity 11.3 Building and Testing the Emergency Defibrillator Circuit
In this activity, you will finish your circuit design, then build and test your circuit. You will label your model circuit and draw a complete circuit diagram.

Activity 11.4 Presenting the Best Circuit
As a member of a group, you will prepare and deliver a multimedia presentation on your model defibrillator circuit to the class and invited guests. You will select your own format (for example, presentation software, audiovisual aids, or poster materials), and demonstrate how your circuit works and why it is an appropriate model for the defibrillator.

ACTIVITY 11.1

Observing Capacitors in Simple Circuits

Getting In Gear

In Chapter 10, you designed and built a single discharging circuit to produce the desired current in your defibrillator. As you saw earlier, defibrillators contain both a charging circuit and a discharging circuit. In this activity, you will see how another circuit component, a capacitor, is used for charging and discharging. Once you learn about the capacitor, you will be ready to begin the final design of the defibrillator circuit.

As you learn about capacitors, think about how they can be used in your model defibrillator circuit. In particular, notice how fast the capacitor reduces the current to zero.

Getting To Work!

To understand how capacitors work, you will

1. Read the overview scenario and project milestone for Chapter 11, and discuss the scenario with your class.

Job Sheet

2. Work in groups and use Job Sheet 11.1 What Do Capacitors Do in Circuits? to investigate capacitors.
   a. Build circuits with capacitors and lightbulbs.
   b. See what happens to lightbulbs when the capacitor charges and discharges.
   c. Observe and compare the behavior of high-current bulbs and low-current bulbs in circuits with capacitors.

3. View and discuss with the class a graph of current change over time in a capacitor.

4. Read Getting the Point: *About Capacitors and Charge,* and answer the Focus Questions.

5. Read Workplace Connection: *Capacitors* as time permits.

Getting The Point

About Capacitors and Charge

What is a capacitor? A capacitor is an important circuit component used in the defibrillator. Capacitors are used in many devices; you could use a capacitor to build a simple radio, for example. Let's learn about the capacitor and how charge moves during the charging and discharging processes.

A capacitor is a storage device for separated negative and positive charges. The capacitor can function like a battery, but only for a very short period of time since it cannot itself provide energy to separate electrons from atoms. A capacitor needs an energy device, usually a battery, to separate charges and push the charges onto the capacitor.

When a capacitor is acquiring charge, it is *charging*. When a charged capacitor is placed in a circuit, it releases its charge. This event is called *discharging*. A capacitor can drive a brief but substantial current when it discharges.

The electric symbol for a capacitor is used in a circuit diagram as follows:

Figure 11.1
Symbol for a Capacitor

CHARGING THE CAPACITOR

A capacitor has two large pieces of conducting material, called plates, separated by a layer of insulation. When a capacitor is in its uncharged state, the two plates have no charge. The capacitor becomes charged when one plate is connected to the positive terminal of a battery and the other plate is attached to the negative terminal. Once the capacitor is connected, electrons will move away from the battery's negative terminal onto the capacitor plate. At the same time, electrons move away from the other plate toward the positive battery terminal, attracted by its concentration of positive charge.

Figure 11.2 (a) shows a capacitor before being charged. Figure 11.2 (b) shows the movement of charge in a circuit that includes a battery, a capacitor, and a bulb as the capacitor is being charged.

Figure 11.2
Charging Circuit

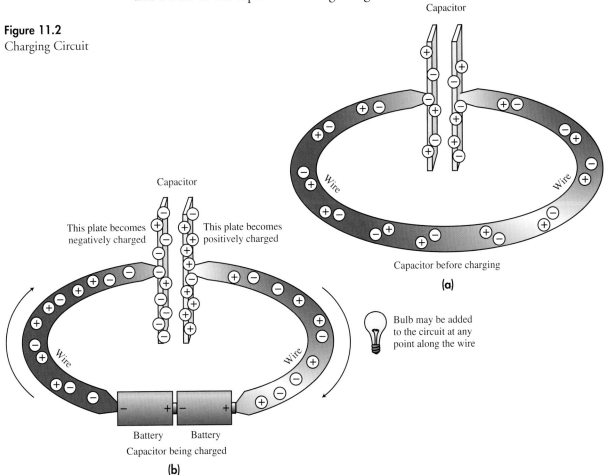

Charging is complete when the accumulated charge on the plates prevents the movement of charges. At that point, it is like having two batteries in the circuit, head to head. The light goes out because there is no flow of charge through it anymore. Now the capacitor has a negative plate and a positive plate, but no current flows.

Figure 11.3
Opposing Voltages

Opposing voltages stop current. This is true
for two batteries wired head to head as well
as for a battery and a charged capacitor.

DISCHARGING THE CAPACITOR

Once the capacitor is charged, it can be switched over to another circuit—without a battery—where it can discharge. The accumulated electrons on the negative plate of the capacitor move freely, no longer opposed by the battery's negative terminal. The jammed-up electrons leave the plate, driven by the force of repulsion. They push against the electrons in the wire, and the charge now moves through the whole circuit toward the positive plate of the capacitor. Figure 11.4(a) represents a capacitor discharging. Figure 11.4(b) represents a capacitor after discharging.

Figure 11.4
Discharging Circuit

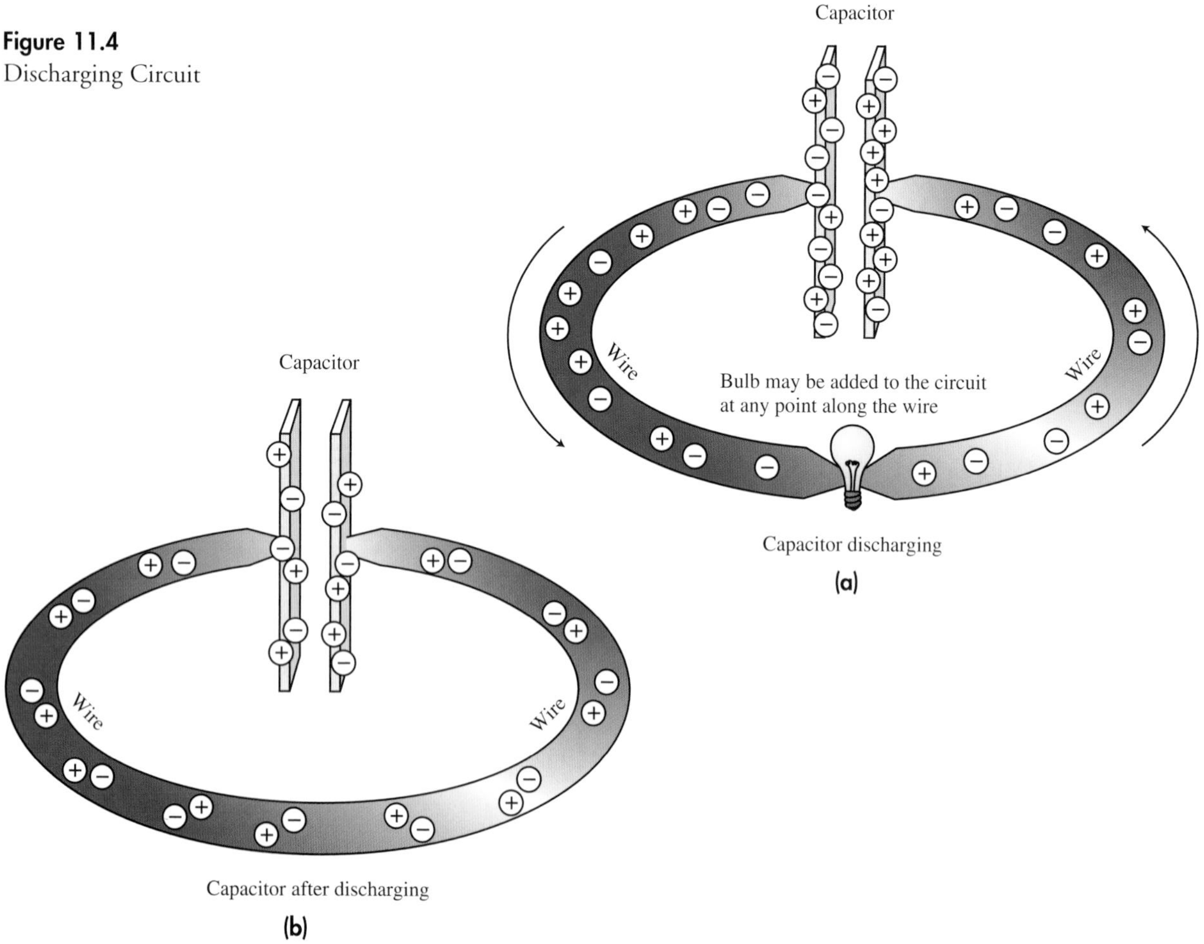

Capacitor

Wire

Wire

Bulb may be added to the circuit
at any point along the wire

Capacitor discharging

(a)

Capacitor

Wire

Wire

Capacitor after discharging

(b)

The current produced by a capacitor is strong but brief. Unlike a battery, a capacitor produces no chemical reactions to keep up the concentration of charge on its plates. Consequently, the concentration of charge disappears quickly, and the charge on each plate reverts to zero. When the capacitor discharges, current in the circuit starts out relatively high but drops very quickly to zero after a few seconds or less. A discharged capacitor has a voltage of 0 volts.

Figure 11.5

Sample Graph of Current versus Time for Discharging Circuit

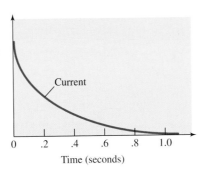

THE STRUCTURE OF THE CAPACITOR

Capacitors usually consist of two pieces of metal foil (the *plates,* which are conductors) separated by air, paper, or some other nonconducting material (the insulator). The conductors allow charge to flow through; the insulator does not. In Figures 11.2 and 11.4, you can see the gap between the two plates; this gap represents the insulator.

Most capacitors are shaped like cylinders. Imagine three very long strips stacked one of top of another: first a strip of foil, then one of wax paper (the insulator), then another one of foil. If you roll up that stack like a sleeping bag, you will get a cylinder-shaped capacitor. One piece of foil is one plate, and the other piece of foil is the other plate. The paper in between prevents electrons from moving across the gap in the capacitor.

Focus Questions

What is the function of a capacitor?

What happens when a charged capacitor is placed in a circuit?

What is the electrical symbol for a capacitor?

How does a capacitor become charged?

When is the charging of a capacitor complete?

What happens to the electrons when a charged capacitor is discharging?

How would you describe the structure of a capacitor?

Workplace Connection: Capacitors

Capacitors come with different voltage ratings and different capacitance. The voltage rating specifies how much energy can be stored in the capacitor and is measured in volts. Capacitance is measured in farads, or more usually in microfarads (one millionth of a farad) or picofarads (one trillionth of a farad). The time it takes for the capacitor to charge is proportional to its capacitance.

There are several different designs of capacitors available. These include axial electrolytic capacitors, radial electrolytic capacitors, film capacitors, ceramic disc capacitors, tantalum capacitors, and variable capacitors.

Figure 11.6
Capacitors

Ceramic disc capacitors   Axial electrolytic capacitors   Tantalum capacitors

RadioShack Product Catalog. Copyright © RadioShack Corporation 2002. Reprinted with permission. http://www.radioshack.com

Figure 11.7
Variable Capacitor

From Palstar Inc., Piqua, OH. "C240 Variable Capacitor."
Reprinted with permission. http://www.palstarinc.com/c240.htm

ACTIVITY 11.2

Charging and Discharging a Capacitor in a Circuit

Using a defibrillator involves a two-step process: charging one circuit and discharging another. In Activity 11.1, you built one circuit to charge a capacitor and another circuit to discharge it. In this activity, you will build a single circuit that contains both a charging circuit and a discharging circuit. You will use this new circuit to help you revise your design for the model defibrillator circuit.

In this activity, you consider why a capacitor is useful in a defibrillator. A capacitor can control the duration of current. The longer current flows the more energy is transferred to the heart. Excess energy could damage the heart and other parts of the body. A defibrillator delivers current for a short time very quickly, in fact, in less than a third of a second. An EMT or emergency room physician could not react fast enough to cut off the current that quickly because people's reaction times are not as fast or reliable.

Getting To Work!

To understand how capacitors are used in defibrillators, you will

1. Work in groups to consider why it might be important to use a capacitor in a defibrillator circuit.

2. Work by yourself and complete Item 1 on **Job Sheet 11.2** How Do You **Charge and Discharge the Capacitor in a Defibrillator Circuit?** to check your understanding of charging and discharging circuits.

3. Work in groups and use Job Sheet 11.2 to design a combined charging/discharging circuit to be used in your defibrillator model.
   a. Propose and then build a single circuit that both charges and discharges a capacitor.
   b. Build charging circuits with two, one, three, and four batteries. Measure voltage across the charged capacitor. Determine the relationship between battery voltage and capacitor voltage.
   c. Modify the design of your model defibrillators to include a combined charging/discharging circuit that provides the same amount of voltage as the model discharging circuit you designed in Activity 9.5.

4. Read Getting the Point: *Voltage Drop across a Component,* and answer the Focus Questions.

5. Read Concept Connection: *Kirchhoff's Voltage Law* and Workplace Connection: *It Takes a Team to Design a Defibrillator* as time permits.

Job Sheet

Getting The Point.

Voltage Drop across a Component

How much does the voltage "drop" across each electric component in the circuit, and how do we measure it? A 1.5-volt battery gives 1.5 joules of electric potential energy to every 1 coulomb of charge passing through the battery. Since this energy is transferred to components in the circuit, the voltage decreases as the current passes through each component.

Figure 11.8
Circuit with 1.5 volt Battery, Light Bulb, and a Resistor

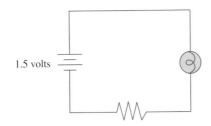

1.5 volts

The voltage drop across a component is the energy per charge that is used by that component. If there is a 0.5-volt potential difference across a lightbulb, every 1 coulomb of charge that passes through it decreases its electric potential energy by 0.5 joules. The electric potential energy is transformed in the lightbulb from electric potential energy to light and heat. If the current passes through a resistor, the energy transforms to heat energy in the resistor.

You can use two methods to find the voltage drop across a component. The most direct method is to turn the current on and use a voltmeter to measure the voltage across the component. Or, you can calculate the voltage drop using Ohm's law. First, while the circuit is off, measure the resistance *(R)* of the component. Then, while the circuit is on, use an ammeter to measure the current *(I)* running through the component. Then use Ohm's law ($V = I \times R$) to calculate the voltage drop *(V)* across the object.

Focus Questions

Why does voltage decrease as current passes through each electric component in a circuit?

What are two methods that can be used to find the voltage drop across a component?

Concept Connection: Kirchhoff's Voltage Law

In a series circuit, the sum of the voltage drops across all of the elements is equal to the total voltage supplied by the battery. You can start at any point in the circuit and travel around the circuit adding up the change in voltage for each component. In the circuit shown below, for example, you would find a drop in the resistor, a drop in the lightbulb, and a gain in the battery. The sum of all the voltage changes around a complete circuit is zero. This is known as Kirchhoff's voltage law.

Figure 11.9

Sample Circuit to Show Kirchoff's Voltage Law

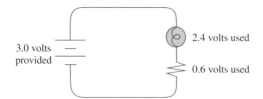

3.0 volts provided

2.4 volts used

0.6 volts used

Kirchhoff's voltage law is an expression of the conservation of energy. In a series circuit, the current can only flow along one route, so the current is the same everywhere. When a given current experiences a voltage change as it passes through electric components, there is a corresponding change in energy. The electric potential energy supplied by the battery is used by the components in the circuit, and transformed to other forms of energy.

Workplace Connection: It Takes a Team to Design a Defibrillator

Teams, not individuals, design new models of defibrillators. The Engineering, Marketing, and Manufacturing Departments bring different skills and have specific responsibilities, but they all influence the defibrillator design. The product manager is in the marketing group. This group runs focus groups, investigates defibrillators on the market, and finds out what customers want. It defines the design problem and writes the initial specifications for the product. The Engineering Department explores how to meet those specifications, and may alter those specifications if it knows better solutions, or find that they are impossible to meet. The Manufacturing Department must build and test the defibrillator. They may find bugs in the engineering or more economical parts, requiring further redesign of the defibrillator. Finally, the Marketing Department writes manuals and promotional material to communicate the final design.

ACTIVITY 11.3

Building and Testing the Emergency Defibrillator Circuit

Getting In Gear

In this activity, you will put together everything you have learned about electric circuits, batteries, capacitors, and resistors, and the function and operation of a defibrillator. You design and build the model defibrillator circuit. Note that as you build and test the model, you continue to refine the design.

By completing this part of milestone four, you demonstrate your understanding of many aspects of electricity, a difficult and demanding subject. You show some of the engineering skills you've acquired by designing and building circuits. You also show how you have organized your work and built upon what you know over a long period of time, in order to complete a complex task. Understanding, skills, and organization are the cornerstones important not only in the classroom but also in the workplace.

Getting To Work!

To complete your work on the model defibrillator circuit, you will

1. Consider with the class how technicians use their knowledge to troubleshoot problems in a defibrillator.

2. Work in groups or individually as indicated and follow the instructions on
   Job Sheet 11.3 Building, Testing, and Documenting the Emergency Defibrillator Circuit.
   a. Draw an initial circuit design that includes the defibrillator safety features listed on the job sheet.
   b. Build a model circuit that uses all the electric components given out and which works correctly when a tester follows the defibrillator operating instructions on the job sheet.

Job Sheet

c. Draw a circuit diagram of the finished model circuit that uses correct electric symbols, and annotate the diagram with a specific set of electric quantities listed on the job sheet.

d. Label all the parts of the finished model circuit, and make a neat and attractive base for it.

3. Read Workplace Connection: *Electrical and Electronics Engineers* as time permits.

Workplace Connection: **Electrical and Electronics Engineers**

Engineers apply the theories and principles of science and mathematics to research and develop economical solutions to technical problems. Their work is the link between perceived social needs and commercial applications.

Electrical and electronics engineers specialize in different areas such as power generation, transmission, and distribution; communications; and electrical equipment manufacturing, or a subdivision of these areas—industrial robot control systems or aviation electronics, for example. Electrical and electronics engineers design new products, write performance requirements, and develop maintenance schedules. They also test equipment, solve operating problems, and estimate the time and cost of engineering projects.

In addition to design and development, many engineers work in testing, production, or maintenance. These engineers supervise production in factories, determine the causes of breakdowns, and test manufactured products to maintain quality. They also estimate the time and cost to complete projects.

Engineers in each branch have a base of knowledge and training that can be applied in many fields. Electronics engineers, for example, work in the medical, computer, communications, and missile guidance fields. Because there are many separate problems to solve in a large engineering project, engineers in one field often work closely with specialists in other scientific, engineering, and business occupations.

A bachelor's degree in engineering is required for almost all entry-level engineering jobs. College graduates with a degree in a physical science or mathematics occasionally may qualify for some engineering jobs, especially in specialties in high demand.

Projected job growth stems largely from increased demand for electrical and electronic goods, including advanced communications equipment, defense-related electronic equipment, and consumer electronics products. The need for electronics manufacturers to invest heavily in research and development to remain competitive and gain a scientific edge will provide openings for graduates who have learned the latest technologies.

Adapted from OCCUPATIONAL OUTLOOK HANDBOOK. "Electrical and Electronics Engineers." U.S. Department of Labor, Bureau of Labor Statistics. http://www.bls.gov/oco/ocos031.htm (June 4, 2002), and "Engineers Build Better World for You." http://www.geocities.com/postbox25/engineer.html (June 11, 2002)

ACTIVITY 11.4

Presenting the Best Circuit

The defibrillator is built, and in this final activity you will complete Project Milestone Four. You also complete the design process by demonstrating how the group's circuit works and why it is an appropriate model for the defibrillator.

The responsibility for this presentation will be divided up among the members of your group—each will discuss a specific aspect of the defibrillator or its design.

Whichever topics your group chooses to present, each group member will want to clearly communicate some of the main features of the design process you followed. During your group's presentation, discuss the problem you set out to solve, the constraints you faced, the solutions that you considered, the testing process that you used, and how you solved problems during the design process.

Don't forget to talk about the ideas that you formed about electricity, circuits, and devices that helped you make sense of this project. This presentation is a way to summarize your learning and communicate it to other people. Because electricity is a difficult topic, some of your ideas may be new to some members of the audience. By clearly explaining the insights you gained, people in the audience will have a chance to learn through and from your experiences.

Getting To Work!

To complete Project Milestone Four, you will

1. Listen to information about the presentation from your teacher, such as where and when it occurs, who is in the audience, your time limit, and dress requirements.

2. Use Job Sheet 11.4 **Presenting the Emergency Defibrillator Circuit** to help you prepare your presentation.
   a. Work with the class to review the presentation requirements for groups and individuals, and develop assessment criteria for presentations.
   b. Work by yourself to prepare a minipresentation and accompanying written report about some aspect of the defibrillator design process. You may need to access unit materials or conduct more research. Make use of available presentation materials, such as software, audiovisual aids, or poster materials.
   c. Work in groups to practice your presentation, and meet with your teacher to review your presentation.

Job Sheet

3. Give your presentation with your group.

4. Review the concepts and answer the questions in What Have You Learned? for homework.

5. Read Workplace Connection: *Writing* as time permits.

Workplace Connection: Writing

"When you establish in your head a good relationship with your audience, suddenly your writing runs strong and clear. You can find words and they are right. You are looking readers in the eye and directing your words right to the center of their brains, not staring at their shoes or mumbling distractedly as you stare at the ceiling. When this works, everything clicks."

From WRITING WITH POWER, by Peter Elbow. Copyright © 1981 Oxford University Press: New York.

What Have You Learned?

Capacitor. A capacitor is a storage device for charge. To discuss capacitors, you must first explain what charging and discharging mean. When a capacitor is acquiring charge, it is charging. When a charged capacitor is placed in a circuit, it releases its charge. This event is called discharging. A capacitor can drive a brief but substantial current when it discharges. Because a capacitor does not separate charges continually like a battery, the current from a capacitor starts out high and rapidly declines as the capacitor loses its charge. The current over time is shown in Figure A.

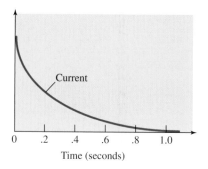

Figure A
Sample Graph of Current versus Time for Discharging Circuit

CONCEPT QUESTIONS

1. Suppose you had a meter to monitor the brightness of the bulb in the circuit in Figure A below.

   How do you think the brightness of the bulb will vary over time when the switch is closed and the capacitor is charged? Use the graph in Figure B to make your prediction. (Use copy of graph from teacher's handout or copy this graph on a piece of paper. Do not write in this book.)

   Figure A

   Figure B

   Continued

2. Why is a capacitor in a defibrillator?

3. If you were going to make a capacitor, which of the following might you do?
   a. Put strips of metals into solutions of other metals.
   b. Bend a strip of metal into a cylinder.
   c. Put strips of metal on top of each other, and connect them.
   d. Put strips of metal next to each other, but do not allow them to touch.

4. As it charges, a capacitor resists the current from the battery. A more fully charged capacitor resists current more than an uncharged capacitor does. Explain why.

5. A battery is used to charge a capacitor. After the capacitor is charged, the battery is flipped over in the holder, reversing the terminals. Does current flow in the circuit? Explain your answer.

APPLYING WHAT YOU KNOW

1. Some devices, such as TVs and radios, have large capacitors. For safety reasons, these large capacitors must always be discharged before any work is done on the devices. Explain why.

2. Which of the following might use a capacitor?
   a. A circuit to run the motor of a toy car.
   b. A circuit to run a flashlight.
   c. A circuit to sound a short alarm when an oven has reached its final temperature.
   d. A circuit to sound a continuous alarm when the oven has finished baking a cake.

3. Capacitors are rated in units called farads. A farad is a ratio of the amount of charge held on a capacitor at a certain voltage. A 1-farad capacitor will hold 1.5 coulombs of charge when connected to a 1.5-volt battery.
   A 1-farad capacitor is charged in a series circuit with two-1.5-volt alkaline batteries. How much charge is held on the charged capacitor?

Generators and Diodes | Building a Better Bike Light

OVERVIEW

For the next 5 or 6 weeks, you will play the role of inventors in a student-owned company called The Green Machine. The name of the company reflects the aspirations of the inventors—to work on designs that are both functional and environmentally friendly. The inventors have gotten together to work on their first project: improving the function of a generator-powered bike light. Because they are powered by a **generator**, the lights in this system are lit any time the bicycle is pedaled. But this system cannot keep the lights on when the bike is stopped. The Green Machine team thinks that generator-powered lights would be more popular if they can be lit at all times, improving the bike's safety and usability. The team wants to find a way to modify the **circuitry** to improve the light.

As you follow in these inventors' shoes, you will spend a lot of time learning about generators. A generator is a device that can change the **energy** of motion into electric energy. Generators—and motors (which turn electric energy into motion)—are common devices. Turbine generators provide most of the electric energy used throughout the world. Motors are present in all kinds of devices that move things.

Another significant system that relates to your work in this unit is the automobile electric system. The automobile contains both a generator, called an alternator, and a rechargeable battery. These two voltage sources work in tandem to start the car, provide current when needed, and keep the battery recharged. Understanding this system and the main parts of its circuit are critical to the success of the project undertaken by The Green Machine.

By the end of this unit, you will have designed and built an electric circuit for the bike light that is powered by both a generator and rechargeable battery, similar to the alternator-battery system used in automobiles. This assignment is your unit project. Like previous projects, the work is divided into project milestones. The three milestones in this unit involve many facets of the design process. In the third and last milestone, you will also research existing bike lights and think about aspects that might make your design marketable. Throughout this unit—from your initial investigation of a generating system to your building of a modified bike light circuit—you will be thinking and working like an inventor/entrepreneur.

Working with
a Generator

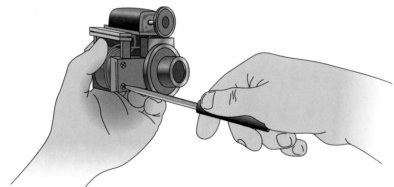

PROJECT MILESTONES

Your unit project is to modify the circuitry of a generator-powered bike light. This assignment is divided into three project milestones.

Project Milestone 1 — Explaining How the Bike Light Generator Works

As one of the student inventors at The Green Machine, you will gather information about a bicycle light that is powered by a generator. You will sketch and name the important parts inside the bike light generator, and explain how they move while the bicycle is being pedaled so that the front and rear lamps will light.

Project Milestone 2 — Creating Specifications and Designs for the Bike Light Circuit

You will create circuit specifications for a modified bike light circuit and brainstorm possible circuit designs.

Project Milestone 3 — Building a Better Bike Light

You will design and build an improved bike light circuit, which can provide energy at all times. You will prepare a presentation to convince "investors" to fund the building and marketing of the improved bike light, and present your sales pitch to the class and invited guests.

ACTIVITIES AND ASSIGNMENTS

Your work on this unit project requires an understanding of generators, an automobile's electric system, and complex circuits. As you progress through the unit, you will complete a number of activities and assignments to help you understand these systems.

Just as there are three project milestones, the activities and assignments in the unit are organized into three chapters. Each chapter focuses on a different aspect of learning.

1. In Chapter 12, you will examine generators. You will see that the generator transfers energy. By investigating the parts inside the generator and experimenting with magnets and wire coils, you will be able to describe how several kinds of generators work.

2. In Chapter 13, you will study an automobile's electric system. You will have an opportunity to visit with an alternator specialist. You will learn the meaning of direct current (DC) and alternating current (AC), and find out how generators can be used to recharge batteries. You will use your knowledge to begin brainstorming possible modifications to the bike light circuit.

3. In Chapter 14, you will build more complex circuits and analyze the transfer of energy and current. With these new skills, you will begin building complex circuits for a new bike light system.

How Does a Generator Work?

OVERVIEW

STARTING THE GREEN MACHINE

You and a group of friends have formed a small company, The Green Machine, with the idea of inventing machines that are environmentally friendly. Several members of the group ride bicycles a lot, and they want to build a better bike light.

"Too many bike lights use batteries," says Joe, who rides his bike home from school every day. "When the batteries are dead, people just throw them away. That contaminates the environment with mercury, and mercury is a poison."

"I have a generator-powered light system," says Sylvia, whose father works in an electronics store. "But the lights only work when you're pedaling. You're not safe when you're stopped, like if you're trying to cross the street."

The group decides on its first project. It will improve the bike light so that it remains on all the time. Thinking like inventors, you have an idea that Sylvia's generator-powered bike light could be modified. You set to work examining Sylvia's light.

Your first milestone:

Project Milestone 1 — Explaining How the Bike Light Generator Works

As one of the student inventors at The Green Machine, you will gather information about a bicycle light that is powered by a generator. You will sketch and name the important parts inside the bike light generator, and explain how they move while the bicycle is being pedaled so that the front and rear lamps will light.

This unit builds on a series of assignments that involve generators and circuits. In this chapter, you will see that a generator transfers energy of motion to electric energy. This transformation is possible because of the connection between electricity and magnetism, which you will study throughout Chapter 12. You will observe how the bike light generator works and look at the parts inside several generators. Then you will study the separate parts of generators, which are magnets, electromagnets, and wire coils. You will see that movement of charge creates a magnet, and that relative motion between a magnet and a wire coil creates current in the coil.

By the end of this chapter, you will use these observations to explain how the bike light generator transforms energy of cycling into electric energy. This work will give you information you need about the system when you attempt the modifications called for in the unit project.

To help you accomplish Project Milestone One, you will do the following activities:

Activity 12.1 Investigating an Ordinary Bicycle Light
What is a bike light generator? In this activity, you will investigate how one works.

Activity 12.2 Examining Generators
You will learn more about generating systems by examining a dismantled alternator, a dismantled generator system for a bike light, and a diagram of a generating system for an electric power plant. Inside you will find magnets and wire coils.

Activity 12.3 Experimenting with Magnets
You will experiment with magnets: observe interactions using two magnets, everyday objects, and a compass; and map the magnetic force.

Activity 12.4 What Is an Electromagnet?
You will place a current-carrying wire over a compass and observe its magnetic effect. Then you will build an electromagnet, and also see that a car alternator contains an electromagnet.

Activity 12.5 Moving a Magnet in a Wire Coil
You will brainstorm how a generator might produce electricity, then observe electromagnetic induction. You will complete Project Milestone One by sketching and naming parts inside the bike light generator, and explaining how they move while the bicycle is being pedaled.

ACTIVITY 12.1

Investigating an Ordinary Bicycle Light

Getting In Gear

You are about to begin a study of generators and complex circuits. Because this is the beginning of a new unit, you will want to know more about your responsibilities and the topics you will be studying. You may ask, What project will I be working on? What are generators? What do they do, and where do I find them? Why are they important to study? More specific questions may include, What is a bike light generator? What does it look like, and how does it work?

This first activity will help answer some of those questions. You will have opportunities to ask questions about the unit project and to discuss what you already know about some of the topics found in this unit. You will also see how a bike generator works.

It is especially important in this first activity for you to take the time to understand the outline of the unit project and of the day-to-day activities throughout the unit. This knowledge will help you see how the work in the unit is connected, will help you gauge your own progress, and will give meaning to the activities in the unit.

Getting To Work!

To understand a bike light generator, your unit project, and the material you will cover in Chapter 12, you will

1. Read the overview for Unit Four, and discuss as a class the unit project and the outline of work throughout the unit.

2. Read the overview scenario and project milestone for Chapter 12, and discuss the scenario with your class.

3. Observe as a class how a bike light generator works, and brainstorm everything you know about generators and where they are found.

4. Work in groups and use 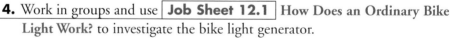 **Job Sheet 12.1** **How Does an Ordinary Bike Light Work?** to investigate the bike light generator.

Job Sheet

   a. Work with others in your group to operate the generator safely and to light the lights.

   b. Sketch the important parts of the bike light system, and record what you notice about how the lights work.

5. Read Workplace Connection: *Light and Generators* as time permits.

Workplace Connection: Light and Generators

[Note: Dynamo is another term for generator.]

The Schmidt Dynamo front (wheel) hub weighs 1.5 lbs and has significantly less drag than tire driven generators. Made by Wilfried Schmidt Maschinenbau in

Tübingen, Germany, the hub is quiet and reliable, and is designed to give 50,000 kilometers of trouble-free riding. The hub powers Lumotec or Lumotec Oval Plus headlamps and taillights made by Busch & Müller in Germany, and modified by Schmidt. The hub is rated at 6 volts and 3 watts.

The Lumotec Oval Plus' circuitry stores some electrical energy (a capacitor) to power an LED "Standlight" when the wheel stops. The LED light isn't nearly as bright as the halogen bulb. But it provides enough light to read your watch face or check a map and provide an added measure of safety when stopped at an intersection. The rear lights also incorporate the "Standlight" feature.

Adapted from *"Lights and Generators."* Peter White Cycle. http://www.peterwhitecycles.com/Schmidt-Lumotec

ACTIVITY 12.2

Examining Generators

Getting In Gear

Do you know what's inside a generator? In Activity 12.1, you observed the operation of the bike light generator. But you probably have very little idea of how a generator works, because you can't see inside the generator attached to the wheel.

In this activity, you will observe what is inside three kinds of generators. You will examine a disassembled bike light generator; an alternator, which is used in a car; and a diagram of an electricity turbine, a third kind of generator. Look carefully at the two disassembled generators, and pick up and investigate all their parts. As you explore the generators, try to develop your own theories about the principles behind their operation.

Getting To Work!

To begin to understand how generators work, you will

1. Work in groups and follow the instructions in ☐ **Job Sheet 12.2** ☐ **What Do All Generators Have in Common?** **Job Sheet**
   a. Visit the three stations that have disassembled generators or diagrams. Spend about 5 minutes at each station, examining its generator system and taking detailed notes.
   b. Work with your group to use your observations and notes from the three stations to form one or more theories about how a generator works.

2. Discuss as a class, and record the ideas and questions about how a generator produces electricity.

3. Read Getting the Point: *Generators,* and answer the Focus Questions.

4. Read Workplace Connection: *Power Plant Operators, Distributors, and Dispatchers,* and check out the Did You Know? reading as time permits.

Generators

A generator does not create energy. Instead, it changes mechanical energy into electric energy. Three types of generators are described below.

The *bicycle generator* typically contains a permanent magnet encased in a cylinder that is mounted on an axle inside coils of wire. The magnet is spun by the rotation of the bicycle wheel, which induces voltage in the coil and causes current to flow in the circuit. Because the magnet rotates, it is called the *rotor*, and the stationary coils of wire are called the *stator*. (In some generators, the magnet is stationary and the coils rotate.)

Figure 12.1

A Disassembled Bicycle Generator (including cross-section view)

Most motor vehicles contain a generator that is called an *alternator* (it is used to recharge the battery). The rotor of the alternator is an electromagnet, which you will learn more about later in this chapter. The engine moves the rotor, which induces voltage in the stator coils and causes current to flow in the electric system of the car. The coils in the rotor and in the stator are electrically isolated from one another.

Figure 12.2

A View Inside a Car Alternator

The primary difference between the bicycle generator and the alternator is that the rotor of the alternator is an electromagnet, while the rotor of the bicycle generator is a permanent magnet.

The *power plant generating system* operates in a fashion similar to the alternator. Like the alternator, it consists of an electromagnet as a rotor that moves relative to the stator. The current to create the rotor's electromagnet is produced by a smaller, permanent-magnet generator. A turbine powered by steam, water, or wind turns the rotors of both generators in a power plant.

Figure 12.3
A Power Plant
Generating System

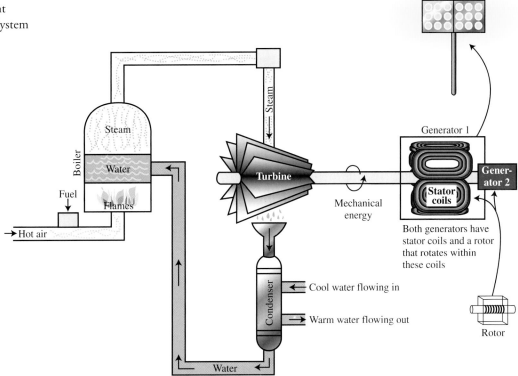

**Focus
Questions**

A generator is a device that changes _____ energy to _____ energy.

What is the rotor of the bike light generator, and what does it do?

What is the stator of the bike light generator, and what does it do?

An electric motor works in the opposite way from a generator. A motor uses electric energy to produce mechanical energy. The turning motion of an electric motor is used to do work. Electric motors are used in many devices: fans, blenders, choppers, grinders, refrigerators, tape or video recorders, and electric toys, for example.

Workplace Connection: Power Plant Operators, Distributors, and Dispatchers

Electricity is vital for most everyday activities. From the moment you flip the first switch each morning, you are connecting to a huge network of people, electric lines, and generating equipment. Power plant operators control the machinery that generates electricity. Power distributors and dispatchers control the flow of electricity from the power plant over a network of transmission lines, to industrial plants and substations, and, finally, over distribution lines to residential users.

Power plant operators control and monitor boilers, turbines, generators, and auxiliary equipment in power generating plants. Operators distribute power demands among generators, combine the current from several generators, and monitor instruments to maintain voltage and regulate electricity flows from the plant. When power requirements change, these workers start or stop generators and connect or disconnect them from circuits. They often use computers to keep records of switching operations and loads on generators, lines, and transformers. Operators also may use computers to prepare reports of unusual incidents, malfunctioning equipment, or maintenance performed during their shift.

Power distributors and dispatchers, also called load dispatchers or systems operators, control the flow of electricity through transmission lines to industrial plants and substations that supply residential electric needs. They operate current converters, voltage transformers, and circuit breakers. Dispatchers monitor equipment and record readings at a pilot board, which is a map of the transmission grid system showing the status of transmission circuits and connections with substations and industrial plants.

Dispatchers also anticipate power needs, such as those caused by changes in the weather. They call control room operators to start or stop boilers and generators, to bring production into balance with needs. They handle emergencies such as transformer or transmission line failures and route current around affected areas. They also operate and monitor equipment in substations, which step up or step down voltage, and operate switchboard levers to control the flow of electricity in and out of substations.

Employers seek high school graduates for entry-level operator, distributor, and dispatcher positions. Candidates with strong math and science skills are preferred. College-level courses or prior experience in a mechanical or technical job may be helpful. Employers increasingly require computer proficiency, as computers are used to keep records, generate reports, and track maintenance. Most entry-level positions are helper or laborer jobs, such as in powerline construction. Depending on the results of aptitude tests, worker preferences, and availability of openings, workers may be assigned to train for one of many utility positions.

Workers selected for training as a fossil-fueled power plant operator or distributor undergo extensive on-the-job and classroom training. Several years of training and experience are required to become a fully qualified control room operator or power distributor. With further training and experience, workers may advance to shift supervisor. Utilities generally promote from within; therefore, opportunities to advance by moving to another employer are limited.

From OCCUPATIONAL OUTLOOK HANDBOOK. *"Power Plant Operators, Distributors, and Dispatchers."* U.S. Department of Labor. Bureau of Labor Statistics. http://www.bls.gov/oco/ocos227.htm (July 5, 2002)

ACTIVITY 12.3

Experimenting with Magnets

Getting In Gear

In activities 12.3, 12.4 and 12.5, you will investigate the structures you found inside the bike light generator and the alternator. In this activity, you will experiment with magnets. As you observe magnetic interactions, consider the following questions: How do magnets work inside a generator? Is there a connection between electricity and magnetism? If so, what is the nature of that connection?

One important phenomenon you will discuss in exploring magnets is their ability to attract or repel each other even when they are not touching. The space around a magnet where magnetic forces are felt is called the magnetic field. At the end of this activity, you will map and view this field using a magnet and a compass.

In Activity 12.4, you will continue to investigate generators by examining the operation of the wire coils in the alternator's rotor.

Getting To Work!

To deepen your understanding of magnetism, you will

1. Listen as a class to a review of your theories about how generators work and the structures that are inside generators (which include magnets).

2. Work in groups and follow the instructions on **Job Sheet 12.3** What Is a Magnet?
   a. Explore interactions between magnets and other materials, identifying aspects of magnetic force.
   b. Explore interactions between a magnet and a compass. Use your results to identify what a compass is made from.
   c. Map the magnetic force around a magnet.

Job Sheet

3. Read Getting the Point: *Magnets and Magnetic Fields,* and answer the Focus Questions.

4. Read Concept Connection: *Magnetic Domains,* and check out the Did You Know? reading as time permits.

Magnets and Magnetic Fields

Certain kinds of materials exert forces on one another that are neither electrical nor gravitational. The ancient Greeks observed these forces in an iron ore found in the region called Magnesia, hence, the name magnets.

If there are two bar-shaped magnets, one end of one bar will be attracted to one end of the other bar and repelled by the other end of the same bar. The ends are called magnetic poles. The poles are commonly called north and south poles; more properly, they are called north-seeking and south-seeking poles.

Figure 12.4
A Sample of Different Types of Magnets

Magnetic poles always come in pairs. If you break a magnet into pieces, each broken piece will have a south magnetic pole and a north magnetic pole. The forces between the poles of two magnets can be summarized as follows: Like poles repel each other, and unlike poles attract each other.

Did You Know?

The Sun, Earth, and most other planets have magnetic fields. Scientists think that iron ores in the core of the Earth form a giant magnet deep underground. The poles of this giant magnet are near but not at the geographic poles. If opposite poles attract, how can the north end of a compass point north? Shouldn't it be attracted to Earth's *south* magnetic pole? In fact, it is. Because of the peculiar way we label magnetic poles, Earth's south magnetic pole is actually located close to the *geographic* North Pole.

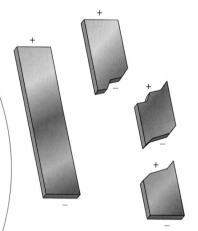

Figure 12.5
Broken Magnets Showing Poles

Some materials are permanently magnetic. However, as you know when you pick up paper clips with a magnet, there are materials that become magnetic when placed near a permanent magnet. Temporarily, the paper clips become magnets.

A compass needle is a magnet; its north pole points to geographic north. When compass needles are placed around a bar magnet, they will respond to the poles of the magnet by lining up in different directions. By drawing arrows to show which way the compass needles point at different locations, you can depict the magnetic environment of the magnet, commonly called its magnetic field (see Figure 12.6).

Figure 12.6
Arrows Show the
Direction of the
Magnetic Field

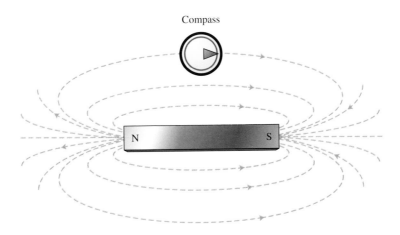

The direction of the lines in Figure 12.6 is the direction of the force on the north pole of the compass needle. In this kind of mapping, the lines will become more closely packed whenever the field becomes stronger. This occurs when the compass is brought nearer the poles of the magnet, or when another bar magnet is placed on top of the first.

**Focus
Questions**

What is the difference between a permanent magnet and a temporary magnet?

What does a magnetic field represent?

Concept Connection: Magnetic Domains

You can make several interesting observations about temporary magnetic materials. When you pick up paper clips with a magnet, the clips are always attracted to the magnet, regardless of the way you hold the magnet. This suggests that something about the paper clip changes in response to the magnet's magnetic field.

You can explore another interesting phenomenon of magnetic materials with a pair of steel scissors and a magnet. If you slide the magnet along the scissors, the scissors become magnetized for a time. Now repeat sliding the magnet along the scissors, and watch what happens. You will see that the scissors become more and more strongly magnetized.

Figure 12.7
Magnetizing a
Pair of Scissors

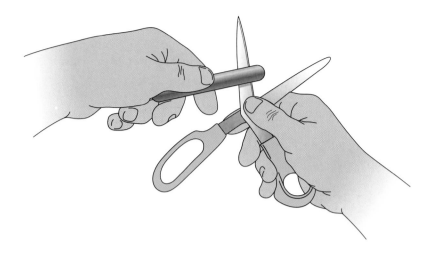

Scientists now think that magnetism in materials occurs because of the magnetic properties of atoms. All atoms are magnetic and have a small magnetic field around them. In most materials, the atoms are arranged randomly, and the small magnetic fields cancel each other out. In magnets, the atoms line up so that the magnetic fields are all pointing in the same direction.

In magnetic materials, the atoms are not lined up, but they are free to rotate. When a magnet is nearby, the atoms turn in response to the magnetic field. This is why a paper clip is always attracted to a magnet.

Scientists now have evidence that when atoms rotate in response to a magnetic field, you will see areas of atoms aligned in different directions. These areas are called magnetic domains. Each time you slide the magnet along the scissors, you make the magnetic domains that are lined up with the magnet larger and larger, and the scissors become more magnetized.

Figure 12.8
Magnetic Domains

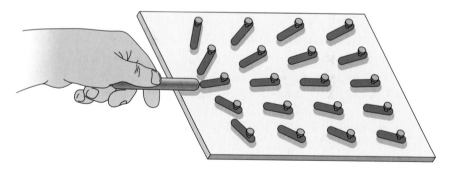

ACTIVITY 12.4

What Is an Electromagnet?

In Activity 12.2, you observed that the rotor of the bike light generator contained a magnet, while the rotor of the alternator contained a wire coil. The alternator rotor is connected to the car battery. When the alternator is in the car, the rotor coil has current going through it. Based on your observations of the disassembled bike light generator, what properties do you expect the current-carrying coil to have?

You might conclude that the wire coil could also have magnetic properties. In this activity, you will make a coil of wire and attach the coil to a battery. Then you can test the idea that the current-carrying wire has magnetic properties.

With this work, you are beginning to investigate the relationships between electricity and magnetism. Understanding that these two phenomena are related is important. Electromagnets, which you study in this activity, are used extensively in many devices from audio speakers to toasters. In Activity 12.5, you will continue to study how electricity and magnetism are connected by observing the principle of electromagnetic induction.

Getting To Work!

To begin your observations of the connections between electricity and magnetism, you will

1. Review the alternator as a class, then observe the effect of putting current through the alternator's rotor.

2. Work in groups and use **Job Sheet 12.4** | **What Is an Electromagnet and How Do You Make One?** to explore electromagnetism.
   a. Observe the effect of a current-carrying wire on a compass, and discuss your results with the class.
   b. Make an electromagnet coil, and test it for magnetic properties.
   c. Figure out how to make the electromagnet stronger, using the materials at hand.
   d. Discuss as a class, and record the results.

3. Read Getting the Point: *Electromagnets,* and answer the Focus Questions.

4. Read Workplace Connection: *Basics of Magnetic Recording,* and check out the Did You Know? reading as time permits.

Job Sheet

Getting The Point.

Electromagnets

The Danish scientist Hans Christian Oersted discovered the connection between electricity and magnetism. This happened by accident when he was demonstrating electricity on a table that had a compass on it. He noticed that the wire caused the compass to move.

Further study of Oersted's observation led to the invention of the *electromagnet.* Coils or loops of current-carrying wire will act just like bar magnets. The magnetic poles are located at each end of the coil, and depend on direction of current.

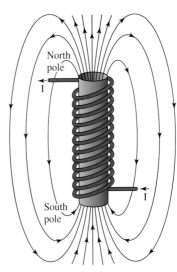
Figure 12.9
Current and Poles of an Electromagnet

Electromagnets are used in many applications because their strength can be easily varied by changing the amount of current, the number of loops in the coil, or by adding magnetic material to the core of the coil. In an electromagnet, the location of the north and south poles can be reversed by reversing the direction of current through the wire.

The invention of the electromagnet eventually led to the invention of the electric motor and the generator, as well.

Electromagnets helped scientists to understand that all magnetic phenomena are caused by electric charges in motion. Present understanding maintains that all atoms exhibit magnetism because the movement of their electrons creates very small currents. In natural magnets, these atomic currents are aligned and exert strong magnetic forces on other moving charges. In other materials, these small atomic currents oppose each other, and the material is not magnetic.

Both magnets and electromagnets have neatly lined up circuit loops. The natural magnet has a huge number of very small circuit loops, and the electromagnet has a few larger circuit loops. (The current through an atomic circuit loop is very small compared to the current through an electromagnet.)

Focus Questions

Describe three ways to make an electromagnet stronger.

What is the current theory of the cause of magnetism?

Workplace Connection: Basics of Magnetic Recording

Read-Rite's recording heads are the miniaturized hearts of disk drives and other magnetic storage devices. While they may appear to be simple components, their design and manufacture require leading-edge capabilities in device modeling, materials science, photolithography, vacuum deposition processes, ion beam etching, reliability testing, mechanical design, machining, air bearing design, tribology, and other critical skills.

One example of data storage applications is a writing head. It is used for writing bits of information onto a spinning magnetic disk. The operation of a writing head is based directly on two magnetic phenomena:

- An electric current produces a magnetic field.
- Some materials are easily magnetized when placed in a weak magnetic field. When the field is turned off, the material rapidly demagnetizes. These are called *Soft Magnetic Materials.*

Simplified sketches of a writing head are shown in Figure 12.10. The view from the top of the writing head (left) shows a spiral coil wrapped between two layers of soft magnetic material; on the right is a cross-section of this head as viewed from the side. Note two things in this figure: at the lower end, there is a gap between these layers, and at their upper end these layers are joined together. The top and bottom layers of magnetic material are readily magnetized when an electric current flows in the spiral coil, so these layers become *North* and *South* magnetic poles of a tiny electromagnet. [In a real head, the distance from the gap to the top of the coil is about 30 microns (or 0.0012 inch).]

Figure 12.10
A Writing Head

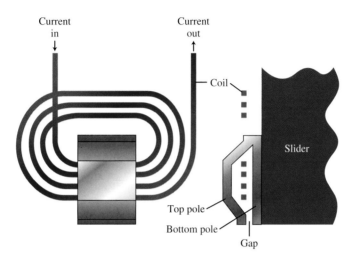

The N-S poles at the gap end of the writing head further concentrate the field to make this region the business end, which is the area where the writing field leaks into space outside the head. When a magnetic storage medium (a spinning computer disk, for example) is put in close proximity with the writing head, the hard magnetic material on the disk surface is permanently magnetized (written) with a polarity that matches the writing field. If the polarity of the electric current is reversed, the magnetic polarity at the gap also reverses.

Adapted from *"Basics of Magnetic Recording."* Text and illustration courtesy of Read-Rite Corporation, Fremont, California. www.readrite.com/html/magbasic.html (June 6, 2002)

ACTIVITY 12.5

Moving a Magnet in a Wire Coil

In this activity, you will finish your investigations into generators. Understanding the bike light generating system is your first step in completing the unit project: creating a bike light circuit that works even when the bicycle isn't moving.

In Activity 12.2, you theorized about how a generator produces electricity. In the subsequent activities, you studied the properties of the parts inside a generator. You now have a stronger understanding of magnetism and electromagnetism, and know that there are important connections between electricity and magnetism.

Specifically in Activity 12.4, you discovered that electric currents are the cause of magnetism. In this activity, you will find that the reverse is true: a moving magnet can cause current. This principle, electromagnetic induction, makes generators and motors possible. Using your understanding of this principle, you will be able to describe clearly how the bike light generator transforms energy of motion into electric energy.

Getting To Work!

To complete Project Milestone One, you will

1. Brainstorm as a class how a generator works, using what you have learned in earlier activities.

2. Watch a demonstration of electromagnetic induction in the alternator.

3. Work in groups and follow the instructions in **Job Sheet 12.5** Describing **How the Bike Light Generator Works.**

Job Sheet

   a. Revisit the bike light generator station. Sketch and name the important parts inside the bike light generator.
   b. Explain how these parts move while the bicycle is being pedaled so that the front and rear lamps will light.
   c. Create a poster summarizing information about the bike light generator.

4. Read Getting the Point: *Generators and Electromagnetic Induction,* and answer the Focus Questions.

5. Review the concepts and answer the questions in What Have You Learned? for homework.

6. Read Workplace Connection: *Design Ideas from Bicyclists (1),* as time permits.

Getting The Point.

Generators and Electromagnetic Induction

After Oersted's discovery that electricity causes magnetism, Joseph Henry and Michael Faraday conducted an experiment to see if magnetism causes electricity. They moved a magnet through a wire coil and measured electric current in the coil. This way of creating voltage current is called *electromagnetic induction,* because the movement of the magnet inside a wire coil induces voltage and current in the coil.

You learned earlier in this chapter that an electric generator is a device that converts energy of motion into electric energy. Generators work because they use the principle of electromagnetic induction discovered by Henry and Faraday. In a generator, you will always find relative motion between magnets or electromagnets and wire coils. This means that either the magnet or the wire coil can move during induction.

A perfect symmetry exists between electricity and magnetism: the movement of charges results in a magnet, and the movement of a magnet results in the movement of charges. We've now learned enough about electric and magnetic forces that we can describe some relationships between them. Both forces are linked by the property of *charge,* as summarized below.

- All charged particles exert an electric force on all other charged particles. This is true whether the charges are stationary or in motion.
- All charged particles in motion exert a magnetic force on all other charged particles in motion.

Focus Questions

Describe the difference between electromagnetism and electro-magnetic induction.

What two kinds of devices are based on the principle of electro-magnetic induction?

Workplace Connection: Design Ideas from Bicyclists (1)

Many bicyclists try out different configurations with their lights, much as you are doing in your unit project. This is the first of two articles on generator light modifications tried out by bicyclists.

Boosting Dynamo Output

(NOTE: DYNAMO IS ANOTHER TERM FOR GENERATOR.)

Bicycle generators are usually specified as 6V, the voltage output you get using normal bicycle light bulbs. At reasonably high speeds, bicycle dynamos are *constant current* generators. The voltage produced can reach high values, depending on speed. The current, however, is limited to 0.5A. This design protects bulbs from blowing out.

The voltage output depends on bulb resistance, which is normally 12 ohms. Using the current limit and Ohm's law, you can calculate voltage output for two bicycle lights in *PARALLEL:*

$$12 \text{ ohm} * 0.5 \text{ A} = 6 \text{ V}$$

However, if you attach your two bicycle lights in *SERIES,* you can get higher voltage output:

$$24 \text{ ohm} * 0.5 \text{ A} = 12 \text{ V}$$

I have been using this setup for more than a year now and it is still working perfectly. The only drawback is that you need to go twice as fast to reach the limit of the 0.5 A, about 10 - 16 km/h.

If you use a rectifier and recharge batteries with your generator, the current is still approximately 0.5 A (minus some losses) and the voltage is given by the batteries. You can charge 6V batteries if you cycle fast enough.

Adapted from *"Boosting Dynamo Output,"* by Mike Fabian. http://www.bath.ac.uk/~bspahh/bikelights/node64.html (June 6, 2002)

What Have You Learned?

Magnets. Magnets are made of special materials that exert magnetic forces on other magnets and on magnetic materials. Magnets have permanent magnetic properties. There are also magnetic materials that act like magnets only when close to a magnet.

All magnets have two ends, called magnetic poles. The poles are commonly called north and south poles; more properly, they are called north-seeking and south-seeking poles. The names for the poles come from compass directions. A compass needle is a magnet, attracted by magnetic ore in the core of the earth that is lined up north to south. If you break a magnet in half, you will have two new magnets, each with a north and a south magnetic pole.

If you bring two bar-shaped magnets together, you will feel attraction between unlike poles and repulsion between like poles.

Magnetic field. When compass needles are placed around a bar magnet, they will respond to the poles of the magnet by lining up in different directions. By drawing arrows to show which way the compass needles point at different locations, you can depict the magnetic environment of the magnet, commonly called its magnetic field (see Figure A). The magnet exerts a force on the compass needle so that the north

pole of the compass points toward the south pole of the magnet. The exact direction of the compass needle is as indicated by the direction of the lines in the figure.

Electromagnet. Electricity and magnetism are related phenomena, which became clear when Oersted discovered that moving charges could create a magnet. Coils or loops of current-carrying wire will act just like bar magnets. These coils are therefore called electromagnets. Electromagnets are used in many applications because their strength can be easily varied by changing the amount of current, the number of loops in the coil, or by adding magnetic material to the core of the coil.

Electromagnetic induction. Moving charges create a magnet. The reverse is true as well: a moving magnet creates a voltage difference. If a magnet is moved inside a closed coil of wire, then the voltage difference results in a flow of charges through the wire. Because an electric effect is being produced by magnetic means, the effect is called electromagnetic induction.

Generator. A generator is a device that uses the principle of electromagnetic induction. It converts energy of motion into electric energy. In a generator, you will always find relative motion between magnets or electromagnets and wire coils.

Figure A
Mapping Magnetic Field Lines

CONCEPT QUESTIONS

1. Why is it that windmills produce more electricity on windy days than on less windy days? How does this relate to the way the bike light generator works?

2. Imagine that you drop a magnet, and it breaks into two similar-size pieces. Draw the broken magnet, and show the locations of the south and north poles on the two broken pieces.

3. What is the difference between the magnet in a car alternator and the magnet in a bicycle generator?

4. Atoms have electrons that move around them. Use this information to explain why each atom is a tiny magnet.

5. What would happen to the magnetic field if you increased the current through the electromagnet? What would happen if you decreased it?

6. Why are electromagnet coils often wrapped around an iron core?

7. List three kinds of generators.

APPLYING WHAT YOU KNOW

1. Explain why materials like iron and steel are attracted to a magnet without being magnetic themselves.

2. Information is stored on computers by using materials that can be magnetized and demagnetized. Explain why magnets should not be placed close to a computer.

3. Research the use of turbines in power plants. What energy sources are used to turn a generator turbine?

Looking Under the Hood

OVERVIEW

WHERE TO GO FROM HERE?

Sylvia, Joe, and Robert get together to discuss progress on the bike light. Robert starts, "We've learned a lot about the bike light generator in the past week. One thing seems clear to me—if the wheel isn't turning, we can't get voltage or current. We have to store that voltage and current somehow."

Sylvia continues. "That sounds like a battery. But we decided before that we don't want to throw away a lot of batteries."

"Well, maybe there's a solution," says Joe. "Perhaps we could use rechargeable batteries. We use them at my house, and you can recharge them lots of times."

Robert says, "My friend who knows about cars says that a car's battery is recharged when the car moves. Maybe we could do the same thing with the bike?"

"What a great idea!," says Sylvia. "Let's take a look at the car!"

Your next milestone:

Project Milestone ②

Creating Specifications and Designs for the Bike Light Circuit

You will create circuit specifications for a modified bike light circuit and brainstorm possible circuit designs.

In the overview scenario, the student inventors at The Green Machine realize that they need to store the generator's energy. Once that energy is stored, then the rider will be able to use it when needed. After brainstorming among themselves, the inventors identified a rechargeable battery as a way to store energy. One of the inventors knew that a car uses a rechargeable battery to store energy generated by the alternator.

In this chapter, you will learn about the electric system in an automobile and begin to think about how to apply its design to the bike light generator. You will look under the hood of a car to see how the electric parts are connected, hear from an alternator specialist, and learn how current is converted to recharge a battery. By the end of this chapter, you will be on your way to modifying the bike light generator.

To help you accomplish Project Milestone Two, you will need to understand all the parts of an automobile's electrical system and how they work together. To reach this second milestone, you will complete the following activities:

Activity 13.1 What's Under the Hood?
Do you know how a car's electric system works? You will brainstorm ideas and look under the hood of a car to see the parts and examine how they are connected.

Activity 13.2 Visit with an Alternator Specialist
You will visit with an alternator specialist and learn how common alternator problems are diagnosed and repaired.

Activity 13.3 Viewing and Interpreting Current Graphs
You will view and interpret current graphs from a battery and a generator. You will see how the rotation of a magnet inside a generator creates alternating current.

Activity 13.4 How Do You Recharge a Battery?
You will learn how a diode changes alternating current from a generator. You will build a circuit with the bike light generator and diode, and recharge a battery.

Activity 13.5 Creating Circuit Specifications and Designs
You will create circuit specifications for a modified bike light circuit to meet the guidelines set out in the unit project, and brainstorm possible circuit designs.

ACTIVITY 13.1

What's Under the Hood?

Getting In Gear

What is under the hood of a car? How are the alternator and its parts connected to the rest of the automobile's electric system? How do the parts work together? How can this system provide a model for a modified bike light generator? In this chapter, you will start to answer those questions.

The automobile system contains both a battery and generator, which have the capacity to provide current whether or not the car is running. The inventors at The Green Machine set out to understand this system. You will do the same. As you observe the parts and connections of an automobile's electric system, think about how the bike light generator could be modified to work in a similar fashion.

Getting To Work!

To begin your investigation into an automobile's electric system, you will

1. Read the overview scenario and project milestone for Chapter 13, and discuss the scenario with your class.

2. Brainstorm as a class everything you know about an automobile's electric system.

3. Review as a class a diagram of the automobile's electric system.

4. Take turns looking under the hood of a car to identify the alternator, alternator belt, battery, and spark plugs.

5. Work in groups and follow │ **Job Sheet 13.1** │ What's Under the Hood?
   a. Describe the role of the alternator, alternator belt, battery, and spark plugs.
   b. Sketch how these parts are connected.

Job Sheet

6. Read Getting the Point: *Overview of the Automobile's Electric System,* and answer the Focus Questions.

7. Read Workplace Connection: *Automotive Service Technicians and Mechanics* as time permits.

Getting The Point

Overview of the Automobile's Electric System

The automotive electric system comprises several components connected in a complete circuit. A lead-acid battery is the primary source of electricity for starting the engine. It also serves as a reserve source of electricity for the electric load of the vehicle when the engine is running.

Figure 13.1

Diagram of Automobile Charging System

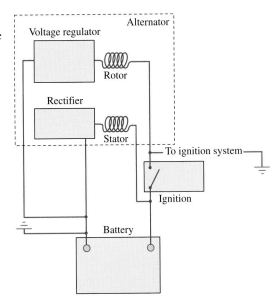

The starter or cranking motor is an electric motor designed to produce a high turning effort, or torque, at high speeds for a short period of time. It is used to start the engine. It has a mechanism to connect it to the engine when starting and to disconnect it when the engine starts.

The charging system, or alternator, consists of a belt-driven generator, a regulator to limit maximum voltage, and a diode to convert or rectify the alternating current produced by the generator to the direct current necessary to charge the battery. The rotor's coil is connected in a complete circuit to the ignition circuit of the car. When the ignition switch is closed, current flows to the rotor through two brushes, creating a magnetic field. The engine produces the mechanical power necessary to turn the alternator rotor through the drive belt. The movement of the magnetized rotor induces current in the stator coils and operates the charging system.

The ignition system consists of a low-voltage primary circuit and a high-voltage secondary circuit. The primary circuit consists of the battery, ignition switch, and a coil or wire. The secondary circuit includes the distributor coil, distributor, and spark plugs. This configuration acts as a transformer to provide the high voltage necessary to fire the spark plugs. Finally, the circuit is completed by wires that connect the devices and the frame of the automobile to one terminal of the battery.

Focus Questions

What source of electricity is used to start the engine?

What kind of current is produced by the generator (alternator)?

What kind of current is needed to recharge the car battery?

What is the name of the component that converts current for battery recharging?

Workplace Connection: Automotive Service Technicians and Mechanics

- Formal automotive technician training is the best preparation for these challenging technology-based jobs.
- Opportunities should be very good for automotive service technicians and mechanics with good diagnostic and problem-solving skills and knowledge of electronics and mathematics.
- Automotive service technicians and mechanics must continually adapt to changing technology and repair techniques as vehicle components and systems become increasingly sophisticated.

NATURE OF THE WORK

Anyone whose car or light truck has broken down knows the importance of the jobs of automotive service technicians and mechanics. The ability to diagnose the source of a problem quickly and accurately—a most valuable skill—requires good reasoning ability and a thorough knowledge of automobiles. Many technicians consider diagnosing hard-to-find troubles one of their most challenging and satisfying duties.

The work of automotive service technicians and mechanics has evolved from simply mechanical to high technology. Today integrated electronic systems and complex computers run vehicles and measure their performance while on the road. Automotive service technicians have developed into diagnostic, high-tech problem solvers. Technicians must have an increasingly broad base of knowledge about how vehicles' complex components work and interact, as well as the ability to work with electronic diagnostic equipment and computer-based technical reference materials.

When mechanical or electrical troubles occur, technicians first get a description of the symptoms from the owner or, if they work in a large shop, the repair service estimator who wrote the repair order. To locate the problem, technicians use a diagnostic approach. First, they test to see if components and systems are proper and secure, and then isolate those components or systems that could not logically be the cause of the problem. For example, if an air conditioner malfunctions, the technician's diagnostic approach can pinpoint a problem as simple as a low coolant level or as complex as a bad drive-train connection that has shorted out the air conditioner. Technicians may have to test drive the vehicle or use a variety of testing equipment, such as onboard and hand-held diagnostic computers or compression gauges, to identify the source of the problem. These tests may indicate whether a component is salvageable or if a new one is required to get the vehicle back in working order.

EMPLOYMENT

Automotive service technicians and mechanics held about 840,000 jobs in 2000. The majority worked for retail and wholesale automotive dealers, independent automotive repair shops, or automotive service facilities at department, automotive, and home supply stores. Others found employment in gasoline service stations; taxicab and automobile leasing companies; Federal, State, and local governments; and other organizations. About 18 percent of service technicians were self-employed.

TRAINING, OTHER QUALIFICATIONS, AND ADVANCEMENT

Automotive technology is rapidly increasing in sophistication, and most training authorities strongly recommend that persons seeking automotive service technician and mechanic jobs complete a formal training program in high school or in a postsecondary vocational school. However, some service technicians still learn the trade solely by assisting and learning from experienced workers.

Adapted from OCCUPATIONAL OUTLOOK HANDBOOK. *"Automotive Service Technicians and Mechanics."* U.S. Department of Labor. Bureau of Labor Statistics. http://www.bls.gov/oco/ocos181.htm (June 7, 2002)

ACTIVITY 13.2

Visit with an Alternator Specialist

Getting In Gear

How much do you know about fixing cars? What symptoms would your car have if the alternator wasn't working properly? Exactly how do alternators work when they are inside a car? How does an alternator recharge the car battery? In this activity, you will visit a repair shop to meet with an alternator specialist who will explain how the alternator works in the electric system of a car. He or she will also explain how to diagnose and repair common alternator problems.

The specialist will also give you some information about careers in automotive repair and technology. Due to the increasing complexity of cars and the computerization of many functions, this field is changing rapidly. Specialization is more and more common, and knowledge of computers is essential for automotive repair technicians.

Repair shops contain oily and sometimes dangerous machinery. Dress appropriately and safely. Wear washable, dark-colored clothing, and tie back long hair.

Getting To Work!

Before, during, and after your repair shop visit, you will

1. Participate in a class discussion about the visit to the repair shop. At this time, you will review the questions on Job Sheet 13.2 A Visit with an Alternator Specialist.

2. Work in groups to develop additional questions about the alternator, the work automotive specialists do, and the specialist's background and training. Practice asking your questions.

Job Sheet

3. Hand in all permission forms, and review information about the transportation arrangements and how missed classes will be made up.

4. View videos (as available) about the careers of automotive repair technicians, electricians, power plant technicians, and electrical or mechanical engineers.

5. Meet with your tour leader at the repair shop. He or she will demonstrate how to diagnose and repair some common alternator problems.

6. Answer the questions on Job Sheet 13.2. Ask questions if you need more information from the tour leader about items on the job sheet or for any other reason.

7. Discuss the visit with the class after the repair shop visit.

8. Write a thank-you letter to your tour leader.

9. Read Workplace Connection: *Automobile Repair Specialization* as time permits.

Workplace Connection: Automobile Repair Specialization

Automotive service technicians in large shops have increasingly become specialized. For example, transmission technicians and rebuilders work on gear trains, couplings, hydraulic pumps, and other parts of transmissions. Extensive knowledge of computer controls, diagnosis of electrical and hydraulic problems, and other specialized skills are needed to work on these complex components, which employ some of the most sophisticated technology used in vehicles. Tune-up technicians adjust the ignition timing and valves, and adjust or replace spark plugs and other parts to ensure efficient engine performance. They often use electronic test equipment to isolate and adjust malfunctions in fuel, ignition, and emissions control systems.

Automotive air-conditioning repairers install and repair air conditioners and service components, such as compressors, condensers, and controls. These workers require special training in Federal and State regulations governing the handling and disposal of refrigerants. Front-end mechanics align and balance wheels and repair steering mechanisms and suspension systems. They frequently use special alignment equipment and wheel-balancing machines. Brake repairers adjust brakes, replace brake linings and pads, and make other repairs on brake systems. Some technicians and mechanics specialize in both brake and front-end work.

Adapted from OCCUPATIONAL OUTLOOK HANDBOOK *"Automotive Service Technicians and Mechanics."* U.S. Department of Labor. Bureau of Labor Statistics. http://www.bls.gov/oco/ocos181.htm (June 7, 2000)

ACTIVITY 13.3

Viewing and Interpreting Current Graphs

Getting In Gear

Activity 13.1, you learned that, in an automobile's electric system, a battery creates direct current and a generator creates alternating current. Direct current is often abbreviated *DC* and alternating current *AC*. You may have seen these abbreviations on electric meters or on other electric equipment. In this activity, you will have an opportunity to understand these terms by viewing how current changes over time in a battery circuit and in a generator circuit.

You will interpret graphs, an important skill. As you view graphs of current change over time, you will need to describe the flow of charge in relation to the graph. By completing this analysis, you will understand the difference between direct current (DC) and alternating current (AC).

In Activity 13.4, you will use your understanding of DC and AC to learn how to recharge a battery.

Getting To Work!

To study direct and alternating current, you will

1. Work in groups and follow the instructions on | **Job Sheet 13.3** | Interpreting Current Graphs.

a. Review and analyze a current-over-time graph for a battery circuit.
b. Review and analyze a current-over-time graph for a generator circuit.
c. Summarize the main difference between direct current and alternating current.
d. View a diagram of the alternator rotor and housing, showing the magnetic environment, and visualize how the magnetic poles rotate inside the stator.
e. Describe how the change in magnetic poles results in current that reverses, or alternates, in direction.

2. Discuss as a class household current, which is alternating current produced by turbine generators in power plants.

3. Read Getting the Point: *Direct and Alternating Current,* and answer the Focus Questions.

4. Read Concept Connection: *How a Speaker Works* as time permits.

Job Sheet

Getting The Point.

Direct and Alternating Current

Direct current (DC) is a flow of charge in one direction through a circuit. Figure 13.2 shows an oscilloscope trace of voltage in a battery circuit. A battery produces direct current. In a battery circuit, electrons are always moving in the same direction away from the negative terminal of the battery, which repels them, and toward the positive terminal of the battery, which attracts them. The straight line on the graph indicates that voltage remains constant in value.

Figure 13.2
Oscilloscope Trace of a Battery Circuit: Direct Current

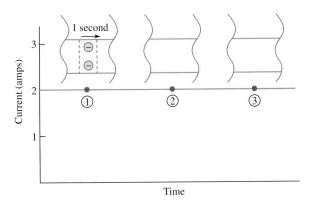

⊖ = 1 coulomb of charge

Alternating current (AC) is a flow of charge that moves first in one direction and then in the opposite direction through a circuit. AC generators produce electricity through electromagnetic induction. Figure 13.3 shows an oscilloscope trace of alternating current in a generator circuit. In the bike light generator, a multipole magnet rotates inside several loops of wire. As the magnet rotates, the change from a north magnetic pole to a south magnetic pole results in current that flows through the wire first in one direction, and then back in the other direction. The result is an alternating current, which has a wave form when graphed. A complete wave is called a cycle, and the frequency of alternation is expressed in cycles per second, called Hertz (Hz). Alternating current from most household outlets is 60 Hertz.

Figure 13.3
Oscilloscope Trace of a Generator Circuit: Alternating Current

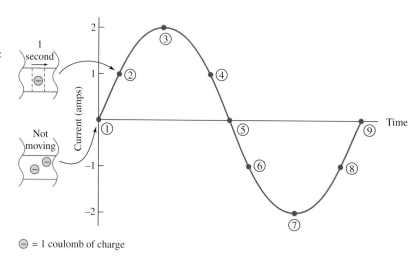

⊖ = 1 coulomb of charge

Both AC and DC circuits cause lightbulbs to glow because charges are moving through the lightbulb filament. It doesn't matter whether they are moving back and forth or in one direction. However, some devices, such as computers, require DC.

Focus Questions

All current is the flow of charge. What is different about charge flow in a DC circuit and in an AC circuit?

What is the frequency of household alternating current?

Concept Connection: How a Speaker Works

Mechanical vibrations cause sound. When our vocal cords, a string, or a drum top vibrate back and forth, they compress the air that they are in contact with. If we are close enough to the vibration, we sense the air compressions as sound. An *audio speaker*, which produces sound, works by converting electric energy into mechanical vibration.

Figure 13.4
An Audio Speaker

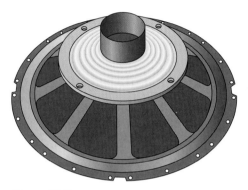

Figure 13.5
A Voice Coil and Cone

A speaker is both a transducer—a device that transforms energy from one form to another—and a communication device, because the energy it receives is in the form of information. Because of its design, the speaker produces nearly the same vibrations that the microphone originally recorded onto a CD or tape.

Each sound we hear is caused by an object vibrating faster or slower. In a speaker, the vibrations are produced by the *cone,* or *diaphragm.* The cone is connected to an electromagnet, called the *voice coil.*

The voice coil electromagnet is placed close to a permanent magnet. When current of different amounts and direction moves through the electromagnet, it moves toward or away from the permanent magnet. This movement vibrates the cone, and sound is produced.

ACTIVITY 13.4

How Do You Recharge a Battery?

In this activity, you will complete your study of the automobile's electric system. You will learn how a battery is recharged from a generator, and you will build a circuit to recharge a battery yourself. By building this circuit and analyzing how it works, you will better understand how an automobile's electric system works to provide and manage electricity.

During recharging, a diode is used (or arrangements of diodes, which are called rectifiers). Diodes are used to convert alternating current into direct current, which is needed to recharge a battery. The direction of current in a recharging circuit must be *into* the negative terminal of a spent battery. Metal ions in the spent battery react with the energetic electrons, forming metal atoms that renew the negative electrode.

As you build the circuit and recharge a battery, analyze current flow in the circuit. This will help you when the time comes to design your modified bike light circuit.

Getting To Work!

To learn how to recharge a battery, you will

1. View as a class the dismantled alternator and a circuit diagram of an automobile's electric system, which shows the connections between the alternator stator coil, the alternator rectifier, and the battery.

2. Learn as a class that a rectifier is made up of three diodes, and that a diode is a circuit component that serves as a one-way gate, allowing electrons to flow through it in only one direction.

Job Sheet

3. Work in groups and use 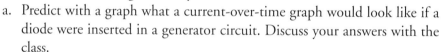 **Job Sheet 13.4** **How Do You Recharge a Battery?** to learn how to recharge a battery.
   a. Predict with a graph what a current-over-time graph would look like if a diode were inserted in a generator circuit. Discuss your answers with the class.
   b. Discuss why direct current is needed to recharge a battery.
   c. Build a recharging circuit with the bike light generator, a diode, and the rechargeable battery.
   d. Take voltage readings while recharging the battery; record the results in Table A on the job sheet.

4. Read Getting the Point: *Diodes and Rectifiers,* and answer the Focus Questions.

5. Read Workplace Connection: *Batteries and the Environment* as time permits.

Getting The Point.

Diodes and Rectifiers

A diode is a circuit component that serves as a one-way current gate. In AC circuits, it allows current to flow through it in one direction and prevents current from flowing through it in the opposite direction. (The diode shown in Figure 13.6 is part of the car alternator shown in Figure 12.2.)

Figure 13.6
A Diode

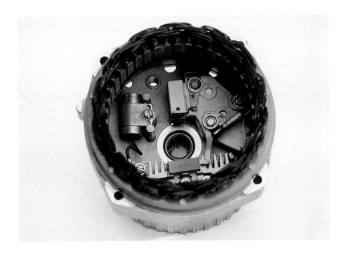

In this activity, you analyzed how a diode affects the current in an AC circuit, as shown in the graph:

Figure 13.7
Graph of Current in
Circuit with a Generator
and a Diode

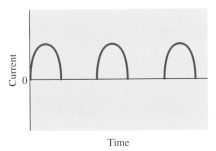

Because half of the AC wave is allowed through the circuit, this effect is called *half-wave rectification*. Half-wave rectification leads to an on-and-off, or pulsating, direct current.

In half-wave rectification, half of the energy from the generator is lost, dissipated as heat from the diode. For that reason, engineers have figured out how to use arrangements of diodes that can convert almost all of the alternating current to direct current. These arrangements of diodes are called *rectifiers*.

Figure 13.8
A Rectifier

Earlier, you saw that the alternator coil and the battery are connected in series with an alternator rectifier. An alternator rectifier is a special arrangement of diodes. Rectifiers can convert all of the alternating current to direct current, as shown in the following graph:

Figure 13.9

Trace of Current in Circuit with a Generator and a Bridge Rectifier

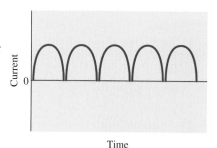

Time

Because the entire AC wave is allowed through the circuit, this effect is called *full-wave rectification*.

With this information about battery recharging, you should have a pretty complete picture of how an automobile's electric system works. When the car is running, the alternator is turning and current is generated both for use during driving and to recharge the car battery. If extra current is needed, the battery can also provide more when it is not being recharged. When the car is off, however, only the battery provides current, most importantly for starting the car.

Focus Questions

What is the role of a diode?

Are diodes used in AC circuits or DC circuits?

What is a rectifier?

Why are rectifiers used in circuits, in place of a single diode?

Workplace Connection: Batteries and the Environment

Batteries are indispensable to most people. They provide portable power for music, tools, hearing aids, telephones, games, and so on. Many types of batteries, however have depended on chemical reactions using toxic chemicals that are hazardous to people and animals. The toxic chemicals in batteries are mercury, lead, and cadmium.

The disposal of these toxic chemicals in regular household trash has contributed to the pollution of the environment. For that reason, most battery manufacturers have developed types of batteries that are free from toxic chemicals.

Another method that reduces the number of batteries thrown away is the use of rechargeable batteries. These batteries can be recharged and reused many times before becoming unusable. There's a catch though: the most commonly used rechargeable battery is the nickel-cadmium battery (also referred to as NiCd or NiCad battery), which uses the toxic chemical cadmium.

Because cadmium is toxic, it is important to dispose of used NiCad batteries properly. (You can find the nearest drop-off point by calling the nonprofit Rechargeable Battery Recycling Corporation at 800-8-BATTERY.)

Battery development is currently focused on improving two newer types of rechargeable batteries, lithium-ion and nickel-metal-hydride (NiMH) batteries. These batteries do not contain toxic chemicals and will not introduce hazardous chemicals into the environment when thrown away.

ACTIVITY 13.5

Creating Circuit Specifications and Designs

Getting In Gear

You now have a much better understanding of the automobile's electric system. You know its main parts—the alternator, battery, and rectifier—and understand how they work together when the car is running. You know that the rectifier is necessary in the circuit to convert the alternating current of the alternator into direct current needed to recharge the battery.

One of your tasks in this activity is to develop some ideas about how a similar system could be used in the bike light generator. You may not be able to wire the circuit right now (in Chapter 14, you will study the circuitry of the bike light generating system)—but you should be able to identify major parts of a modified circuit. You will also need to describe, as clearly as possible, the operation of your modified circuit by a rider.

Getting To Work!

To complete Project Milestone Two, you will

1. Work by yourself to answer Question 1 on ⎸ **Job Sheet 13.5** ⎸ **Creating Circuit Specifications and Designs.** Discuss your answer with the class.

2. Review as a class the charge of the unit project—to modify the circuitry of the bike light generator so that the bike light can stay on when the bike is stopped.

Job Sheet

3. Work in groups to complete Job Sheet 13.5.
   a. List the parts you think you will need to improve the bike light generator.
   b. Describe the circuit specifications for your improved bike light. (Specifications describe what the circuit will do and how it works.)
   c. Brainstorm initial circuit designs for the improved bike light generator.
   d. "Build" proposed circuits by placing regular and rechargeable batteries, a lightbulb, and a diode on chart paper and drawing connections.

4. Review the concepts and answer the questions in What Have You Learned? for homework.

5. Read Workplace Connection: *Cars and Onboard Computers* as time permits.

Workplace Connection: Cars and Onboard Computers

There are more computers aboard a car today than aboard the first spacecraft. A new car has from 10 to 15 onboard computers, operating everything from the engine to the radio. Some of the more advanced vehicles have global positioning systems (GPS), Internet access, and other high-tech features integrated into the functions of the vehicle. Therefore, knowledge of electronics and computers has grown increasingly important for service technicians. Engine controls and dashboard instruments were among the first components to use electronics, but now, everything from brakes to transmissions and air-conditioning systems to steering systems is run primarily by computers and electronic components. In the past, a specialist usually handled any problems involving electrical systems or electronics. Now that electronics are so common, it is essential for service technicians to be familiar with at least the basic principles of electronics. Electrical components or a series of related components account for nearly all malfunctions in modern vehicles.

In addition to electronics and computers, automotive service technicians will have to learn and understand the science behind the alternate fuel vehicles that have begun to enter the market. The fuel for these vehicles will come from the dehydrogenation of water, electric fuel cells, natural gas, solar power, and other nonpetroleum-based sources. Some vehicles will even capture the energy from brakes and use it as fuel. As vehicles with these new technologies become more common, technicians will need additional training to learn the science and engineering that makes them possible.

Adapted from OCCUPATIONAL OUTLOOK HANDBOOK. *"Automotive Service Technicians and Mechanics."* U.S. Department of Labor. Bureau of Labor Statistics. http://www.bls.gov/oco/ocos181.htm (June 7, 2002)

What Have You Learned?

KEY CONCEPTS

Direct current (DC). Batteries, and some types of generators, produce voltage that does not reverse, and therefore current in a battery circuit always travels in the same direction. This kind of current is called direct current (DC).

Alternating current (AC). Some types of generators produce a voltage that reverses or alternates rapidly; the current it generates also reverses its direction in response to the change in voltage. This kind of current is called alternating current (AC). A voltage versus time graph of an AC circuit would look like a sine wave. A complete AC wave is called a cycle, and a cycle per second is called a Hertz (Hz).

Conversion of alternating current to direct current. Alternating current can be converted to direct current by using one of several arrangements of diodes.

Diode. A diode is a circuit component that serves as a one-way current gate. In AC circuits, it allows current to flow through it in one direction and prevents current from flowing through it in the opposite direction.

CONCEPT QUESTIONS

1. List the two major parts of an automobile's electric system. Briefly describe the main function of each part.

2. Do you need direct or alternating current to recharge a battery?

3. Consider that electronic devices, such as computers and stereos, must use direct current (DC) even though they are plugged into an AC outlet. Is it likely that these devices contain a diode or rectifier? Explain your answer.

4. Draw a schematic of a circuit that would recharge a battery. In your diagram, indicate the direction the electrons travel.

5. When the magnet in the bike light generator rotates, the voltage reverses in the loop of wire. Explain why.

6. In alternating current (AC), current changes direction as it travels through the wire. What other differences, if any, are there between alternating current and direct current (DC)?

APPLYING WHAT YOU KNOW

1. In what ways does a turnstile, like that used as an entry and exit gate, act like a diode?

2. List three devices that use rechargeable batteries.

3. Figure A shows the arrangement of magnetic poles on the rotor of one brand of bike light generator. Draw a representation of the AC wave that results when the rotor turns one full circle.

Figure A
Arrangement of
Magnetic Poles
on One Bicycle
Generator Rotor

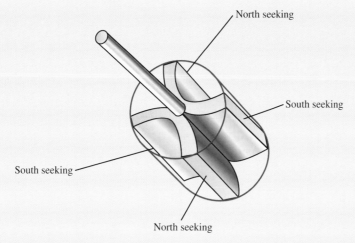

North seeking

South seeking

South seeking

North seeking

4. A transformer is used to convert AC current from one value of voltage to another. Research transformers and find out how they are used in the power industry.

Building a Better Bike Light

MODIFYING CIRCUITS

After checking out the car system, the inventors continue their discussion. Robert is excited now that the project seems to be on its way. "The Green Machine needs to develop a plan to share its ideas with potential investors. Let's come up with a definite idea."

"OK," says Joe. "We know we can recharge the battery with DC current. We know how to do that: put a diode in the bike light circuit. And then we can light the light either with the generator current *or* the battery current."

"We know how to do it in theory," says Sylvia. "But I have a hunch that actually building our new circuit is going to be complicated. You know, we haven't even looked at our existing bike light circuit thoroughly."

Robert and Joe realize that Sylvia has a good point, and the three inventors study the bike light circuit. Because of the connections through the bicycle frames, it's hard to figure out what's happening. They begin taking off wires and reattaching them. One of the things they discover is that each light can be on independent of the other light.

"You're right," says Robert to Sylvia. "This is pretty complicated. Why don't we plan more time to look at this circuit?" The inventors go back to looking at the bike light circuit. They figure out that the circuit is a parallel circuit.

"Now we have to build our improved light," says Joe. "It should be easy. We know how to recharge the battery, so let's add the recharging circuit to the bike light circuit."

The inventors put together the two circuits. They're positive that the batteries are being recharged, but the light doesn't work when the bike isn't being pedaled. "Why doesn't this work?" Sylvia asks. "With all these wires and batteries, I can't figure out what's going on. Let's draw the circuit we've built and try to figure out what's wrong."

Sylvia starts diagramming the circuit they've built. Robert helps her trace the different circuit paths. At last they have a schematic to look at. The three inventors trace the current flow through the circuit they've built, from the battery only. "Oh!" says Joe. "I see why it doesn't work." He points to the diode. "This can't be here."

The inventors puzzle over the drawing. "Then where should it go?" asks Sylvia.

Robert points to the schematic. "Here might work."

"Let's try it," Joe says. The inventors begin again to make a circuit. Joe starts writing down why the other circuit didn't work as Sylvia and Robert build the new circuit.

"Hey," says Sylvia, "how come you're not helping?"

"But I am. I'm keeping track of all our work," says Joe. "Remember, we have to meet with a couple of potential investors soon, and I want them to know that we understand what we're doing."

Your last milestone:

Project Milestone 3 | Building a Better Bike Light

You will design and build an improved bike light circuit, which can provide energy at all times. You will prepare a presentation to convince "investors" to fund the building and marketing of the improved bike light, and present your sales pitch to the class and invited guests.

In the overview scenario, the student inventors found that applying what they learned about the automobile's electric system to the bike light circuit was not as easy as they had hoped. First, Sylvia, Joe, and Robert had to understand the bike light circuit. Then they had to modify this circuit in a way that increased its complexity. As they built their final circuit, the inventors kept track of their work at each step with a circuit diagram. This documentation was very important. Sylvia, Joe, and Robert used one of the diagrams to analyze the circuit when it didn't work as expected.

In this chapter, you too will study circuits with multiple current paths and circuits with multiple voltage sources. Building on everything you have learned throughout this unit, you will have modified the bike light circuit by the end of this chapter and accomplished part of Project Milestone Three. To help you complete this milestone, you will do the following activities:

Activity 14.1 Tracing the Bike Light Circuit
You will trace and diagram the bicycle's generator and light circuit, which is a parallel circuit.

Activity 14.2 Finding "Circuit Rules" for Parallel Circuits
You will explore parallel circuits, take measurements of voltage and current, and deduce new "circuit rules" for these kinds of circuits.

Activity 14.3 Designing and Building the Better Bike Light Circuit
You will begin Project Milestone Three, and design, build, test, and document the better bike light circuit.

Activity 14.4 Presenting the Better Bike Light Circuit
You will convince an "investor" to fund the building and marketing of the new bike light design. Your presentations may include data on competing products and possible sales.

ACTIVITY 14.1

Tracing the Bike Light Circuit

Getting In Gear

You have seen that an automobile's electric system contains both a battery and generator, and has the capacity to provide current whether the car is running or not. In Activity 13.5, you began thinking about how to apply this model to the bike light generator system.

You probably had questions about the bike light circuit. What components are in the circuit? How does the circuit work? Is the circuit similar to other circuits that you've seen before? How would you break the circuit and add components? In this activity and the next, you will study the bike light circuit and try to answer those questions. What you learn will assist your work on modifications to the bike light circuit.

In this activity, you will trace the bike light circuit and see how it is arranged. Because the bicycle generator system can be difficult to operate, you will also make a model of its circuit using one battery and two bulbs.

Getting To Work!

To study the bike light circuit configuration, you will

1. Read the overview scenario and project milestone for Chapter 14, and discuss the scenario with your class.

Job Sheet

2. Work in groups and follow the instructions on | **Job Sheet 14.1** | Tracing the Bike Light Circuit.
   a. Examine the bike light circuit, and attempt to trace its circuit path.
   b. Disconnect the headlight and taillight in turn, and see the effect on the circuit.
   c. Model the bike light circuit using a battery and two flashlight bulbs. The completed circuit is a parallel circuit.
   d. View different, but equivalent, diagrams of a parallel circuit.
   e. Draw a detailed circuit schematic of the bike light circuit that clearly indicates the generator, both lights, the circuit connections, and the places where the circuit can be easily broken.

3. Read Getting the Point: *Review of Circuits,* and answer the Focus Questions.

4. Read Concept Connection: *Riding at Night* as time permits.

Getting The Point.

Review of Circuits

Electricity occurs when electric charges have both enough energy and a path to flow from one place to another. Like the fall of matter toward the Earth, the movement of charges is not random. Charges flow away from charges that repel them and toward charges that attract them. In the circuits you study, negative charges flow away from other negative charges and toward positive charges.

The flow of charge is called current, and the paths current travels in are called circuits. Because only some materials contain free-moving charges (conductors and semiconductors), circuits are made up of a closed path of these materials.

Even if you have a circuit of conducting materials, charges would not move in a specific direction through the circuit unless they first gained energy. Charges gain energy when they are separated from opposite charges (to which they are attracted). This energy is measured per unit of charge and is called voltage.

Electricity is used widely because circuits both transfer energy and transform energy. All kinds of electric components, such as lights, heaters, fans, and so forth, are designed to transform electric energy into another form of energy.

Although electricity can be generated in nature in several ways, people use batteries and generators to create electricity. A battery makes electricity by capturing the energy of chemical reactions. A generator makes electricity by capturing the energy of motion through the principle of electromagnetic induction. When we connect batteries or generators to circuits, we have electricity.

Circuits can be arranged in several ways. Bulbs, batteries, or generators, and other circuit elements can be connected in series or in parallel, or in circuits combining both types of connections.

Figure 14.1
Ways That Circuit Elements Can Be Connected

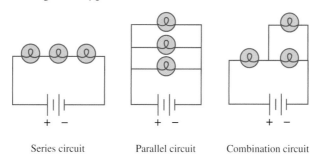

Series circuit   Parallel circuit   Combination circuit

A short circuit is a complete circuit that includes a battery and wire but no other components. A short circuit can start a fire. Figure 14.2 shows two examples of short circuits. A, Represents a circuit with only wire and a battery. In B, the current can also "follow" a short circuit path including only the wire and battery—but not the light bulb.

Figure 14.2
A Short Circuit

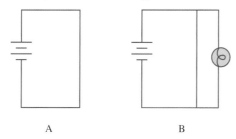

A   B

Focus Questions

What are the two major devices used to generate electricity?

Why is a circuit made of a closed path of conductors or semiconductors?

Concept Connection: Riding at Night

If you use your bicycle for transportation, sooner or later you'll find that you have to ride at night. To ride at night, you need lights. Even when streetlights show you the way, you need lights so other people can see you against the glare of car headlights. A white headlight identifies the front of all vehicles. A bicycle is always required by law to have a headlight at night. A front reflector, such as those sold on new bicycles, is not sufficient. A red taillight may be required, though sometimes a rear reflector is permitted as a substitute. It's a good idea to use both a taillight and rear reflector.

Three major types of lights are available for bicycles: small battery lights, generator systems and high-powered battery systems. Choose your lights depending on where you ride. Small battery lights are most useful for riding under streetlights. Aim the headlight level, so it looks as bright as possible to people ahead of you. Rechargeable batteries will cut the cost of operating small battery lights. Hardware stores and electronics stores sell these batteries and chargers.

Unlike small battery lights, a good generator system is bright enough to light your way on dark roads. It's the best choice for long-distance touring, since you may not be able to buy or recharge batteries. Most generator systems go dark when you stop riding; a disadvantage in stop-and-go city riding. Some generator systems have a battery backup that keeps them lighted when you stop.

High-powered battery lights are brightest of all. They're best for night riding under demanding conditions: on dark roads or off-road. They're more expensive and heavier than other bicycle lights, and they need recharging frequently.

When riding at night, carry spare bulbs and batteries for your lights. It's also a good idea to carry a small battery light as a spare to get you home in case your main lighting system fails. Mount a generator or high-powered battery light low, so its beam pattern extends longest and reveals surface irregularities. Aim taillights and small battery headlights level. Test aim by rolling the bike toward and away from a wall. The center of the beam should stay at the same height.

Riding at night is reasonably safe if you equip yourself correctly. You must use at least a headlight and rear reflector. A taillight and additional reflectors can make you more visible, and are required by law in some places. Brightly colored clothing can also help, as can reflective strips on your baggage, clothing, or helmet. Reflective patches on the backs of your gloves allow you to make a flashing turn signal by rotating your wrist.

If you are properly equipped, riding at night is not much different from riding in daylight hours, though some situations are better avoided because of increased risk of physical attack or of a crash.

Adapted from BICYCLING STREET SMARTS, by John S. Allen. Copyright © 1988, 2001 Rodale Inc. Reprinted with permission of Rubel BikeMaps, Cambridge MA. http://www.bicyclingstreetsmarts.com (June 7, 2002)

ACTIVITY 14.2

Finding "Circuit Rules" for Parallel Circuits

Getting In Gear

In Activity 14.1, you made a model of the bike light circuit using one battery and two bulbs. This model made it easier to understand the arrangement of the generator and two lights. This kind of arrangement may have been new to you because this circuit has multiple paths that current can follow. You learned that these kinds of circuits are called parallel circuits.

In this activity, you will examine the characteristics of parallel circuits by comparing them to series circuits. Although understanding parallel circuits is a challenge, the investigations in this activity will help you understand them. This knowledge will help you complete the unit project. And because parallel circuits are used widely, knowing how these circuits work will help you understand how circuits are wired in homes and businesses.

Getting To Work!

To become more familiar with parallel circuits, you will

1. Discuss as a class the main ideas of Getting the Point: *Review of Circuits* in Activity 14.1.

2. Work in groups and follow the instructions on **Job Sheet 14.2** Finding **"Circuit Rules" for Parallel Circuits.**
   a. Build series and parallel circuits. Make and record voltage and current measurements.
   b. Compare the measurements from different circuits, and deduce new circuit **Sheet** rules that apply to parallel circuits.

   Job

3. Share and review parallel circuit rules as a class.

4. Work by yourself at the end of Job Sheet 14.2 to check your recognition of series, parallel, combination, and short circuits.

5. Discuss as a class how to build wiring.

6. Read Getting the Point: *Parallel Circuits,* and answer the Focus Questions.

7. Read Workplace Connection: *Electricians* as time permits.

Getting The Point.

Parallel Circuits

When a circuit has more than one path that current can follow, it is called a parallel circuit (or a combination circuit depending on its complexity). The name *parallel* comes from the fact that, in a circuit diagram, the multiple paths are usually drawn side by side like parallel lines.

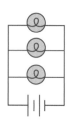

Figure 14.3
A Parallel Circuit

Most of us do not have an intuitive sense of how series circuits work, and parallel circuits are even more complex. To get a better understanding of parallel circuits, you need to build them, see how they work, and take and analyze measurements. One easy way to understand a parallel circuit is to think of each path as a separate series circuit connected to the same battery.

Because parallel circuits have multiple paths, they can be very advantageous. Our household circuits are parallel circuits. Every plug has its own path. You can turn each plugged-in appliance and device on and off without disturbing anything else on the circuit.

Household circuits also give us a clue as to how energy is provided in parallel circuits. The energy provided from each plug is the same, whether or not something else is on. You observed that fact in this activity when you measured the voltage across the bulb in each path. Remember, *each path of a parallel circuit has the same voltage drop as the voltage source.*

You also observed that the *current from parallel branches adds together*—Kirchhoff's current law. The same is true in your home; if you turn too many devices on that are on one circuit, the current can get too high, and the circuit will be shut off by a safety fuse or circuit breaker. This safety feature helps to prevent fires caused by an overheated wire.

Focus Questions

Describe the difference in current path between a series circuit and a parallel circuit.

List the two main reasons we use parallel circuits in our homes.

Workplace Connection: Electricians

SIGNIFICANT POINTS

1. Job opportunities are expected to be excellent for qualified electricians.

2. Most electricians acquire their skills by completing a formal 4- or 5-year apprenticeship program.

3. About one-third of all electricians work in industries other than construction.

NATURE OF THE WORK

Electricity is essential for light, power, air conditioning, and refrigeration. Electricians install, connect, test, and maintain electrical systems for a variety of purposes, including climate control, security, and communications. They also may install and maintain the electronic controls for machines in business and industry. Although most electricians specialize in either construction or maintenance, a growing number do both. Electricians work with blueprints when they install electrical systems in factories, office buildings, homes, and other structures.

Blueprints indicate the locations of circuits, outlets, load centers, panel boards, and other equipment. Electricians must follow the National Electric Code and comply with state and local building codes when they install these systems.

In factories and offices, they first place conduit (pipe or tubing) inside designated partitions, walls, or other concealed areas. They also fasten to the wall small metal or plastic boxes that will house electrical switches and outlets. They then pull insulated wires or cables through the conduit to complete circuits between these boxes. In lighter construction, such as residential, plastic-covered wire usually is used instead of conduit. Regardless of the type of wire used, electricians connect it to circuit breakers, transformers, or other components. They join the wires in boxes with various specially designed connectors. After they finish the wiring, they use testing equipment, such as ohmmeters, voltmeters, and oscilloscopes, to check the circuits for proper connections, ensuring electrical compatibility and safety of components.

In addition to wiring a building's electrical system, electricians may install coaxial or fiber optic cable for computers and other telecommunications equipment. A growing number of electricians install telephone systems, computer wiring and equipment, street lights, intercom systems, and fire alarm and security systems. They also may connect motors to electrical power and install electronic controls for industrial equipment.

EMPLOYMENT

Electricians held about 698,000 jobs in 2000. About two-thirds were employed in the construction industry. About one-third worked as maintenance electricians and were employed outside the construction industry. In addition, about 8 percent of electricians were self-employed. Because of the widespread need for electrical services, jobs for electricians are found in all parts of the country.

TRAINING, OTHER QUALIFICATIONS, AND ADVANCEMENT

Most people learn the electrical trade by completing a 4- or 5-year apprenticeship program. Apprenticeship gives trainees a thorough knowledge of all aspects of the trade and generally improves their ability to find a job. Although more electricians are trained through apprenticeship than are workers in other construction trades, some still learn their skills informally, on the job. Apprenticeship programs may be sponsored by joint training committees made up of local unions of the International Brotherhood of Electrical Workers and local chapters of the National Electrical Contractors Association; company management committees of individual electrical contracting companies; or by local chapters of the Associated Builders and Contractors and the Independent Electrical Contractors Association. Training also may be provided by company management committees of individual electrical contracting companies and by local chapters of the Associated Builders and Contractors and the Independent Electrical Contractors. Because of the comprehensive training received, those who complete apprenticeship programs qualify to do both maintenance and construction work.

Regardless of how one learns the trade, previous training is very helpful. High school courses in mathematics, electricity, electronics, mechanical drawing, science, and shop provide a good background. Special training offered in the Armed Forces and by postsecondary technical schools also is beneficial. All applicants should be in good health and have at least average physical strength. Agility and dexterity also are important. Good color vision is needed because workers must frequently identify electrical wires by color. Most apprenticeship sponsors require applicants for apprentice positions to be at least 18 years old and have a high school diploma or its equivalent. For those interested in becoming maintenance electricians, a background in electronics is increasingly important because of the growing use of complex electronic controls on manufacturing equipment.

Adapted from OCCUPATIONAL OUTLOOK HANDBOOK. *"Electricians."* U.S. Department of Labor. Bureau of Labor Statistics. http://www.bls.gov/oco/ocos206.htm (June 7, 2002)

ACTIVITY 14.3

Designing and Building the Better Bike Light Circuit

Getting In Gear

In this activity, you will begin Project Milestone Three. You will use what you have learned about generators, AC and DC current, battery recharging, and parallel circuits to design and build a modified bike light circuit. By completing this part of the unit project, you will demonstrate your understanding and application of these subjects, and your facility with the engineering design cycle.

You will also show how you have organized your work and built upon what you know over a long period of time, in order to complete a complex task. Understanding, skills, and organization are the cornerstones important not only in the classroom but also in the workplace.

Getting To Work!

To complete your work on the bike light circuit, you will

1. Review as a class your assignments for Project Milestone Three.

2. View a demonstration of a lightbulb powered by two voltage sources in parallel. Find out that the lightbulb always "sees" the parallel voltage that is strongest.

3. Work in groups or individually and follow the instructions on
   Job Sheet 14.3 Designing and Building the Better Bike Light Circuit.
   You may need to refer to previous job sheets to complete some of the tasks.
   a. Review the requirements for the modified bike light circuit.
   b. Determine the switches you will need and the number of batteries required to light the headlight. Draw an initial circuit design for the modified bike light system. In this circuit, the generator should recharge the battery and light the bulb, and the battery should light the bulb when the generator is off.
   c. Build your circuit from the circuit design. Test the circuit to see if it meets the circuit use requirements listed on the job sheet. Troubleshoot and revise your design as needed.

Job Sheet

d. Draw a circuit diagram of the finished modified circuit; use correct electric symbols. Annotate the diagram with the current paths through the bike light system that occur during different operating modes.

4. Present your circuits and schematic to the class. Discuss the different design options.

5. Read Concept Connection: *Design Ideas from Bicyclists (2)* as time permits.

Concept Connection: Design Ideas from Bicyclists (2)

Many bicyclists try out different configurations with their lights, much as you are doing in your unit project. This is the second of two articles on generator light modifications tried out by bicyclists.

The schematic below shows a regulator for a 6V/3W bicycle generator system. The purpose is to switch to rechargeable batteries when the generator is idle. In addition, the device limits the voltage across the bulbs when the generator operates at a high speed.

Figure 14.4

A Regulator for a Bicycle Generator System

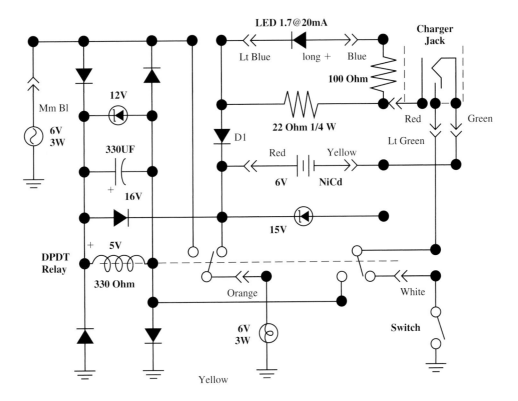

As you can see, the circuit is purely electrical. I kept the regulator on the bike for 2 years during which the circuit operated fairly satisfactorily. Thereafter, I moved on to an electronic regulator optimized for the operation with a hub dynamo.

When the main switch is in the on position, and the generator is not running, the bulbs are fed by five AA nicads. A running generator feeds the relay, which switches the bulbs to the generator in place of the nicads. Excess voltage across the generator is used to recharge the batteries. The Zener diodes are for protection. The batteries can be further recharged through the charger jack. I use a 7.2V Radio Shack Battery Charger, but another might be suitable with changed resistor values in the charging part if NiMH batteries are used in place of NiCd.

As is seen, the circuit, generator, and lights share the ground. All unmarked diodes are 1A Schottky. D1 is some generic all-purpose 1A diode. The low-current polarized DPDT (double-pole double-throw) relay was purchased from Electronic Goldmine. Since many relay manufacturers start their lineup with such relays, you might be able to get one from elsewhere. The relay's line of action goes horizontally across the figure. Different connections and colors are for my own reference.

All elements can be nicely packed onto a 1-3/4″ × 1-3/4″ circuit board and placed, with the 5 AA batteries, switch, mounted LED, and the charger jack, in a 1-5/8″ × 2″ × 2-3/4″ aluminum box. I used 800mAh nicads from Radio Shack, which I soldered in series.

I mounted the regulator box on my wire basket. Using reflector holders, it could be mounted on the frame.

I use a FER 2001 generator and lights with a halogen bulb in the front and with a regular bulb in the back. The regulator ensures that motorists see me at an intersection while I'm standing. The device genuinely gives me more security; the drivers respect me more.

We do not have any hills here, so I cannot assess the operation for a steep climb. A possibility is to include a trimmer resistor in series with the relay for adjustments.

The schematic shown above is the most conservative, letting the generator take over whenever there is a slightest sign of life from that generator. As the system performed reliably, I decided, eventually, to tip the balance more towards the batteries. Thus, I reduced the capacitor value to 75uF (the capacitor affects the delay in the reaction of the regulator) and I put a resistor of 270ohm in series with the relay (the resistor affects the threshold at which the generator takes over). The particular values would, generally, depend on the relay and on the taste, and should be experimented with. In my case, the batteries now take over when the light driven by a generator gets quite dim.

Experiences to share with would-be designers:
- The use of Zener diodes for protection, when dealing with such large inductances as that of a generator, or of a charging transformer, is absolutely essential. Without the diodes, you will fry the delicate relay poles in no time. Capacitors are useless for the purpose.
- Finding a right charging adapter turned out to be quite tricky. I tried a number of them using the generous Radio Shack return policy and buying individual adapters from different outlets.
- Do not count on the different relay poles to fire simultaneously.
- Solar cells can deliver a respectable charging current in bright sun. However, the current becomes abysmal under cloudy winter skies. Around here (Michigan) these cells offer no alternative to a generator.
- Standard battery holders are not practical on a bicycle. The batteries easily pop out.

Adapted from *"Bicycle Regulator,"* by Pawel Danielewicz. Reprinted with permission. http://www.nscl.msu.edu/~daniel/regulator.html (June 7, 2002)

ACTIVITY 14.4

Presenting the Better Bike Light Circuit

Getting In Gear

The bike light circuit is complete. In this final activity, you will prepare a presentation to persuade an investor to back your product. You will complete the design process by demonstrating how the group's circuit works and why it can meet specifications that a rider might have.

The responsibility for this presentation will be divided among the members of your group—your team will need to present three aspects of design or marketing for the modified bike light system. Whichever topics your group chooses to present, each of you will want to clearly communicate your designs, research, and conclusions.

Because you are trying to persuade a person to fund your design, this presentation may be different from others you have made. If you have entrepreneurial interests, this is an opportunity to gain valuable experience. Don't forget to talk about the ideas that you formed about generators, electromagnetic induction, and the automobile's electric system. These experiences helped you to complete this project and show people that you understand how to make your product.

Getting To Work!

To complete Project Milestone Three, you will

1. Learn about the presentation from your teacher, such as where and when it will occur, who will be in the audience, your time limit, and dress requirements.

2. Use **Job Sheet 14.4** Presenting Your Better Bike Light Circuit to help you prepare your presentation.
   a. Work as a class to review the presentation requirements for groups and individuals, and develop assessment criteria for your presentations.
   b. Work by yourself or in a small team to prepare an individual minipresentation and accompanying written report about some aspect of the modified bike light circuit design process, including potential marketability. You may need to access unit materials or conduct more research. Make use of available presentation materials, such as software, audiovisual aids, or poster materials.
   c. Work in groups to practice your presentation, and meet with your teacher to review your presentation.

Job Sheet

3. Give your presentation.

4. Review the concept and answer the questions in What Have You Learned? for homework.

5. Read Workplace Connection: *What Can Be Patented* as time permits.

Workplace Connection: What Can Be Patented

The patent law specifies the general field of subject matter that can be patented and the conditions under which a patent may be obtained.

In the language of the statute, any person who "invents or discovers any new and useful process, machine, manufacture, or composition of matter, or any new and useful improvement thereof, may obtain a patent," subject to the conditions and requirements of the law. The word "process" is defined by law as a process, act or method, and primarily includes industrial or technical processes. The term "machine" used in the statute needs no explanation. The term "manufacture" refers to articles that are made, and includes all manufactured articles. The term "composition of matter" relates to chemical compositions and may include mixtures of ingredients as well as new chemical compounds. These classes of subject matter taken together include practically everything that is made by man and the processes for making the products.

The Atomic Energy Act of 1954 excludes the patenting of inventions useful solely in the utilization of special nuclear material or atomic energy for atomic weapons.

The patent law specifies that the subject matter must be "useful." The term "useful" in this connection refers to the condition that the subject matter has a useful purpose and also includes operativeness, that is, a machine which will not operate to perform the intended purpose would not be called useful, and therefore would not be granted a patent.

Interpretations of the statute by the courts have defined the limits of the field of subject matter that can be patented, thus it has been held that the laws of nature, physical phenomena, and abstract ideas are not patentable subject matter.

A patent cannot be obtained upon a mere idea or suggestion. The patent is granted upon the new machine, manufacture, etc., as has been said, and not upon the idea or suggestion of the new machine. A complete description of the actual machine or other subject matter for which a patent is sought is required.

From GENERAL INFORMATION CONCERNING PATENTS: *"What Can Be Patented."* United States Patent and Trademark Office. http://www.uspto.gov/web/offices/pac/doc/general/what.htm (June 7, 2002)

What Have You Learned?

KEY CONCEPT

Parallel circuit. A parallel circuit is a circuit that branches into two or more paths that later rejoin. This configuration allows current to flow through multiple paths, each a complete circuit. Voltage across each parallel path is the same, but current varies with the total resistance of components placed in each path. Total current in the circuit is the sum of currents in all branches, as described by Kirchhoff's current law.

CONCEPT QUESTIONS

1. What is the role of the mounting bracket and the bike frame in the bike light circuit you used in class?

2. What is the voltage across each branch of a parallel circuit that is powered by a 3-volt battery pack?

3. A parallel circuit has two parallel paths. The current in each path is 0.8 amps. What is the total current in the circuit?

4. How would you explain the difference between a series circuit and a parallel circuit to a new student in the class?

5. In a parallel circuit, why can one bulb light while another remains unlit? Could that happen in a series circuit? Explain your answers.

6. If your front and rear bike lights were configured as a series circuit, what would happen to the front light if the rear light burned out? Explain your answer.

7. What happens to the total current in a parallel circuit if more parallel paths are added?

APPLYING WHAT YOU KNOW

1. Imagine a new product, and develop a marketing plan to promote and sell it.

2. View an ad on TV for a product, and identify the strategies and arguments made to persuade you to purchase the product.

3. Draw a picture showing coulombs of charge moving through a parallel circuit. The picture should accurately represent voltage and current relationships in a parallel circuit.

Energy | Live from WPTW!

OVERVIEW

This unit entails building, testing, and operating a radio transmitter that you will use to send a series of notes from an instrument, which you will also build. Much of the work of this unit focuses on energy, its transfer, and its conservation. You will need to explore these principles to understand how the components of your radio transmitter work.

You will build on your previous work with electric circuits and the concepts that explain the flow of current, voltage, and resistance. Using these ideas as stepping stones, you will broaden your view of electronics, sound, and communication by examining the concepts of electric power, heat transfer, and electromagnetic radiation.

In each milestone, you will consider how the energy that drives electric devices is transferred or changed as one type of energy is translated into another. At each stage, you should be able to explain how these energy transfers take place. This is the key to understanding how radio communication occurs.

PROJECT MILESTONES

Your unit project is to build the components necessary to establish a working radio station for your classroom. This assignment is divided into three project milestones.

Project Milestone 1 Building a Thumb Piano

You will build a thumb piano to use in your final milestone to transmit a series of notes to an FM receiver. You will also write a short essay that describes the transfers of work and energy that occur from the production of a single note on your thumb piano to the perception of that note by the brain.

Project Milestone 2 Building a Speaker and Microphone

You will build a working speaker and microphone, linking the concepts of electromagnetic induction from your previous work to the principles of how speakers and microphones work. You will explain the energy transfers that take place from playing a note on your thumb piano to the reception of the sound by your ear—tracing the energy transfers through both the speaker and the microphone circuits.

Project Milestone 3 Building and Testing a Radio Transmitter and Operating the Radio Station

You will build a radio transmitter that converts sounds into radio waves. You will then test and adapt your radio "station" for the clearest signal and maximum possible range, and send your thumb piano notes to an FM receiver (and your audience!). You will explain the energy transfers that occur from the playing of a note to the brain's recognition of the note coming from the receiver's speaker.

ACTIVITIES AND ASSIGNMENTS

Your work on this unit project requires an understanding of electricity and circuits. In fact, many of the milestones cannot be fully completed unless you gain familiarity with specific aspects of electricity. As you progress through the unit, you will complete a number of activities and assignments to help you understand the complex and often invisible processes of electricity.

Just as there are three project milestones, the activities and assignments in the unit are organized into three chapters. Each chapter focuses on a different aspect of energy and its transmission.

1. In Chapter 15, you will explore work and energy in a qualitative way. You will explore how humans and animals communicate, and you will build a musical instrument to use in your final milestone. You will also visit an audio specialist.

2. In Chapter 16, you will investigate the quantitative aspects of not only work and energy, but also power in electric circuits and sound. Your work will lead you to an understanding of speakers and microphones, the end product and milestone of this chapter.

3. In Chapter 17, you will put together the components of your classroom radio transmitter. Beginning with a study of the electromagnetic spectrum, you will build an FM receiver and explore the world of radio communication. In your final project, you will build a radio transmitter, and then test it for maximum clarity of sound and range.

Making Music

OVERVIEW

MAKING WAVES

Have you ever dreamed of being a DJ? Ever want to host sports talk radio, perform, or interview TV and movie stars over the airwaves? Well, in this unit you will have the opportunity to build a mini–radio station from the ground up, and then test it, use it, and maximize its range to reach your largest possible audience.

But first, to understand radio you have to understand energy. Not the high-pitched squeal of bad advertising from used-car dealers, but rather the transfer of energy from one form to another. Energy has many identities, forms, and functions. You will focus on how sounds can be transferred from your throat or a musical instrument to a radio receiver in your school building.

In this chapter, you are going to build some simple instruments to help you understand how they make sound and how that sound is transmitted to your ears. This is your first step toward creating the WPTW school radio station.

Your first milestone:

Project Milestone | Building a Thumb Piano

You will build a thumb piano to use in your final milestone to transmit a series of notes to an FM receiver. You will also write a short essay that describes the transfers of work and energy that occur from the production of a single note on your thumb piano to the perception of that note by the brain.

By the end of this chapter, you will have explored the nature of different types of energy, their transfer, and conservation in a qualitative way. The production of sound will be examined as a result of doing work—culminating in the construction of a simple musical instrument—a thumb piano. The thumb piano, modeled after a traditional African percussion instrument called a kalimba, is used during the final milestone of this unit to transmit a simple tune to a receiver.

To help you accomplish Project Milestone One, you will do the following activities:

Activity 15.1 Energy to Spare
You will begin your study of energy by considering a steel ball rolling down a ramp. You then examine how energy can be stored (potential energy) and used in different contexts. Using a balloon rocket, you apply your ideas to relate kinetic and potential energy to the sounds produced by the balloon.

Activity 15.2 Working with Energy and Sound
You will investigate the concepts of energy and work by doing an activity that explores the transfer of work to potential and kinetic energy to produce vibrational (or acoustical) energy. You then learn about these concepts via hands-on activities: creating sounds on stretched rubber bands, creating sounds using bobby pins, and observing a mass oscillating on a spring.

Activity 15.3 Sound Off!
You will explore the concepts of energy transmission through longitudinal waves and then investigate sound frequencies, wavelengths, and velocities of waves with Slinkys and tuning forks. Here you begin to examine the energy pathway for your final project milestone—making a sound into a microphone and transmitting it to a radio receiver.

Activity 15.4 A Visit to an Audio Specalist
You will visit an audio specialist to learn about electronics, sound, and energy in the workplace.

Activity 15.5 Transmitting Sounds
You will learn about conservation of energy and work in a different context—how humans and other members of the animal kingdom receive and transmit sounds. You follow the paths of work and energy transfer involved in producing sound in human speech and receiving sound by the human ear. You then search the Internet to apply the

concepts of wave transmission and wave characteristics to compare the sounds made by animals to those made by humans.

Activity 15.6 Building a Thumb Piano

You will build a musical instrument to perform a 15-second tune or series of notes at the end of the unit. You identify the transfers of work and energy that occur from the moment you produce a note on your thumb piano to the moment the brain recognizes the sound as a note.

ACTIVITY 15.1

Energy to Spare

Getting In Gear

Ever wonder how the music comes out of your radio or your favorite program shows up on your TV? Most kids start out thinking that miniature people are in the radio singing and playing instruments. Even more puzzling are the little people we see on our TV screen. As we grow up, we realize that they couldn't possibly be inside our radio or TV sets. But then how do they appear?

The answers to these questions involve various forms of energy and how one form of energy is converted into another form. This first activity will examine the concept of energy in a qualitative way using a balloon rocket. Experimenting with rockets will help you begin to understand energy, its transfer and conservation.

Getting To Work!

To begin your investigation of energy, you will

1. Read the overview for Unit Five, and discuss as a class the unit project and the outline of work throughout the unit.

2. Share your ideas about energy by responding to the questions your teacher poses.

3. Read the overview scenario and project milestone for Chapter 15, and discuss the scenario with your class.

4. Work in groups and obtain $\boxed{\textbf{Job Sheet 15.1}}$ Thinking about Energy? Follow the directions to build a balloon rocket. You will investigate the relationships among work, sound, and two types of energy—kinetic and potential.

Job Sheet

5. Participate in a class discussion about potential energy and energy conversion.

6. Read Getting the Point: *Work and Energy,* and answer the Focus Questions.

7. Check out Workplace Connection: *Pile Driver Operator* and the Did You Know? reading as time permits.

Wonder about the physics involved when riding your favorite roller coaster? Read concept connection: *Energy Transformation on a Roller Coaster.*

Getting The Point.

Work and Energy

The word *work* means different things to different people. In science, work means that you are applying a force and moving a mass in some direction. When work is done, the object having work done to it gains energy of some kind. Energy gained can be transferred or changed several times before sound or heat energy is produced. Sound is produced when a vibration is created in a *medium* (any material, such as wood, metal, or a rubber balloon).

One way to think about energy is to relate it to movement. A moving object is said to have *kinetic energy*. When a moving object hits a body, the object's energy is transferred to that body. A baseball that has just been hit by a bat has kinetic energy. Moving masses often change their *potential energy* as well. Potential energy is the energy of position and is "stored" for later use. When you lift a hammer, for instance, you have done work (you applied a force straight up on the mass of the hammer), and for a brief moment "stored" it before you let the hammer fall and hit the nail on its head. There are many kinds of potential energy. You know one of them, electric potential energy, by the name *voltage*.

Energy can change from one form to another, but is never created or destroyed. The total amount of energy is always the same. This is the *Law of Conservation of Energy.* Electric circuits provide a way to transfer electric energy to light energy, heat energy, mechanical energy, or sound energy.

Energy transfers occur all around you each day, and the chain of transformations is almost infinite. Only when all things in the universe have the same amount of energy will transformations cease.

Focus Questions

How does a scientist's definition of work differ from your own?

How does kinetic energy differ from potential energy?

What is a medium?

Concept Connection: Energy Transformation on a Roller Coaster

A roller coaster ride is a thrilling experience that involves a wealth of physics. The ride begins with a chain and motor exerting a force on the train, lifting it to the top of a very tall hill. Once the initial work is done, gravity takes over and the remainder of the ride is a symphony of energy transformations (and screams!).

At the top of the hill, the cars possess a huge quantity of potential energy. As the cars drop straight down, they lose much of this potential energy and subsequently gain lots of kinetic energy. Thus, their original potential energy is transformed into kinetic energy (revealed by their high speeds). As the ride continues, the train of cars is continuously losing and gaining height. Each gain in height corresponds to the loss of speed as kinetic energy is transformed into potential energy. Each loss in height corresponds to a gain of speed as potential energy is transformed into kinetic energy.

After a minute or two of breathless excitement and continuous energy transfer, the coaster hits the level surface and brakes must be applied, which convert the remaining kinetic energy into heat, and the ride is done.

Adapted from *"Work and Energy: Energy Transformation on a Roller Coaster."* The Physics Classroom and Mathsoft Education & Engineering, Inc. http://www.physicsclassroom.com/mmedia/energy/ce.html (June 10, 2003)

Workplace Connection: Pile Driver Operator

Pile drivers convert energy from one form to another at construction sites. Work is done on a heavy object that is lifted and then dropped onto other objects in order to drive them into the ground.

JOB DESCRIPTION: PILE DRIVER OPERATOR

Pile drivers work with pile-driving rigs that drive metal, concrete or wood piling into the earth during the early stages of construction. They are usually the first workers at a commercial job site. They drive metal sheet piling to hold back dirt during excavations, drive concrete, metal and wood pilings as part of the foundation system for skyscrapers and drive wood and concrete pilings to hold up docks, wharves and bridges. Some may work on offshore oilrigs as commercial divers involved in underwater construction. Pile drivers work with a variety of hand and portable power tools, and frequently cut, join, and fasten metal construction materials using welding equipment and oxy-acetylene torches.

WORKING CONDITIONS

Pile driving work is very physical and involves climbing, kneeling, lifting, and squatting. Work is done inside and outside, depending on the construction. Travel is often required. Pile drivers work where it is warm and dry, cold and wet, and at depths of 100 feet below or above ground. Pile drivers must be in good health, meet certain strength requirements, be agile and have good hand-eye coordination.

Did You Know?

A common gag purchased at joke stores is a "whoopee cushion." When someone sits on a whoopee cushion, a loud flatulence noise emanates from it. In a balloon, like a whoopee cushion, when we do work by sitting on it, we let the air out and it makes a sound. In a whoopee cushion, all the stored potential energy is converted to sound by giving the air molecules kinetic energy, forcing them to move. What we hear are the collisions of the rubber flaps on the orifice caused by the kinetic energy of those now moving air molecules. Those colliding pieces of rubber vibrate the outside air at the same frequency as the rubber. The kinetic energy of the moving air reaches our ears and is converted to electric energy (still kinetic energy, moving electric charges), and we hear it. We laugh and use even more of our stored potential energy. Laugh more (kinetic energy); eat more (potential energy).

WAGES*

Beginning apprentices start at 60 percent of the journey-level wage. Upon successful completion of required class work and on-the-job hours, wages increase usually every six months, until the journey-level rate is achieved.

LENGTH OF APPRENTICESHIP*

This apprenticeship lasts four years. Apprentices must complete a minimum of 120 related classroom hours per year and 8,000 on-the-job training hours.

MINIMUM QUALIFICATIONS*

Apprenticeship applicants must be at least 18 years of age. In addition, they must provide proof of high school graduation or general education development (GED) equivalent.

*Information refers to the current (2002) apprenticeship standards adopted in the state of Oregon. This information may not apply to other states.

From *"The Oregon Apprenticeship Guide: Pile Driver."* State of Oregon Apprenticeship Standards, June 2002. Copyright © 2002 Bureau of Labor and Industries. Reprinted with permission. http://www.boli.state.or.us/ apprenticeship/piledriver.html (June 1, 2002)

ACTIVITY 15.2

Working with Energy and Sound

Getting In Gear

Picture yourself across the room from a person playing a guitar. She strums the guitar strings with her fingers, and suddenly you hear music. How does that happen? How do the guitar strings make music? Why does one string have a different sound than another? You will create your own sounds with a variety of "instruments" in your classroom.

Getting To Work!

To create sounds of your own on various instruments, you will

1. Participate in a class discussion about sound.

Job Sheet

2. Obtain │ **Job Sheet 15.2** │ **Working with Energy,** and explore the apparatus at each of three stations as directed by your teacher. Follow the instructions on the job sheet, and answer all the questions regarding the stations.

3. Obtain │ **Job Sheet 15.3** │ **Homework for Work.** Answer the questions in class or for homework, as directed by your teacher.

4. Check out Workplace Connection: *Noise in the Workplace* and the Did You Know? reading as time permits.

Ever wonder about the history and acoustics of bells? Read Concept Connection: *Bells Are Ringing.*

Concept Connection: Bells Are Ringing

Bells have been an important part of almost every culture in history. Bells have served as musical instruments, as signaling devices, in religious worship, to communicate, and to sound warnings.

Many ancient Chinese bells, some more than 3000 years old, remain from the time of the Shang and Zhou dynasties. Most of these bells, being oval or almond-shaped, sound two distinctly different notes, depending upon where they are struck. Although small ornamental bells may have existed in India, Assyria, and Egypt as early as 2000 B.C., the bells that remain from these early civilizations do not compare to the ancient Chinese bells in size or in quality.

The art of designing and casting ancient bells reached its peak in China during the Western Zhou (1122-771 B.C.) and Eastern Zhou (770-249 B.C.) dynasties. Most musical bells were manufactured in scaled sets or chimes. Chimes of bells were frequently buried in the tombs of royalty and noblemen, and that is how large numbers of ancient bells have been well preserved through the ages. The most remarkable set of bells discovered to date is the 65-bell set discovered in the tomb of Zeng Hou Yi (Marquis Yi of Zeng) in 1987. These richly-inscribed bells survived in excellent condition since about 433 B.C. due to the tomb filling with water.

After the 3rd century A.D., round temple bells gradually replaced two-tone bells. Many cities placed large bells in towers to announce the time of day. The most famous temple bell in Korea is the magnificent King Songdok bell, cast in 771 A.D. during the Silla dynasty. Standing 3.66 m high, it has a mass of nearly 20,000 kg. The largest known Chinese bell, standing over 4.5 m high, was cast in the 15th century during the reign of the Ming emperor Yongle.

Bells developed as Western musical instruments around the 17th century when bell founders learned how to tune their partials harmonically. The founders in the Low Countries, especially the Hemony brothers (Francois and Pieter) and Jacob van Eyck, took the lead in tuning bells, and many of their fine bells are found in carillons today.

Handbells date back at least several centuries B.C., although tuned handbells of the present-day type were developed in England in the 19th century. In recent years, handbell choirs have become popular in schools and churches, some 40,000 handbell choirs have been reported in the United States alone. Tuned handbells are generally made of cast bronze, which has been the traditional bell material for many centuries.

Demand for handbells of lower and lower pitches has led to the development of bass bells as low as G0 (fundamental frequency of 24.5 Hz). Bronze handbells tuned to this pitch radiate inefficiently, however, since the vibrational waves travel considerably slower in the bells than they do in the air nearby, thus creating a sort of acoustical "short circuit." In order to obtain a higher radiation efficiency and thereby enhance the sound of bass bells, the Malmark Company has created a new bell design using aluminum rather than bronze. These new bells are larger in diameter and radiate much more efficiently than bronze bells, yet they are lighter in weight.

Adapted from *"Acoustics of Eastern and Western Bells, Old and New,"* T.D. Rossing, Popular version 2p MU1, 133rd Meeting, Acoustical Society of America, 1997. Reprinted with permission.

Workplace Connection: Noise in the Workplace

Workplace sounds can be steady (such as the continuous hum from a ventilation system or a computer), intermittent (sound which comes and goes), or impact (sounds of short duration, such as the snap of an electric stapler).

A variety of sounds can be heard in the average office—anything from the sound of a ringing telephone to the background hum of a ventilation system. Some sources of noise can be minimized with minor adjustments. Others, such as the noise from the ventilation system, may require major alterations to building systems.

Sources of equipment-generated noise include telephones, photocopiers, computers, or other office equipment. Equipment-generated noise is usually transient and the sensitivity to equipment sounds varies from person to person. For example, the noise generated by running a photocopier may not annoy the operator, but it may be distracting to people in adjacent work spaces.

If you plan to purchase new office equipment, keep in mind the amount of noise produced. High-quality office equipment should function with a minimum of noise. Some types of equipment (e.g. photocopiers) will produce a lot of noise no matter what model you buy. Noisy equipment should be grouped together in an area away from workstations, preferably in a separate room. Don't place noisy equipment against a hard wall or in a corner as the sound will be reflected back into the workplace.

Practice good maintenance to prevent noise from squeaking chair bearings, door hinges, moving equipment parts and other sources by lubricating them.

Occupant-generated sounds can be a major source of noise in the office. They include in-person as well as telephone conversations, radios, and movement within the office. Occupant-generated sounds can usually be dealt with by no more than a friendly reminder to keep the volume down. Encourage people to speak in lowered voices and to carry on conversations where they will not disturb others.

Music in the workplace, either from piped-in music or from a radio, is sometimes used to mask sounds. Music can provide mental stimulation while performing monotonous tasks that can help to reduce stress levels in the office. Some people, however, find music in the office *intensely* annoying.

From *"Noise and Acoustics: Sources of Noise in the Office."* Copyright © 2002 Canada Safety Council. Reprinted with permission. http://www.safety-council. org/info/osh/noise.htm (June 10, 2003)

Did You Know?

A new analysis of what is believed to be the world's oldest musical instrument has produced a noteworthy result: Neandertals may have used the same seven-note scale that forms the basis of Western music.

Bob Fink, a musicologist in Saskatoon, Canada, analyzed the spacing of holes on a primitive bone flute—a piece of bear thigh bone found in July 1995 by Slovenian archaeologist Ivan Turk in a cave in what was formerly northern Yugoslavia. He concluded that the instrument, which is believed to be more than 43,000 years old, produced four notes that correspond to the third, fourth, fifth, and sixth notes of a minor diatonic scale (one composed of half tones and whole tones).

From *"Neandertals Lived Harmoniously,"* Daily Insight, Academic Press, April 3, 1997. American Association for the Advancement of Science. http://darwin.apnet.com/inscight/04031997/grapha.htm (June 10, 2003)

ACTIVITY 15.3

Sound Off!

Getting In Gear

So what does sound have to do with energy? How does sound get from an instrument to your ear? It all has to do with waves, not the kind you find in the ocean, but sound waves that move through the air. You will play with a Slinky to model sound waves and learn about their properties.

Getting To Work!

To learn about sound waves, you will

1. Discuss with your classmates and teacher how sounds are produced in nature and by musical instruments.

2. Obtain | Job Sheet 15.4 | Hey, That Hertz! Do all three parts of the activity set up by your teacher.

3. Read Getting the Point: *Waves,* and answer the Focus Questions.

4. Obtain | Job Sheet 15.5 | Sound Bytes. Answer the questions in class or for homework, as directed by your teacher.

5. Check out the Did You Know? readings as time permits.

Job Sheet

Job Sheet

Wonder about how sonar locates fish? Read Workplace Connection: *Finding Fish with Sonar.*

Getting The Point

Waves

In this unit, you will create a transmitter that conveys musical notes through space to a receiver. How does this process of transfer occur from the initial work being done to produce the note to its reception on an FM radio? The answer has much to do with *waves.* Waves are disturbances in a medium that carry energy with them as they move through air, solids, liquids, or the vacuum of space. Ocean waves occur when wind works on the water (applying a force over a distance) to create the disturbance. The ocean waves carry this energy vast distances until the waves encounter the shore, where this energy is converted to mechanical energy—the pounding surf. Only two types of waves are important to your project: transverse and longitudinal. Both have some similar characteristics, or properties.

Transverse waves have a crest, the highest point of the wave, and a trough, the lowest point. They are called transverse since the motion of the crests and troughs is at a 90° angle to the direction that the wave moves. Waves are periodic, meaning that the same wave pattern is repeated over and over.

Figure 15.1

Components of a
Transverse Wave

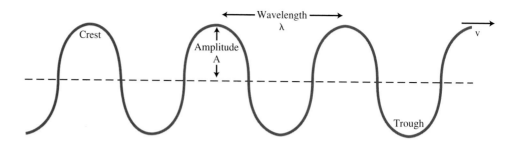

In Figure 15.1, the dotted line represents the flat surface that would exist if there were no waves. The *amplitude* (A) is the distance from this surface to the highest point of the wave. The amplitude determines the intensity of the wave.

The distance between adjacent crests or adjacent troughs is called the *wavelength.* The Greek letter λ (pronounced lambda) is used to denote this measurement.

The *frequency* of a wave is a measure of how many crests pass a given point per second. For instance, if you are standing on the beach and waves are lapping quickly over and over again on your toes, then those waves have a relatively high frequency. If only one wave comes up on the beach per minute, those waves have a relatively low frequency. The letter f is often used to denote the frequency of a wave.

The total *speed,* or *velocity* of a wave equals the wavelength times the frequency ($v = f\lambda$) This means that the speed is equal to the length of one wave times the number of waves that pass a point in 1 second. If the speed of the wave is constant, then as the wavelength increases, the frequency of the wave must decrease and vice versa.

Longitudinal waves are similar to transverse waves, but the energy in the medium moves back and forth in the same direction as the wave moves.

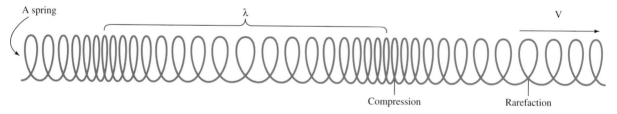

Figure 15.2

Components of a Longitudinal Wave

Instead of having crests, longitudinal waves have *compressions;* instead of troughs, they have *rarefactions.* Wavelength is measured from compression to compression, or from rarefaction to rarefaction. Sound waves are longitudinal in nature. The speed of sound waves varies with temperature and the material through which it travels. In air, sound travels at a rate of 340 meter/second at room temperature.

Focus Questions

What is a wave?

What are two differences between transverse and longitudinal waves?

The amount of energy carried by the wave is related to what feature of the wave?

Workplace Connection: Finding Fish with Sonar

People have been fishing for thousands of years. Every person fishing has had the same problem—finding fish and

Did You Know?

The inventor of the Slinky actually invented an energy conversion gadget.

Like so many other great inventions, the Slinky, a favorite of both kids and physics teachers, was just a grand accident. Richard James, a naval engineer, "discovered" this enduring toy in 1943.

Working to help the war effort, James was developing an anti-vibration device for ship instruments when he knocked over some springs and was fascinated by the way the springs appeared to "walk" down the shelves. James showed his invention to his wife, Betty, who provided the name.

The Jameses took their first batch of 400 Slinkys to Gimbel's department store in Philadelphia during the winter of 1945, right in time for Christmas shopping. They were so desperate to sell the toy, they paid a friend $1 to buy one and start the feeding frenzy. Ninety minutes later, not one Slinky remained. And the rest is Slinky history.

Some other little known facts:

- Slinkys were among the first toys to travel into space.
- During the Vietnam War, U.S. soldiers would toss a Slinky into a tree for use as a makeshift radio antenna.
- If stretched end-to-end, the Slinky toys sold since 1945 (about 250 million) would wrap around the world 126 times.

From ASK YAHOO! *"Who Invented the Slinky?"*
http://ask.yahoo.com/ask/20000606.html (June 10, 2003)

getting them to bite. Sonar is a technological system that transmits sound waves underwater and then receives the reflected waves that bounce off of objects below the ship—in this case, fish. Although sonar can't make the fish bite, it can solve the problem of finding fish. You can't catch them if you're not fishing where they are—and the Lowrance sonar will prove it.

In the late 1950s, Carl Lowrance and his sons Arlen and Darrell began scuba diving to observe fish and their habits. This research, substantiated by local and federal government studies, found that about 90 percent of the fish congregated in 10 percent of the water on inland lakes. As environmental conditions changed, the fish would move to more favorable areas. Their dives confirmed that most species of fish are affected by underwater structure (such as trees, weeds, rocks, and drop-offs), temperature, current, sunlight and wind. These and other factors also influence the location of food (baitfish, algae and plankton). Together, these factors create conditions that cause frequent relocation of fish populations.

During this time, a few people were using large, cumbersome sonar units on fishing boats. Working at low frequencies, these units used vacuum tubes which required car batteries to keep them running. Although they would show a satisfactory bottom signal and large schools of fish, they couldn't show individual fish. Carl and his sons began to conceptualize a compact, battery operated sonar that could detect individual fish. After years of research, development, struggle and simple hard work, a sonar was produced that changed the fishing world forever.

Out of this simple beginning, a new industry was formed in 1957 with the sale of the first transistorized sportfishing sonar. In 1959, Lowrance introduced "The Little Green Box," which became the most popular sonar instrument in the world. All transistorized, it was the first successful sportfishing sonar unit. More than a million were made until 1984, when it was discontinued due to high production costs. We've come a long way since 1957. From "little green boxes" to the latest in sonar and GPS technology, Lowrance continues to lead in the world of sportfishing sonar.

ACTIVITY 15.4

A Visit to an Audio Specialist

Getting In Gear

Who makes a living dealing with sound? Well, other than ear doctors, there are also the people who make equipment for recording studios, speakers for concerts, and other types of audio communication. You are going to visit an audio specialist and see what kind of work he or she does.

Getting To Work!

To explore the workplace of an audio specialist, you will

1. Discuss with your teacher the trip logistics, safety concerns, and behavior suitable for a visit to a site that houses expensive, and sometimes delicate equipment.

2. Obtain │ **Job Sheet 15.6** │ **A Visit to an Audio Specialist,** and go over the questions before you leave on your trip.

3. Take notes during your trip, and complete the job sheet as homework.

4. Read the Getting the Point: *Analog and Digital Audio,* and answer the Focus Questions for homework.

5. Check out the Did you Know? reading as time permits.

6. Write a thank-you letter to your tour leader.

Ever wonder about the acoustics of the special events held during the Super Bowl? Read Workplace Connection: *The Sound of Super Bowl XXXII.*

Job Sheet

Getting The Point.

Analog and Digital Audio

The term analog means something that is similar in function or position. The varying voltage produced by a microphone is analogous to the pressure variations of a sound wave. On a cassette tape, variations in magnetic flux in a metal coating on the tape represent pressure variations in the sound wave. On vinyl records, variations in the width of the groove correspond to the pressure variations. The position along the groove or tape corresponds to time.

In an analog audio system, voltages represent sound pressures. These signals are amplified from the millivolt level (1000th of a volt) produced by microphones, playback heads and phono cartridges by about 1000 times (60dB) to the levels found inside stereo preamps. A power amp boosts the voltage level from the preamp to a loudspeaker, which creates sound waves in the air by vibrating rapidly in response to the audio signal.

DIGITAL AUDIO

In digital audio, the representation of the audio signal is no longer directly analogous to the sound wave. Instead, the value of the signal is sampled at regular intervals by an analog-to-digital (A/D) converter (or ADC), which produces numbers (digits) that represent the value of each sample. This stream of numbers represents a digital audio signal, which can be stored as a computer file and transmitted across a network. In order to listen to a digital audio signal, it must be converted to analog by a digital-to-analog (D/A) converter (or DAC). In most home stereo systems, the D/A conversion takes place inside the CD player. Computer sound cards, MiniDisc recorders and DATs have both A/D converters (for recording) and D/A converters (for playback). Many home systems have a combination of digital and analog components, but all audio systems end with analog signals at the speakers or headphones.

The sampling rate is how many times per second the voltage of the analog signal is measured. CD audio is sampled at a rate of 44,100 times per second (44.1 kHz). DAT (Digital Audio Tape) supports sampling rates of 32, 44.1 and 48 kHz. Other commonly used sampling rates are 22.05 kHz and 11.025 kHz. The sampling rate must be at least twice as high as the highest frequency to be reproduced. The range of human hearing is roughly from 20 to 2,000 Hz, so a sampling rate of at least 40 kHz is needed to reproduce the full range.

Higher sampling rates allow the use of filters with a more gradual roll-off. This reduces phase shift, which can affect the stereo image at higher frequencies. The 44.1 kHz sampling rate for CDs was chosen to allow headroom for filters and other types of signal processing. MPEG AAC and DVD Audio support rates up to 96 kHz.

RESOLUTION

The resolution of a digital signal is the range of numbers that can be assigned to each sample. CD audio uses 16 bits, which provides a range of binary values from 0 to 65,534 (216). The binary value of 0000000000000000 (zero) corresponds to -32,768 (the lowest possible level), and the value 1111111111111111 (65,535) corresponds to 32,767 (the highest possible level). Higher resolution increases the dynamic range and reduces quantization distortion and background noise.

QUANTIZATION

Quantization is the process of selecting whole numbers to represent the voltage level of each sample. The A/D converter must select a whole number that is closest to the signal level at the instant it's sampled. This produces small rounding errors that cause distortion. Quantization distortion increases at lower levels because the signal is using a smaller portion of the available dynamic range, so any errors are a greater percentage of the signal. A key advantage of audio encoding schemes, such as MP3, is that more bits can be allocated to low-level signals to reduce quantization errors.

DITHERING

A process called dithering introduces random noise into the signal to spread out the effects of quantization distortion and make it less noticeable. Some audiophiles don't like the notion of noise that is deliberately added to a signal, but the advantages of digital audio are so great that the end result is still better than most analog systems.

CLIPPING

Levels in a digital audio signal are usually expressed in dB, measured by their relationship to 0 dB, the highest possible level. One of the rules of digital audio is that a signal can never exceed 0 dB. If the level of a signal is raised too much, the peaks will be clipped at the 0 dB level. Clipping causes extreme distortion and should be avoided at all costs.

BIT-RATES

The term "bit-rate" refers to how many bits (1s and 0s) are used each second to represent the signal. The bit-rate for digital audio is expressed in thousands of bits per second (kbps) and correlates directly to the file size and sound quality. Lower bit-rates result in smaller file sizes but poorer sound quality, and higher bit-rates result in better quality but larger files. The bit-rate of uncompressed audio can be calculated by multiplying the sampling rate by the resolution (8-bit, 16-bit, etc.) and the number of channels. For example, CD Audio (or a WAV file extracted from a CD) has a sampling rate of 44,100 times per second, a resolution of 16 bits and two channels.

SIGNAL-TO-NOISE RATIO

The signal-to-noise ratio is the ratio of the background noise (hiss, hum and static) level to the highest level that can be reproduced. Each additional bit of resolution corresponds to an increase of 6 dB in signal-to-noise ratio. Audio CDs achieve about a 90 dB signal-to-noise ratio.

ENCODING

Encoding is the process of converting uncompressed digital audio to a compressed format such as MP3. The algorithm used in the encoding (and decoding) software is referred to as a codec—as in coding/decoding. There is often more than one codec for a particular format, and different codecs can vary widely in quality and speed, even for the same format.

ADVANTAGES OF DIGITAL AUDIO

For years, audiophiles and engineers have debated the merits of digital audio versus high-end analog systems, and to this day, there are audiophiles who swear by their analog systems. Digital audio has emerged as the winner by most accounts, but it's still useful to understand the advantages of digital versus analog audio, because many audio systems contain a mix of digital and analog components. The advantages of digital audio can be summed up as follows: wider dynamic range, increased resistance to noise, better copy ability and the ability to use error correction to compensate for wear and tear. Many types of digital media, such as CDs and MiniDiscs, are also more durable than common analog media, such as vinyl records and cassette tapes.

Adapted from *"The MP3 and The Internet Audio Handbook: A Digital Audio Primer,"* by Bruce Fries. Copyright © 2000 TeamCom Books. Reprinted with permission. http://www.teamcombooks.com/mp3handbook/11.htm (June 10, 2003)

Focus Questions

What represents differences in sound pressures in analog systems?

What is meant by sampling rate?

What is meant by signal-to-noise ratio?

List four advantages of digital over analog audio.

Workplace Connection: The Sound of Super Bowl XXXII

Super Bowl XXXII in San Diego delivered something most of its predecessors have not: a memorable, closely fought game not decided until the final minute and unsurpassed audio quality.

The stellar halftime production featured a tribute to Motown music delivered to the more than 70,000 in attendance at San Diego's Qualcomm Park and hundreds of millions of television viewers by an intricate, high-fidelity audio system. The system was designed and provided by ATK/Audiotek of Burbank, California, a performance audio company that's no stranger to large scale, mega-events.

In addition to the halftime production, ATK also handled pre-game and on-field trophy presentations, all without a hitch. An all-star team of engineers and technicians were under the direction of ATK's Executive In Charge Mike Stahl and Chief Engineer Scott Harmala. They assembled a system of top components that was commensurate with the important, critical nature of the live event.

Months of planning and coordination go into assembling the staff and equipment, yet it all comes down to three weeks, a time as frenzied as the media hype leading up to the big game. And the entire production, including the massive sound system, had to be completely set on the field within five minutes of the end of the game's first half.

"I think a lot of the success that we experienced had to do with the amount of planning we put into this event," explains Scott Harmala, chief engineer for ATK. "By the time the volunteers arrived, three days prior to the game, the entire system had been up and running for over a week. It had been checked and doublechecked a hundred times over. Having that accomplished allowed us to concentrate on making sure that the production end of the event was well-rehearsed and carried out in the allotted time frame."

PLANNING MAKES PERFECT

ATK began working on the Super Bowl project before being awarded the contract. The final bid entailed many hours of prep work that, according to Harmala, provided them with invaluable insight to the job before it actually started. In October the work began in earnest.

Between October and January 5, the scheduled departure date for San Diego, ATK specified the distributed sound reinforcement system, designed the mobile carts for the system, and worked out the broadcast logistics. Routing and cabling schemes, right down to accounting for each and every pin connect, were meticulously documented as well.

"Our goal was to show up with all of the major components ready to roll," adds Harmala. "All of the time spent diagramming really paid off. We had all of the cable runs and patches set up three days ahead of schedule."

The next hurdle was to assemble 18 mobile sound reinforcement carts for the distributed system. When outlining the system, Entertainment System Designer Pat Baltzell specified a loudspeaker that could evenly cover all areas of the stadium. After careful evaluation, they decided upon L-ACOUSTIC V-DOSC cabinets. When arrayed in a group of four, V-DOSC cabinets are designed to cover larger areas with very little variation in frequency response and SPL—exactly what ATK was looking for.

"The V-DOSC boxes can be arrayed and arranged easily," adds Baltzell. "They have excellent sound characteristics and are light enough to simplify the mobile aspect of the system."

QSC Audio PowerLight 4.0 amplifiers were chosen to power the system because of their sonic quality and reliability. Their lower than average weight was an additional plus that helped to keep the carts as light as possible making moving them that much easier. The PowerLight 4.0 amplifiers were rack-mounted on each cart with the V-DOSC arrays. In addition, one to two ATK proprietary M5 cabinets were securely affixed to the carts to provide monitor coverage for the performers on the field during pre- and half-time entertainment.

10 DAYS TO SUPER BOWL DAY

With the cabling in place and the mobile sound reinforcement carts ready to roll, it was time to tie it all together. Given its location, one of the stadiums baseball dugouts was the most convenient location for the entertainment FOH (Front of House) and monitor mix positions to tie into. Quickly converted into the central cable room, the dugout was also where half of an audio distribution system made up of QSC Audio's RAVE (Routing Audio Via Ethernet) as well as the main Telex intercom communications systems and more than 20 Aphex Model 120A servo-balanced distribution amplifiers.

The RAVE system provided a simple way of routing 64 channels audio via standard Fast Ethernet and fiber optic cable to the other half of the RAVE system located in the broadcast truck. The distance to the truck, located at the ATK compound in the stadium parking lot, stipulated the use of fiber as the transport medium. The full 64 channels of audio were utilized with 40 channels of audio sent from the stadium cable room to the broadcast truck and 24 channels of audio playback returning to the cable room. Sixteen of the playback channels were then routed to the FOH so Baltzell could re-mix the audio specifically for the stadium. The nature of the RAVE system also helped to eliminate potential ground loop problems which could have introduced hum and noise into the system. Instead, the sonic quality of the sound reinforcement system remained superb.

"The RAVE system made providing audio playback and broadcast feeds easy," notes Harmala. "We had one single strand of fiber running from point A to point B instead of multiple cable runs. Because fiber can carry up to 64 channels, it gave us the flexibility to provide Pat with what he needed to make the system sound as good as possible."

The Aphex Model 120A servo-balanced distribution amplifiers played another key component in the distribution of audio signal. Servo-balanced by design, each output of the 120A also has its own amplifier and level control for maximum versatility and isolation. In totality, more than 90 Aphex 120As were used throughout the system. In order to minimize the potential of a line split affecting the entire signal chain, ATK assigned every split signal to a channel on a 120A.

Communication distribution was equally important in an event of this size. The communications systems were also housed in the dugout. A mix of a Telex RTS Adam CS 64 x 64 digital matrix system coupled to a custom VMA 20wire dial up and distribution system allowed for conventional beltpacks and headsets distributed throughout the stadium in key locations. The Telex RTS Communications system allowed all key members of the production to communications as needed. The intercom crew, which consisted of John Arenas, Mike Mason and Dave Free, along with the support Telex RTS, were vital parts of the success and smooth operation of the event.

John Arenas, intercom designer for Super Bowl XXXII and owner of Vista Manufacturing Alternatives (VMA), says, "One of the most important aspects when deciding which intercom system to use for Super Bowl XXXII was reliability and ease of use. The system also needed to be capable of integrating 2-wire, 4-wire, 2 way radios and NBC facility interfacing while still remaining transparent to the operator. The Telex RTS product line and ADAM system performed excellent under these conditions."

THE MIX POSITIONS

Unlike most live entertainment events, the Super Bowl system consists of five mix positions—entertainment FOH, stadium FOH, monitor and two playback positions. In addition to being the system designer, Baltzell also performed the duties of FOH engineer.

"I chose the Yamaha PM3500 because I needed a reliable, quiet console in a reduced size," notes Baltzell. "It has all of the features, improved headroom and signal-to-noise ratio as the PM4000, but it fit the limited space I had to work with much better."

Baltzell was referring to the 6′ × 7′ platform built above a stairwell at the 36-yard line for FOH use. Located about 75 feet from the field, the platform positioned Baltzell in the sound field but did not take up any of the valuable seats. In addition to the 52-channel PM3500, the FOH position was also home to ten Aphex Model 661 Tube Compressor/Limiters and two Aphex Model 106 Easyrider Four-Channel Compressors, all for use on live vocals. Four Klark Teknik DN410 Parametric Equalizers assisted in equalizing the entertainment system.

A Yamaha PM4000M-52 monitor console, handled by engineer Mike Parker, was used to mix monitors for all of the entertainment foldback needs. Positioned on the AFC 50-yard line just above field level, the board was chosen for its versatility.

"The board is great in this situation because it has a lot of outputs, so you can create different assignments for different acts and not be limited to a certain number of auxes to work with," explained Mike Parker, monitor engineer for the event. "It is very flexible and quite easy to use."

The Yamaha PM4000M is equipped with 52 inputs and 22 outputs, as well as built-in parametric input and output EQ that Parker was familiar with and assisted greatly in cutting back on outboard gear. Again, space was at a premium, so the less gear required, the better. Other equipment utilized at the monitor position included six Garwood in-ear monitoring systems paired up with six Aphex Model 720 Dominator II peak limiters, two Klark Teknik DN3600 programmable graphic equalizers and two Klark Teknik DN360 graphic equalizers.

Largely in deference to television, the vast majority of entertainment audio for the production was set to tape. The playback positions were located in two production trucks situated on the ATK compound. Le Mobile was where all pre-game entertainment, national anthem, game and post-game playback originated. Andrew Waterman, veteran of several Super Bowls and other large-scale live events, manned the Le Mobile truck. From there, he not only provided the audio playback, which was sent to the central cabling room, entertainment system and monitor system, but also sent the mix directly to the NBC broadcast truck as well as other organizations requiring live broadcast feeds.

Waterman's final mix featured an Aphex Model 2020 FM Pro. Designed for FM processing, the 2020 has features that make it equally as valuable in mastering, studio and PA applications. The pre-game show tape was unique in that it was actually mastered in the stadium while listening to the entertainment sound system. Using the 2020 as a flat processor, Waterman utilized the wideband leveling, 4-band compressions and split band peak limiting features for the final show mix. All audio channels were eventually routed through Aphex Model 120A servo-balanced distribution amplifiers before leaving Le Mobile.

The second playback position, located in the second truck on the ATK compound, was the source of the audio playback for the half-time entertainment. Ed Green, with the assistance of a Yamaha PM3500 console, a plethora of outboard gear, and an assortment of Aphex signal processing equipment, provided a MoTown mix that sounded like the real thing.

IT TAKES TWO TO TANGO

One of the biggest stumbling blocks ATK encountered was tying into the existing stadium audio system. Not only was it incomplete in some areas but also in less than optimal shape. Although the stadium system would not be used for any of the entertainment, it would still play an important role in game announcements. As a result, ATK re-timed all of the delay systems, some boxes had to be replaced and, in some areas, loudspeakers had to be installed from scratch.

Once the system was primed, Stadium Sound System Engineer Dan Schipper was given the task of coordinating the stadium system with the entertainment system.

"For our own peace of mind, we directly by-passed the front end of the stadium system and tied directly into their drive racks," explained Harmala. "This gave us better drive and total control of their system."

Did You Know?

Loudness is subjectively how we perceive different sound intensities. The sound intensity of a jet taking off 200 feet away is about 120dB SPL (decibel sound pressure level), or a million times more intense than the threshold of hearing. The sound intensity of rustling leaves is about 20dB SPL, or 10 times higher than the threshold of hearing. The sound of the jet is 100,000 times more intense than the rustling leaves (100dB). We actually perceive the jet to be about 1000 times louder than rustling leaves rather than 100,000 times louder.

Adapted from *"The MP3 and The Internet Audio Handbook: A Digital Audio Primer,"* by Bruce Fries. Copyright © 2000 TeamCom Books. Reprinted with permission. http://www.teamcombooks.com/mp3handbook/11.htm (June 10, 2003)

Schipper used a Soundcraft Series V console and a large assortment of Aphex signal processing gear to optimize the system. When game day rolled around, both systems were working together seamlessly.

GAME DAY

Super Bowl Sunday dawned a beautiful sunny day in San Diego and all systems were primed and ready to roll. The entire event was performed without a hitch and the audio systems were superb.

"On game day we were ready," notes Harmala. "After all of the hours spent detailing, planning, practicing and implementing—there wasn't a stone left unturned. Even the over 100 volunteers that assisted in setting up the performance stages and sound reinforcement system were ready, and it all showed. It was a great game and a great event."

Note: Because of the performance and superior sound quality provided by Audiotek at Super Bowl XXXII, the NFL awarded Super Bowl XXXIII to them in January 1998.

From *"Major Audio Players Assist at Super Bowl XXXII."* Copyright © 1998 QSC Audio Products Incorporated. Reprinted with permission of QSC Audio Products Inc. http://www.qscaudio.com/press/in_news/sprbowl.htm (June 16, 2003)

ACTIVITY 15.5

Transmitting Sounds

Getting In Gear

Y ou have seen how rubber bands, bobby pins, and tuning forks produce sounds. How are sounds produced in human speech? How are they transmitted through the air to the human ear? Most of the answers come from a simple three-word phrase—transfer of energy.

You will explore how the energy contained in a wave, coming from a source like your voice, is translated into a recognizable sound by your ears, and finally by your brain.

Getting To Work!

T o explore how sound is transmitted, you will

1. Discuss with your teacher and classmates how humans and other animals make sounds. How do humans hear sounds?

2. Obtain **Job Sheet 15.7** **Hearing and Making Sounds: A Transfer of Energy.**

Job Sheet

3. Read Getting the Point: *Part A—Hearing the Sounds,* and answer the question on your job sheet.

4. Read Getting the Point: *Part B—Speaking the Sounds,* and answer the questions in Part 2 on your job sheet.

5. Work in groups of four. Obtain **Job Sheet 15.8** Transmitting Sounds by **Land and Sea.** Follow the directions on the job sheet to investigate how sounds are made by four different animal species.

Job Sheet

6. Obtain a piece of white tagboard or butcher paper from your teacher. Draw a picture of your animal, and add the answers to Step 2, Questions a-g on Job Sheet 15.8 to your picture in some organized and legible way.

7. Review your summary posters, and discuss the similarities and differences among your animals' methods of communication.

8. Check out the Did You Know? readings as time permits.

Worried about occupations that could jeopardize your hearing? Read Workplace Connection: *Hearing Loss in the Workplace.*

Getting The Point.

Part A—Hearing the Sounds

The first stop for sound waves once they are inside your head is the tympanic membrane, also called the eardrum. The eardrum is too far inside your ear for you to see it, although a doctor can with an instrument called an otoscope. When the sound waves that were collected by the external ear strike the tympanic membrane, the membrane moves back and forth. The sound waves are now converted back to vibrations. Since the tympanic membrane touches the middle ear, the membrane's movement sends the vibrations to the middle ear.

The middle ear is a cavity that contains the ossicles—three small bones called the hammer (malleus), anvil (incus), and stirrup (stapes). The vibrations travel from the hammer, to the anvil, and then to the stirrup. The stirrup is the final part of the middle ear. When the vibrations reach the stirrup, they are then transferred to the oval window, which separates the middle and inner ear.

The vibrations finally reach the last part of the ear, the cochlea. The cochlea makes up the inner ear and looks a little bit like a snail because of its coiled tube. The cochlea is filled with fluid, and the vibrations now pass through fluid instead of through air. Several parts make up the cochlea, but the part that we are most concerned with for the purposes of hearing is the organ of Corti. The organ of Corti is made up of hair cells, also known as cilia. When the vibrations that have moved from the oval window to the inner ear strike the cilia, these hair cells bend. Different hair cells are stimulated, depending on the frequency of the vibrations. Therefore, based on the music you are listening to, the teacher who is complimenting you, or your friend who is talking to you, different hair cells will move.

At this point, the mechanical force of the vibrations is converted into electric impulses. The cilia are next to a nerve called the cochlear nerve. When the cilia bend, electric, or nerve impulses begin in the cochlear nerve, and then travel to the brain. These electric impulses are sent to the brain via neurons, the major transportation system in the nervous system.

Figure 15.3
Diagram of a Human Ear

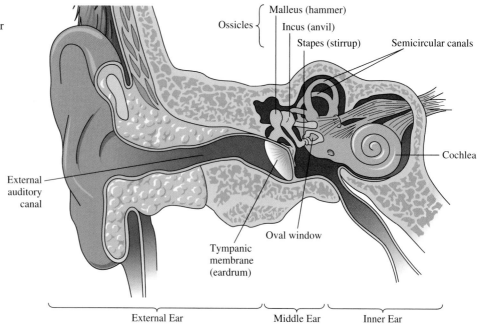

Ossicles { Malleus (hammer)
Incus (anvil)
Stapes (stirrup)

Semicircular canals

Cochlea

External auditory canal

Oval window

Tympanic membrane (eardrum)

External Ear   Middle Ear   Inner Ear

Getting The Point.

Part B—Speaking the Sounds

You are playing basketball and want one of your friends to pass you the ball. How are you able to communicate this? One way is by yelling over to her, "Pass the ball," or "I'm free . . . over here." How do you create these sounds so that your friend knows what you want her to do? These sounds are produced thanks to your respiratory and nervous systems.

Before you even form the words that eventually come out of your mouth, your brain has been at work sending messages from one lobe to another, and from the brain to the rest of the body. These messages are sent via neurons that transmit nerve impulses. A nervous impulse is the transmission of an electric charge. Three parts of your brain are involved with the production of speech and the transmission of messages about the formation of words. After hearing or reading something to which you want to respond, Wernicke's area, in the temporal region of your brain, sends a nerve impulse to Broca's area, located in the frontal lobe. From Broca's area, impulses are sent to the primary motor cortex, which initiates the mechanical movements necessary for speech.

The primary motor cortex controls the human sound production system that is responsible for the mechanical movements of speech. Included in the human sound production system are the lungs, trachea (windpipe), larynx (containing the vocal cords), throat, mouth, nose, and lips. The larynx, throat, mouth, and lips are grouped together and are considered the vocal tract. Once the brain has relayed information to the human sound production system, how do you actually make words? The beginning of a sound starts in the lungs, as air is mechanically pushed through the lungs to the rest of the body. The primary motor cortex controls the lungs through nervous impulses and forces air in the

Figure 15.4
Human Vocal Chords

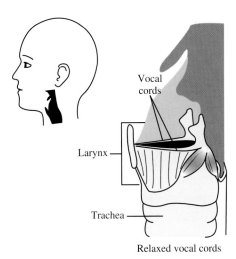

Vocal cords

Vocal cords

Larynx

Trachea

Relaxed vocal cords

Tensed vocal cords

lungs to go through the trachea and then to the larynx. The air that began in the lungs, reaches the larynx and causes the vocal cords to vibrate back and forth. These vibrations create sound waves.

The type of sound produced depends on three factors: pitch, loudness, and word control. The pitch of the sound waves is controlled by the tension of the vocal cords. Increasing the tension in the vocal cords creates a high pitch. If the vocal cords are more relaxed, lower pitches can be produced. If you have ever played with a rubber band to make sounds, you know that the more tense the rubber band is, the higher the pitch. If the rubber band is very loose, it makes a low sound. This is exactly the same as with your vocal cords. In addition to controlling pitch, you may wish to control the loudness of what you are saying. For example, if you were in the library, you would need to speak much more softly than if you were on the basketball court. Fortunately, you can control how loudly you speak by changing the force of the air that is passing through your vocal cords. To speak very loudly, your lungs need to send very strong currents of air to your larynx. The air sent when you want to speak quietly enters the vocal tract with much less force.

In addition to pitch and loudness, you need to control what words the sound waves make. To control the sound waves and to

Did You Know?

How do big brown bats avoid crashing into objects when they are searching for food?

This bat utilizes echolocation to avoid obstacles and to capture flying insect prey. It can track insects into vegetation and intercept them while also avoiding the obstacles vegetation may present. These bats emit volleys of calls through their open mouths. The duration of each call and interval between calls varies depending on whether the bat is in search, approach, attack, or terminal phase. They are able to get acoustic images by integrating information from echoes in relation to their outgoing calls.

Adapted from *"Eptesicus fuscus: Big Brown Bat,"* by Michael Mulheisen and Kathleen Berry. Animal Diversity Web. The University of Michigan Museum of Zoology. http://animaldiversity.ummz. umich.edu/accounts/eptesicus/e._fuscus$narrative.html (June 10, 2003)

There is general agreement in the scientific community that hearing is probably the primary sense of whales, dolphins, and other marine species, as vitally important to them as seeing is to us. Most marine mammals depend on sound as they hunt for food, detect predators, find mates, and keep their herds together in the darkness of the sea. For the great whales and others, much of this activity takes place in the low frequencies, in the band below 1000 Hertz. Unfortunately, that part of the spectrum is also occupied by some of the loudest human sources of sound.

The impact that one of these sources can have on an animal depends partly on its distance. At close range a powerful sound can cause tissue in the lungs, ears, or other parts of the body to rupture and hemorrhage. Farther away, the same sound can induce temporary or permanent hearing loss. And at even greater distances, it can affect behavior, leading animals to swim off course, or abandon habitat, or stop vocalizing, or turn aggressive. In addition, any loud noise has the potential to drown out other sounds—calves, mates, predators—around the same frequency, a phenomenon known as "masking."

From *"Sounding The Depths: Supertankers, Sonar, and The Rise of Undersea Noise,"* by Michael Jasny. Natural Resources Defense Council, 1999. http://www.nrdc.org/wildlife/marine/sound/exec.asp (June 10, 2003)

create words, you change the shape of different parts of your vocal tract, including your mouth, tongue, and lips. If you were not able to convert the sound waves into the words you wished to produce, no one would be able to understand if you wanted the basketball, a ride to the movies, or a new pair of sneakers. With the help of the primary motor cortex, which controls the vocal tract, you can form the words successfully, which started simply as thoughts in the Wernicke's area of your brain.

Workplace Connection: Hearing Loss in the Workplace

The kinetic energy of moving parts in many machines is converted into the kinetic energy of air molecules resulting in sounds that may produce hearing losses in the workplace.

Work-related hearing loss continues to be a critical workplace safety and health issue. The National Institute for Occupational Safety and Health (NIOSH) and the occupational safety and health community named hearing loss one of the 21 priority areas for research in the next century. Noise-induced hearing loss is 100 percent preventable but once acquired, hearing loss is permanent and irreversible. Therefore, prevention measures must be taken by employers and workers to ensure the protection of workers' hearing.

Approximately 30 million workers are exposed to hazardous noise on the job and an additional nine million are at risk for hearing loss from other agents such as solvents and metals.

Noise-induced hearing loss is one of the most common occupational diseases and the second most self-reported occupational illness or injury. Industry specific studies reveal:

- 44% of carpenters and 48% of plumbers reported that they had a perceived hearing loss.
- 90% of coal miners will have a hearing impairment by age 52 (compared to 9% of the general population); 70% of male, metal/nonmetal miners will experience a hearing impairment by age 60.

While any worker can be at risk for noise-induced hearing loss in the workplace, workers in many industries have higher exposures to dangerous levels of noise. Industries with high numbers of exposed workers include: agriculture; mining; construction; manufacturing and utilities; transportation; and military.

Adapted from *"Work-Related Hearing Loss."* Centers for Disease Control and Prevention. http://www.cdc.gov/niosh/hpworkrel.html? (June 10, 2003)

ACTIVITY 15.6

Building a Thumb Piano

Getting In Gear

Time is getting short; your radio transmitter is slated to begin operation for the first time about a month from now. For the inaugural performance transmitted from your station to your audience, you will play a short tune on a musical instrument called a kalimba, or thumb piano. You will construct the instrument and compose a 15-second tune for your big debut.

Getting To Work!

To complete Project Milestone One, you will

1. Obtain **Job Sheet 15.9** Building a Thumb Piano.

2. Read Getting the Point: *The Thumb Piano* and answer the Focus Questions.

3. Discuss safety issues with your teacher.

4. Gather all necessary materials and build the thumb piano.

5. Place your name(s) on the bottom of your piano, and give it to your teacher to store. You will need it to complete your final milestone.

6. Check out Workplace Connection: *Yamaha Internships* and the Did You Know? reading as time permits.

7. Review the concepts and answer the questions in What Have You Learned? for homework.

Job Sheet

Ever wonder about what's "electric" in an electric guitar? Read Concept Connection: *How Does an Electric Guitar Work?*

The Thumb Piano

The thumb piano is one of many instruments developed in African cultures. Some native African instruments allow solo harmonization, although harmony in African music serves only as an embellishment or variation to the given theme. The most sophisticated of these primitive instruments is the sanza, or mbira in Zimbabwe.

The mbira is a popular African instrument. Particularly in Zimbabwe, the mbira is used as a solo instrument as well as to accompany other musicians and dancers. Although it is also known as a "thumb piano," because one uses their thumbs to pluck the six metal strips that are keyed to particular notes, the mbira is actually in the percussion family. The mbira consists of a number of split cane metal tongues (10 or more) over a wooden resonator; the tongues are supported with a lateral bar. The other ends are free to be plucked with the thumbs.

The metal keys are plucked with the thumbs, or with thumbs and fingers. Often, the thumb-piano is made from old spoon handles, bicycle spokes or spring wire that is cut and hammered to the desired shape.

There is a variety of similar instruments in different regions of Africa. The appropriated names are: e.g. kalimba in Kenya, ikembe in Rhuanda, and likembe in the Congo.

The kalimba is made from a board box or calabash: wooden or metal keys are attached to the top. The kalimba is known as a lamellaphone in Eastern Central and South West Africa.

Descriptions and pictures of thumb pianos as well as a wide variety of African instruments can be found at the following web site.

Focus Questions

Is a kalimba more like a piano or a snare drum?

How many notes are played on a typical thumb piano?

Concept Connection: How Does an Electric Guitar Work?

In the construction of "electric guitars," there are essentially two main technologies—both very effective and widely utilized. The Fender company is famous for their "single coil" pickup, a coil of lacquered copper wire wound around 6 small cylinder magnets, strategically placed under each of a guitar's six strings. As a string vibrates, the vibrations "interfere" with the magnetic flux "lines" of each magnet, changing the field and inducing a current analagous to the string's motion.

The system widely used by Gibson uses the so-called "humbucking" pick ups, so called because they combat the transmission of hum and other "airborne" noise in the audio output. Humbuckers are two single coil pickups, placed side by side in a yoke, wired in series, but one is wired clock-wise and the other counter-clockwise. The magnetic poles (two for each) are also situated so as to present opposite polarities. Therefore, the outputs are actually in phase with each other, but because of the wiring and magnet polarity, the noise that may be on the audio output is cancelled. (Note that + polarity plus − polarity, when combined in equal proportion, equals phase cancellation.) What happens is that the audio, which initially was out of phase, is returned to proper phase, while the noise which had been in positive phase on both outputs, is phase reversed, causing removal of the noise, with no audible effect on the audio output.

In practical use, an amplifier is usually called upon to output relatively small amounts of power (on average in the less than 5 Watt range, often less than 1 Watt). But the sudden dynamic nature of live music or digitally encoded music makes it necessary for an amplifier to provide huge amounts of power in a very short period of time. Measured in milliseconds, this time is specified as an amplifier's "slew rate"—how fast, and at what amount of distortion the amplifier can respond. Without this capability, high quality sound would be impossible. A perceived increase of 10 dB in amplitude, generally perceived by most people as "twice as loud" requires 10 times more amplifier power.

In the "live performance" world, every sound person always carries redundant equipment, ready to go "on line" in moments. Guitarists usually also have duplicate instruments on stage with them.

Just as an aside, it has become very common for a sound company working a rock concert in a large arena, to provide more than 100dB of Sound Pressure Level (SPL) in the audience. This level of volume requires a large amount of amplifier power, but in order to not completely obliterate the audience's ears, it must be very low in distortion, not an easy task. Clubs often provide in excess of 120 dB in the venue; this certainly would be considered an OSHA violation, requiring proper ear protection.

Leon Janikian, Associate Professor of Music, Northeastern University. Reprinted with permission.

Workplace Connection: Yamaha Internships

Companies that manufacture musical instruments offer a wide variety of career opportunities. Examples include the internships at the Yamaha Company.

At Yamaha, interns are responsible for a wide range of duties and projects including: data management, product research, inventory management, editing printed publications, designing brochures, ads, and promotional flyers, analyzing industry trends, and helping to manage workshops, clinics, and institutes. Weekly seminars provide interns with the chance to learn about all operations of a musical instrument manufacturing and marketing facility, including: product design, production, quality control, shipping, accounting, and customer service.

The piano, so popular today among musicians all over the world, is only the last in a long series of keyboard instruments used in the civilized world for centuries. The trouble with all the predecessors of the piano, like the harpsichord or clavichord, was that they could not produce dynamic changes, but always sounded at the same level of loudness. That's because their strings were plucked rather than being struck with a hammer. The piano was invented by Bartolomeo Cristofori in Italy in 1709. It had only four octaves, but it embodied the principle that when you struck a key, that threw a hammer at the string and you could adjust loudness and softness by how hard you struck. Hence it was called a *fortepiano,* Italian for loud and soft. Since then, countless improvements have been made, such as increasing range to seven and a half octaves and adding pedals to sustain the notes or to dampen and soften the sound. We call it *pianoforte* to distinguish it from the earlier version, and of course, *piano* for short. But progress never stops. Today, the electronic keyboard is used widely in concert halls as well as in pop recordings. What's next?

An internship is a valuable "calling card" for a career in any field. Former Yamaha interns have gone on to take important positions with some of the leading companies in the music industry.

What are the qualifications?

Yamaha seeks outstanding candidates for its internship program, recognized as one of the most innovative in the music industry.

For internships in music marketing, interested applicants should be completing their senior year or already possess a college degree, and have an exceptional academic record in either music, music education, music business, or a combination thereof.

Candidates should also possess:

- Outstanding spoken and written communication skills
- An adaptive personality; enjoy working with many people in different situations
- Creative problem solving abilities
- A working knowledge of computers, Macintosh and/or IBM platforms
- Experience with a variety of software including: Microsoft Word, Excel, PowerPoint, Pagemaker, QuarkXpress

What Have You Learned?

Work. Work is the act of applying a force to an object and moving it from one point to another. When work is done on an object, energy is transferred from one form to another.

Kinetic energy. Kinetic means "of motion." Kinetic energy is the energy of an object by virtue of its motion.

Potential energy. The potential energy of an object or a system is the energy that is stored and has the potential to be released to do work.

Voltage. Voltage is a measure of electric potential energy, such as the energy stored in a battery.

Law of Conservation of Energy. The total amount of energy of a system always remains the same. Energy can change from one form to another within the system, but is never created or destroyed.

Frequency. The frequency of a wave is the number of oscillations executed per second within that wave.

Wave. A wave is a general term for a disturbance in a medium, such as a sound (wave) in air (medium).

Transverse wave. Transverse waves are created when the oscillations of the wave occur at right angles to the direction of motion of the wave as in a water wave.

Longitudinal wave. Longitudinal waves are created when the oscillations of the wave occur parallel to the direction of motion, as in a sound wave.

General wave equation. The equation, velocity = frequency × wavelength ($v = f\lambda$), governs all types of waves, both transverse and longitudinal.

CONCEPT QUESTIONS

1. If you push on a wall with a force of 50 newtons for an hour, why, according to physics, do you do no "work" on the wall?

2. Describe the kinetic and potential energy of a pendulum after the initial work is done to set it in motion.

3. Why is an inflated balloon a good example of a system with potential energy?

4. Describe how you would find the frequency of the ocean waves at the beach.

5. How are the words *crest, trough, rarefaction,* and *compression* related?

6. Explain why there is a time delay between the time you see a flash of lightning and the time you hear the clap of thunder that results from a strike.

Continued

1. When a moving car slowly stops without braking, its kinetic energy is
   a. transferred to potential energy.
   b. lost.
   c. changed to heat energy due to friction.
   d. transferred to the driver.

2. The time required for the sound waves produced by a 512 Hertz tuning fork ($v = 340$ m/sec) to travel 20 meters is
   a. 0.20 second.
   b. 2.9 seconds.
   c. 17 seconds.
   d. 0.059 second.

3. It takes 5 seconds for four wave crests to hit the side of a rowboat. What is the frequency of the waves?
   a. 0.8 waves/second.
   b. 1.25 waves/second.
   c. 0.6 waves/second.
   d. 1.4 waves/second.

4. What is the wavelength of the 512 Hertz tuning fork in Problem 2?
   a. 16 meters.
   b. .66 meter.
   c. 6.66 meters.
   d. 1.51 meters.

Transfer of Energy

OVERVIEW

ENERGETIC SOUNDS

Getting sound from here to there is the essence of communications. You can pluck a string, or a spring, or a thumb piano, but how does the listener on the other side of the room sense it as music?

Audio equipment uses transmitters to send sound and receivers to receive it. In this chapter, you will build a microphone to amplify the sound energy you create with your vocal chords, and build speakers that turn sound waves into acoustical energy—energy we can hear.

Completing the second milestone by building a working speaker and microphone will take you another step along your journey to radioland.

Your next milestone:

2 | **Project Milestone** | **Building a Speaker and Microphone**

You will build a working speaker and microphone, linking the concepts of electromagnetic induction from your previous work to the principles of how speakers and microphones work. You will explain the energy transfers that take place from playing a note on your thumb piano to the reception of the sound by your ear—tracing the energy transfers through both the speaker and the microphone circuits.

By the end of this chapter, you will have modeled and explained two of the major components of your radio station as parts of your transmitter/receiver system. Since you are experienced in the qualitative concepts of electric circuits, you will now delve into the quantitative side of the concepts and test your ability to think scientifically to solve problems.

Using your knowledge of basic circuits, you will build electric devices and test and maximize their performance by changing components and measuring the resulting changes. You will again be asked to analyze the energy changes and transfers that take place in each more complex electric circuit.

To help you accomplish Project Milestone Two, you will do the following activities:

Activity 16.1 Energy by the Numbers
You will examine energy units and complete some practice problems to instill a quantitative understanding of the concepts from Chapter 15. You will then be introduced to the concept that different types of energy and work are related and conserved in a closed system.

Activity 16.2 Electric Energy
This activity introduces the concepts of heat, specific heat, electric energy, and the dissipation of heat in resistors and electric circuits. You will build a simple circuit to explore the relationship between power, heat, current, and voltage as steps in the development of Joule's law.

Activity 16.3 Science of Sound
You will do a lab that qualitatively depicts what happens as light and sound travel over a distance. Then you will be introduced to the concepts of sound intensity, the inverse square law, and the decibel scale.

Activity 16.4 Speaking of Speakers
You will build a working speaker and microphone, linking the concepts of electromagnetic induction with the production of sound and acoustical energy. You then compare the structure and function of the parts of your speaker and microphone with those of a commercially-produced model. Finally, you analyze the transfers of energy involved in speaker and microphone circuits.

ACTIVITY 16.1

Energy by the Numbers

Getting In Gear

So many types of energy; what do they all mean? When we say we are getting to work, we mean we are getting ready to do something. Could it be anything? What types of actions do you think of when you think of work? Kinetic energy is the energy of a moving object, and potential energy is stored energy that is sitting around just waiting to do something. Are you full of potential energy? If so let's get to work!

Getting To Work!

To explore different forms of energy and its transformations, you will

1. Review the overview scenario and project milestone for Chapter 16, and discuss the scenario with your class.

2. Discuss units of energy with your teacher and classmates. Are there any that you are familiar with?

3. Read Getting the Point: *Work, Kinetic Energy, and Potential Energy,* and answer the Focus Questions.

4. Complete | **Job Sheet 16.1** | **Energy by the Numbers** in small groups.

5. Check out Workplace Connection: *What Nuclear Power Plant Operators Do* and the Did You Know? reading as time permits.

Job Sheet

Ever wonder about alternatives to gasoline-powered cars? Read Concept Connection: *Steam-driven Automobiles.*

Getting The Point.

Work, Kinetic Energy, and Potential Energy

You've already learned a lot about work, kinetic energy, and potential energy. In this reading you'll find some simple equations you can use to calculate the quantity of each. Table 16.1 shows the units for each quantity you calculate.

WORK

Work (W) is a force (F) × distance (d) when the movement of the object is in the same direction as the force:

$$\text{Work (W)} = \text{Force (F)} \times \text{distance (d)} = F \times d = Fd$$

The units of work are:

$$\text{newton(s)} \times \text{meter(s)} = \text{newton-meter(s)} = nm$$

Although newton-meters (nm) can be used to describe quantities of work, these units can be expressed in other ways. A newton is a kilogram × meter/second^2, so

$$\text{newton(s)} \times \text{meter(s)} = (\text{kilogram} \times \text{meter/second}^2)$$
$$\times \text{meter} = kg \times m^2/sec^2$$

Table 16.1

Quantity	Quantity Abbreviation	Unit	Unit Abbreviation
Force	F	newton	n
Distance	d	meter	m
Height	h	meter	m
Velocity	v	meter/second	m/sec
Acceleration due to gravity	g	meter/second^2	m/sec^2
Work	W	Kilogram $\times$ meter^2/second^2 *or* newton-meter *or* Joule	Kg $\times$ m^2/sec^2 *or* nm *or* J
Kinetic energy	KE	Kilogram $\times$ meter^2/second^2 *or* newton-meter *or* Joule	Kg $\times$ m^2/sec^2 *or* nm *or* J
Potential energy	PE	Kilogram $\times$ meter^2/second^2 *or* newton-meter *or* Joule	Kg $\times$ m^2/sec^2 *or* nm *or* J

Scientists have given this large assemblage of units a single name—the Joule (J), after James Prescott Joule, a 19th-century pioneer in the physics of energy conversion.

Sample Problem: When you play your thumb piano, how much work do you do as you push the end of a bobby pin down a distance of 1 centimeter with a force of 4 newtons? (Note: Don't forget to convert all distance units in all energy calculations to meters!)

Solution: W = F $\times$ d = 4n $\times$ 0.01 m = *.04 nm or .04 kg $\times$ m^2/sec^2 or .04 J*

KINETIC ENERGY

The kinetic energy, or energy of motion, of an object (KE) is equal to one half the product of its mass (m) and the square of its velocity (v).

$$\text{Kinetic Energy (KE)} = 1/2 \times \text{mass (m)} \times \text{velocity (v)} \times \text{velocity (v)} = 1/2 \ mv^2$$

The units of kinetic energy are:

$$\text{kg} \times \text{m/sec} \times \text{m/sec} = \text{kg} \times \text{m}^2/\text{sec}^2 = \text{nm} = \text{J}$$

Notice that the units for kinetic energy are the same as the units for work.

Sample Problem: What kinetic energy is produced when a .5-kilogram mass is accelerated to a velocity of 5 meters/second as it is released?

Solution: KE = .5 mv^2 = .5 $\times$ .5 kg $\times$ (5 m/sec)^2 = 6.25 kg $\times$ m/sec^2 = *6.25 nm = 6.25 J*

POTENTIAL ENERGY

As you learned in Activity 15.1, different types of potential energy exist. For example, there is chemical (energy "locked" in coal, wood, gas, and oil, for example); electric (voltage); nuclear (fission); and mechanical (gravitational, elastic). This discussion focuses on gravitational potential energy; the energy stored in an object when it is lifted.

The gain or loss of gravitational potential energy of an object (PE) is equal to the product of its mass (m), the value of the acceleration due to gravity (g), and the change in its vertical height (h):

Potential Energy (PE) = mass (m) × gravity (g) × height (h) = mgh.

The value of acceleration due to gravity (g) on the earth's surface is nearly constant and equals 9.8 m/sec^2; this means that an object's speed increases by 9.8 m/sec^2 during each second that it falls freely toward the earth because of the force of gravity, without encountering a significant force of air resistance.

The units of potential energy are:

$$\text{kg} \times \text{m/sec}^2 \times \text{m} = \text{kg} \times \text{m}^2/\text{sec}^2 = \text{nm} = \text{J}$$

Notice that the units for potential are the same as the units for both work and kinetic energy.

Sample Problem: If you lift a 250-gram mass vertically through a distance of 2 meters, how much potential energy is created? (Keep in mind that mass should be converted to kilograms.)

Solution: PE = mgh = .25 kg × 9.8 m/sec^2 × 2m = 4.9 kg × m^2/sec^2 or 4.9 J

Notes:

1. The weight of the object you are lifting is its mass (m) × acceleration due to gravity (g). The change in potential energy is the weight multiplied by the vertical distance or height that the object has moved.

2. The potential energy that is stored when the mass is lifted 2m is converted to kinetic energy when the object falls back down 2m.

   After falling a vertical distance (d), the velocity (v) of a free falling object is

   $$v = \sqrt{2\,gd}.$$

   At this velocity, its kinetic energy is

   $$KE = 1/2 \times m \times v \times v = 1/2 \times m \times \sqrt{2\,gd} \times \sqrt{2\,gd}$$
   $$= 1/2 \times m \times (2\,gd)$$

   $$\text{or} \quad KE = mv^2/2 = mgd$$

So, if the 250-gram mass in the sample problem is released and falls 2m, its kinetic energy is: KE = mgd = .25 kg × 9.8 m/sec^2 × 2m = 4.9 kg × m^2/sec^2 or *4.9 J*

Focus Questions

What is the fundamental unit of energy in the metric system?

Describe what happens to an object's potential energy as it free-falls from a height of 6 meters.

Concept Connection: Steam-Driven Automobiles

Have you ever heard the whistle of a tea kettle? Steam has a lot of kinetic energy. You have probably witnessed that rapidly moving water vapor vibrates the small opening of a tea kettle, producing sound.

The most frequently raised objection to steam automobiles is the claim that they are less efficient and use more fuel than other cars.

This objection is based on a simplistic and unfortunately widespread misinterpretation of the results obtained in laboratory efficiency tests. These tests, usually called "net thermal efficiency" tests, measure the percentage of potential energy in the fuel that is converted into horsepower measured at the crankshaft.

In laboratory tests, gasoline car engines running at maximum power are about 24% efficient. Steam car powerplants running at maximum power test out at about 15-17% efficient. So the steam car will use more fuel, right?

Not quite. The problem with this thinking is that it overlooks other, more important test results. Now run these same engines at part load. In a car, these engines will run at part load most of the time. When the gasoline car engine is throttled down to run at these real-world average-driving horsepower levels, its efficiency drops to as little as 7%, and typically to 11-13%, for a number of complex engineering reasons. When the steam car powerplant is throttled down to the same output, tests show its efficiency drops to . . . 11-13%.

Thus, in city driving, the steam car gets about the same fuel mileage as a comparable gas car, or better. On the highway, the gas car gets only slightly better fuel mileage than the steamer, because even then it is still not running at the full power which is required for its 24% maximum efficiency.

From *"The Efficiency of Steam and Other Cars,"* by Peter Brow. Reprinted with permission. http://www.geocities.com/MotorCity/Shop/3589/efficiency.html (June 10, 2003)

Workplace Connection:
What Nuclear Power Plant Operators Do

Electricity is vital for most everyday activities. From the moment you flip the first switch each morning, you are connecting to a huge network of people, electric lines, and generating equipment. Power plant operators control the machinery that generates electricity. Power distributors and dispatchers control the flow of electricity from the power plant over a network of transmission lines, to industrial plants and substations, and, finally, over distribution lines to residential users.

Power plant operators control and monitor boilers, turbines, generators, and auxiliary equipment in power generating plants. Operators distribute power demands among generators, combine the current from several generators, and monitor instruments to maintain voltage and regulate electricity flows from the plant. When power requirements change, these workers start or stop generators and connect or disconnect them from circuits. They often use computers to keep records of switching operations and loads on generators, lines, and transformers. Operators also may use computers to prepare reports of unusual incidents, malfunctioning equipment, or maintenance performed during their shift.

Operators in plants with automated control systems work mainly in a central control room and usually are called control room operators and control room operator trainees or assistants. In older plants, the controls for the equipment are not centralized, and switchboard operators control the flow of electricity from a central point, whereas auxiliary equipment operators work throughout the plant, operating and monitoring valves, switches, and gauges.

The Nuclear Regulatory Commission (NRC) licenses operators of nuclear power plants. Reactor operators are authorized to control equipment that affects the power of the reactor in a nuclear power plant. In addition, an NRC-licensed senior reactor operator must be on duty during each shift to act as the plant supervisor and supervise the operation of all controls in the control room.

Power distributors and dispatchers, also called load dispatchers or systems operators, control the flow of electricity through transmission lines to industrial plants and substations that supply residential electric needs. They operate current converters, voltage transformers, and circuit breakers. Dispatchers monitor equipment and record readings at a pilot board, which is a map of the transmission grid system showing the status of transmission circuits and connections with substations and industrial plants.

Dispatchers also anticipate power needs, such as those caused by changes in the weather. They call control room operators to start or stop boilers and generators, to bring production into balance with needs. They handle emergencies such as transformer or transmission line failures and route current around affected areas. They also operate and monitor equipment in substations, which step up or step down voltage, and operate switchboard levers to control the flow of electricity in and out of substations.

Did You Know?

How much energy does each person on Earth convert from one form into another? On a worldwide basis, the mean annual per capita energy consumption is 59 gigajoules (1 gigajoule = 947,800 BTUs). However, the median per capita value is much lower than the 59 gigajoules because the developed nations consume energy at a rate that is one or two orders of magnitude than that of developing countries. For example, Mexico, Malaysia, and Argentina have per capita consumption near the mean value (59, 52, and 60 gigajoules respectively) and the per capita consumption in the United States is 317-319 gigajoules. At the lower end of the scale are Nigeria (7), Bangladesh (3), and Haiti (1).

Adapted from INCREASE IN FOSSIL FUEL UTILIZATION IN THE TWENTY-FIRST CENTURY: ENVIRONMENTAL IMPACT AND LOWER CARBON ALTERNATIVES, by Hal Gluskoter. U.S. Department of the Interior, U.S. Geological Survey. http://energy.er.usgs.gov/products/papers/acs_2-99/acs-2-99.pdf (June 10, 2003)

From OCCUPATIONAL OUTLOOK HANDBOOK. *"Power Plant Operators, Distributors, and Dispatchers."* U.S. Department of Labor. Bureau of Labor Statistics. http://www.bls.gov/oco/ocos227.htm (June 10, 2003)

Electric Energy

Getting In Gear

Have you ever tried to change a lightbulb just after it burned out? Ouch! Those bulbs can get pretty hot. In fact, an electric stove or heater uses the same processes to purposely generate heat. It is the transfer of electric energy to heat, and it happens all around us. You will study Joule's law, which quantifies the relationship between work and heat, especially as it applies to the electric system for your radio station.

Getting To Work!

To explore Joule's law, you will

1. Participate in a class discussion on your initial ideas on the nature of "power" in electric circuits, your home, and industry. What exactly is it, and how is it produced?

2. Obtain │ **Job Sheet 16.2** │ **Power Play: Electricity and Heat,** and construct the circuit to explore the concept of power.

Job Sheet

3. Read Getting the Point: *Feel the Power!*, and answer the Focus Questions.

4. Read Getting the Point: *Heat and Electric Energy,* and answer the Focus Questions.

5. Complete │ **Job Sheet 16.3** │ **Heating Things Up;** answer the questions in class (or for homework), as directed by your teacher.

6. Read Concept Connection: *Really Big Circuits,* and the Did You Know? reading as time permits.

Job Sheet

Ever think about becoming a recording professional? Read Workplace Connection: *Recording Engineer.*

Getting The Point.

Feel the Power!

So far, you have concentrated on the concepts of energy, its transfer, conservation, and transmission. The rate at which any type of energy is transferred from place to place is called *power.* So power equals work or energy divided by time, or $P = F \times d/t$, or E/t. And like energy, power comes in several forms. Unlike energy, several different units for power are commonly used. Horsepower, for instance, is an old term still used to rate the power of automobile engines. James Watt derived the unit for horsepower (hp) in experiments that he performed with large Scottish farm horses in 1746. He found that the average horse on his farm could lift 550 pounds (F), through a distance of 1 foot (d), in 1 second (t). The definition of 1 *horsepower* (hp) is 550 feet × pounds/second. The metric unit for power is newtons × meters/second or Joules/second. Scientists renamed this group of units the *Watt* (W). So, does that mean a lightbulb stamped with 100 watts delivers 100 Joules per second of light? Well, if you have ever grabbed a lit bulb, you know very well that that's not true! In fact, only about 45 Joules of the 100 is converted to light. The rest is the "wasted" heat energy that burns your fingers.

In electric circuits, power is governed by how much energy is being transported by the flow, and by the rate at which it is flowing. You might recall that *voltage (V)* is the electric potential energy of the electrons in a circuit or component. We say that voltage is W/q or Joules/Coulomb. A battery that has "6 V" marked on its side means that every coulomb or charge (6.25×10^{18} electrons) coming from the negative terminal carries 6 Joules of potential energy, which will be delivered to the circuit. But at what rate will it be delivered? You might recall from the definition of the *current* in the circuit that the amp is a measure of how many coulombs of charge are sent from the voltage source each second.

Electric power is then a combination of these two terms:

$$P = VI = J/C \times C/sec = J/sec = Watts$$

Remember that Ohm's law states that $I = V/R$, so the electric power formula can be revised by several mathematical substitutions:

$$P = VI \text{ but } I = V/R, \text{ so } P = V \times V/R \text{ or } P = V^2/R$$

Similarly, $P = VI$, but $V = IR$, so $P = IR \times I$, or $P = I^2R$.

Focus Questions

What is electric power?

If the current in a circuit is 2 amps when hooked up to a 6-volt battery, what power is expended in the circuit?

How many 100-watt lightbulbs would a 2 horsepower engine light up?

Getting The Point.

Heat and Electric Energy

In Job Sheet 16.2, you found that power is how fast energy is delivered through a wire to an electric component. All the energy provided by the battery was dissipated in heating the wire and the resistor. However, in many circuits even the dissipated energy is useful, like the energy emitted by the heated wires in a toaster or the filaments of a lightbulb. James Prescott Joule discovered the relationship between heat energy and electric energy in the 19th century.

Traditionally, heat has been measured in *calories* (1 calorie = the energy required to heat 1 gram of water, 1° Celsius). Joule discovered through experiments (where he measured the heat produced while brass cannon barrels were being bored out with cutting tools) that 1 calorie was equivalent to 4.2 Joules. This is called the *mechanical equivalent of heat.*

Work can produce heat energy in the same way that charges flowing through a circuit can produce heat in a resistor. The *first law of thermodynamics* states that the total change of energy in a system is equal to the heat added to the system minus the work done by the system. $\Delta\mu = Q - W$, where U is the energy of the system, Q is the heat added to the system, and W is the work done by the system.

To compute how much heat energy is absorbed or lost by a quantity of material like water or air, the mass of material (m), its temperature change (T), and a factor called specific heat (c), are multiplied together. Specific heat is the number of joules that it takes for 1 gram of the material to change in temperature by 1° Celsius. Combining these factors:

$$\text{Amount of heat energy} = Q = mcT \text{ (units} = \text{g} \times \text{J/gC} \times \text{C} = \text{J)}$$

The amount of electric energy that a circuit can supply depends on the power. Remember from the reading Getting the Point: *Feel the Power!* that power is the rate of energy per time:

$$P = E/t, \text{ or we can rewrite this as}$$

$$\text{energy} = \text{power} \times \text{time}$$

Since electric power is voltage times current, or $P = VI$, then $E = (VI)t$ is the electric energy going through the wire. So if all of the heat energy dissipated from current going through a wire is then absorbed by the surroundng material,

$$\text{the heat energy dissipated} = \text{the heat energy absorbed}$$

$$VIt = mcT$$

or, using $P = I^2R$, this can be rewritten as $mc\Delta t = I^2Rt$

or using $P = V^2/R$, this can be rewritten as $mc\Delta t = V^2t/R$

The *second law of thermodynamics* states that natural processes tend to move toward a state of disorder. For instance, if a teacup falls to the ground, it breaks into many pieces. It is highly unlikely that those pieces will spontaneously recombine to make the teacup whole again. The system will not naturally move toward a more ordered state. When electricity moves through the wire, some of that energy is converted to heat, as described by Joule's law. The reverse is not true. Energy in the form of heat does not spontaneously convert to electric energy.

Focus Questions

What three factors determine the quantity of heat gained or lost by an object?

How many calories are released by 100 grams of hot water as it cools from 50° to 25° Celsius?

How many seconds would it take a heating coil to deliver 10,000 calories of heat energy to a pot of water if the circuit was on a 110-volt line and drew a current of .5 amps?

Does the conversion of electric energy to heat in the wire follow the second law of thermodynamics? Why or why not?

Concept Connection: Really Big Circuits

The traditional model of electric power generation and delivery is based on the construction of large, centrally located power plants. "Central" in this case would ideally mean that the power plants are located on a hub surrounded by major electrical load centers. For instance, a power plant may be located close to a city to serve the electrical loads in the city and its suburbs, or a plant may be located in the midpoint of a triangle formed by three cities.

In reality, many other factors come into play when siting power plants, including the availability of fuel resources, the need for a cooling water source, environmental considerations, and other factors. In the West, for instance, several large coal plants are located close to coal mines to minimize the cost of shipping coal. And most of the power for the Pacific Northwest comes from hydroelectric plants that are located far from the cities that depend on their power.

Regardless of where power plants are located, their power must be brought from the plant to the users, and that's the purpose of the electricity grid. The grid actually consists of two separate infrastructures: the high-voltage transmission systems, carrying electricity from the power plants and transmitting it, if needed, hundreds of miles away, and the lower-voltage distribution systems, which draw electricity from the transmission lines and distribute it to individual customers.

High voltage is used for transmission lines to minimize electrical losses; however, high voltage is impractical for use in distribution lines. The interface between the two is the electrical substation, which features transformers that "step down" the voltage from the transmission voltages, ranging from 138 kV to 765 kV, to lower voltages for the distribution systems. Transformers located along the distribution lines further step down the voltage to 120 V or 240 V for household use.

Substations also include electrical switchgear and circuit breakers to protect the transformers and the transmission system from electrical failures on the distribution lines. Circuit breakers are also located along the distribution lines to locally isolate electrical problems (such as short circuits caused by downed power lines).

From *"How The Electricity Grid Works."* U.S. Department of Energy. Energy Efficiency and Renewable Energy Network. http://www.eere.energy.gov/der/grid_WORKS.html (June 10, 2003)

Workplace Connection: Recording Engineer

You are relaxing at home listening to the radio, a CD, or even surfing the net. Perhaps you are enjoying a film at a movie theater, watching VH-1 on TV, even viewing a filmstrip at school. Well, if you can hear it, a recording engineer recorded it.

Recording engineers are not engineers as we commonly think of that profession. They are experts in capturing, storing, and disseminating audio. As a matter of fact the term used in Europe, Tonnmeister, may be more accurate to describe this work. Literally, Tonnmeister means "master of sound." Recording professionals must combine significant musical skills with an underlying knowledge of the nature and physics of sound, its transmission, and its perception by human beings.

For years I have posed this question to my students. "What does a guitar sound like?" A simple question, but to answer the question a recording engineer needs to ask many other questions. What musical role does the guitar play in the recording? What kind of guitar is it? How skilled is the player? What genre of music are we recording? Will the guitar occupy a supporting or a leading role in the finished recording? What timbre (combination of "overtones") do I feel is best to maximize the effect this guitar will have in the recording? What microphone is best to capture the sound I expect? Will my choices sound good when the recording is played at home? What is the medium that is likely to be used to play this recording back? These questions are complex and difficult to answer in words. A recording speaks for itself just as a painting does. Success is gauged by the perception of quality and enjoyment a recording provides to its listeners. A recording professional understands all of the issues very well. By combining knowledge and years of experience, fine-tuned by trial and error, recording engineers very often produce a successful recording. But it is not an easy task!

Recording professionals are keenly aware of the underlying quality of playback systems they use. It is imperative that they hear what is contained on the recording itself with brutal accuracy. Simply put, the engineer cannot work with a playback system that is "coloring" the sound in any way. The system must be absolutely accurate within the range of human hearing, which the recording industry specifies as 20-20,000 Hertz (cycles per second). Further the system must not deviate more than 3dB at any point in the audible range! In other words, my system must play back an audible signal that is no more than 3dB higher or lower in amplitude (volume level) than any other audible signal. If this is true, the engineer is working with a "flat response system."

The system's frequency response, when plotted on a decibel scale, appears as a nearly flat line. The engineer can be confident that the playback system is not playing tricks with the audio signals. When an adjustment is needed, the engineer is certain that the basis for perceiving the necessity for adjustment is real. But, to this must be added the fact that we are humans, not test instruments. Our ears are not "flat response" devices. The researchers Fletcher and Munson, and later Robinson and Dadson, have plotted the frequency response curves of typical human beings at varying levels of amplitude. These curves show that human beings perceive sound most linearly in the 80-90 dB SPL range. For this reason engineers typically mix and monitor productions in the 80-90 dB SPL range for maximum perceived quality. The response curves are widely used as a basis for designing recording venues that will allow recording engineers to enjoy truly predictable flat frequency response, not on a test instrument, but at their listening position in a recording control room. Now the Tonnmeister must have knowledge of music and physics, plus an understanding of how sounds move through air, its perception by the brain, and how to physically design a room for best sound.

Recording professionals work as artists, technologists, and even acoustics designers. By moving seamlessly from one to the other, the new discipline of Sound Recording Technology has been created.

Leon Janikian, Associate Professor of Music, Northeastern University. Reprinted with permission.

ACTIVITY 16.3

Science of Sound

Getting In Gear

How loud do you like your music? Deafening amplitude so it rattles the rafters, or gentle soothing volumes so that you can have a conversation? The preference for volume is a personal choice, but the physics behind how loud a sound is can be understood with a bit of math. You will investigate how sound intensity diminishes as you move away from the source.

Getting To Work!

To explore sound intensity, you will

1. Observe your teacher's demonstration.

2. Complete the inverse square activity as described on **Job Sheet 16.4** An **Intense Activity.**

Job Sheet

3. Read Getting the Point sections *The Inverse Square Law* and *Sound Intensity.* Complete the Focus Questions for both of the readings.

4. Answer Questions 6 through 8 on Job Sheet 16.4.

5. Check out Workplace Connection: *Hearing Conversation in the Workplace* and the Did You Know? readings as time permits.

Ever wonder about the computer technology involved in architectural acoustics? Read Concept Connection: *Acoustics in Architecture.*

Getting The Point.

The Inverse Square Law

You have probably seen how, when you shine a flashlight at a wall, the light's brightness changes as you move toward or away from the wall. The brightness, or *intensity,* of the light increases the closer you are to the wall and diminishes as you move away.

But isn't the flashlight always giving off the same amount of light? If so, why does the brightness change? When you are close to the wall, the circle of light is quite small. All the flashlight's light is concentrated into this small area. The light intensity per square inch is high, making it very bright. When you move the flashlight back, the illuminated circle increases in size. Now, the flashlight's light is spread across a larger area. There is less light available per square inch of this larger circle; the light is dimmer—its intensity is less.

When light radiates from a point source, such as the sun, it travels evenly in all directions, forming a sphere around the source. In fact, anything that radiates in straight lines, like sound, also behaves the same way. As the energy spreads out, its intensity per unit area decreases. At one *unit distance,* a distance you define, the energy covers one patch of a sphere. However, by the time they have traveled two unit distances, the energy is spread across four of these patches. At three unit distances, the energy now covers nine patches. As with the flashlight, you can have either a small, brightly-lit area or a large, dimly lit one. With sound coming from a speaker, you hear a loud sound at one unit of distance, while at 2 units the sound is one-fourth as intense, and at 3 units it is one-ninth its original intensity. The intensity of light or sound varies with distance in a predictable, measurable way described by a mathematical formula called the *inverse square law.* Gravitational, electric, and magnetic force are three other quantities that follow the same mathematical relationship.

Figure 16.1
The Inverse Square Distribution of Light

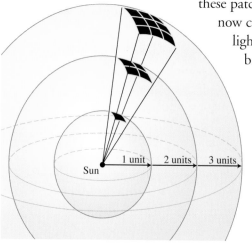

Sun 1 unit 2 units 3 units

Reprinted from LIFE ON EARTH . . . AND ELSEWHERE? ASTROBIOLOGY IN YOUR CLASSROOM. EDUCATOR RESOURCE GUIDE, by Chris Randall. For TERC (Cambridge, MA) and NASA Astrobiology Institute. Fall 2000.

Focus Questions

If you are standing twice as far away from a lightbulb than your friend is, to which of you will the light appear brighter? By how much? Twice as bright? Four times as bright?

Name several types of phenomena that follow the inverse square law.

Getting The Point.

Sound Intensity

The human ear is extremely sensitive to the pressure variations in sound. It can detect pressure changes as small as 2 ten-billionths of ordinary air pressure. When pressure variations become a million times greater than this (but still only 2 ten-thousandths of ordinary pressure), it becomes painful to our ears. As the size of the pressure variations increases, the *intensity* of the sound wave increases. Notice that it is not the total amount of air pressure but the size of the *change* from normal pressure that your ear detects. When audio specialists and sound engineers talk about *sound pressure level* (SPL), they are really referring to the size of the pressure *variations.*

Our human sound detection system—meaning our ears plus our brain, which tells us what our ears detected—responds to sound in rather peculiar ways. Typically, for example, you will have to multiply the intensity of a sound wave by about 10 to make the sound seem twice as loud. That's just the way our ears and brain work. So physicists and engineers have come up with a sound level scale that reflects this peculiarity. It is called the *decibel (dB) scale.* Originally, the units chosen were called Bels after Alexander Graham Bell, inventor of the telephone. But the decibel (deci- means "a tenth of") was found to be a unit of more convenient size. The capital B in the abbreviation dB reminds us that it is named after Bell.

The decibel scale is based on a comparison of the actual sound level to the minimum sound level that our ears can detect. The minimum intensity of sound wave that the typical human ear can detect is $I_{min} = 10^{-12}$ W/m^2. (That's only a trillionth of a watt crossing each square meter of surface.) To compare other values of the intensity I to this one, we ask "How many times as big is it?" so that each value of I can be written as

$$I = 10^{-12} \text{ W/m}^2 \times \text{"the number of times as big"}$$

The decibel scale is related to the number of times as big. Mathematically, the relationship may look a little daunting at first:

$$\text{the number of times as big} = 10^{dB/10}$$

dB stands for the numerical value in decibels.

Putting the pieces together, we get

$$I = I_{min} \times 10^{dB/10}$$

or

$$I = 10^{-12} \text{ W/m}^2 \times 10^{dB/10}$$

To see how this works, suppose we have a 50 decibel sound. What is the intensity of this sound in watts per square meter (W/m^2)?

$$I = 10^{-12} \text{ W/m}^2 \times 10^{dB/10} = 10^{-12} \text{ W/m}^2 \times 10^{50/10} = 10^{-12} \text{ W/m}^2 \times 10^5$$
$$= 10^{-7} \text{ W/m}^2$$

Notice from the next to the last step that the number of times as big is 10^5, or 100,000. A 50 decibel sound (about the level of the background noise in an average suburban home at night) is 100,000 times as intense as the minimum sound you can hear. But this doesn't mean it is 100,000 times as loud. Each time the value in decibels increases by 10, the loudness roughly doubles. (We say "roughly" because each person's hearing is a little different. Also, your hearing is not equally sensitive to all frequencies. So a high-pitched sound with a certain intensity may not seem as loud to you as human speech sounds with the same intensity.) The minimum audible sound level in decibels is zero, so 50 decibel is five tens higher, and the loudness has doubled roughly five times from the minimum loudness you can hear. It is about $2 \times 2 \times 2 \times 2 \times 2$, or 32 times as loud.

Table 16.2 shows sound levels in decibels for a variety of everyday and some less everyday sounds. The formula above calculates the intensities in W/m^2 from the sound levels in decibels (dB). Although audio specs often are in "dB SPL" for sound pressure level, remember that increased pressure means increased intensity as well.

Table 16.2
Intensity of various types of sound.

	Type of sound	Decibels SPL	"number of times as big" as I_{min}	Intensity in W/m^2
L	Eardrum rupture	160	1016	104 or 10000
O	Gun shot (at 8 m)	140	1014	102 or 100
U	Fire engine siren (at 30 m)	130	1013	101 or 10
D	THRESHOLD OF PAIN			
	Rock concert (at 3 m)	120	1012	100 or 1
	Loud thunder	110	1011	10–1 or 0.1
	New York City subway train	100	1010	10-2 or 0.01
	Heavy traffic (at 2 m)	90	109	10–3 or 0.001
	Cabin noise, 767 jet	80	108	10–4
	Traffic on mildly busy street	70	107	10-5
	Normal conversation at 1 m	60	106	10-6
	Typical suburban home (background at night)	50	105	10–7
	Quiet auditorium	40	104	10–8
S	Quiet whisper	30	103 or 1000	10–9
O		20	102 or 100	10–10
F	Normal breathing	10	101 or 10	10–11
T	Softest audible sound	0	100 or 1	10–12

Focus Questions

Use the data in Table 16.2 to answer the following questions:

1. What is the difference in intensity between a loud clap of thunder and a whisper?

2. What is the intensity difference in decibels between a soft whisper and a jet? What is the difference in loudness?

3. How many decibels would someone experience if she were 6 meters away instead of 3 meters away from a rock concert?

Concept Connection: Acoustics in Architecture

The Technical Committee on Architectural Acoustics (TCAA) was established in 1960. TCAA serves as the focus for interested ASA [Acoustical Society of America] members and guests at its biannual meetings to plan future technical sessions, to coordinate and support activities and other initiatives in architectural acoustics. The scope of TCAA is as follows:

- Room acoustics.
- Airborne and impact transmission in building structures.
- Airborne and structure-borne noise control.
- Noise control of building systems.
- Electro-acoustics systems.
- Psychophysics and psycho-acoustics.

The 20th century concluded with an enormous increase in knowledge in all of the above areas. Now, through the widespread areas of affordable computer-aided acoustical measurement, analysis, and design techniques, the acoustical environments of practically any architectural space can be rapidly evaluated in advance of construction. Very soon, the technology to actually "auralize" a space will be commonplace as well, so that architectural acousticians and architects alike will be able to virtually "see and hear" building spaces beforehand. The Technical Committee on Architectural Acoustics will remain the focus of activity in architectural acoustics both in encouraging research and in promoting its practical applications. The 21st century promises to be an exciting one for architectural acoustics. . . . Stay tuned!

Adapted from *"Technical Committee on Architectural Acoustics (TCAA) of the Acoustical Society of America (ASA),"* by William Cavanaugh. http://www.nonoise.org/quietnet/tcaa/ (June 10, 2003)

Workplace Connection: Hearing Conservation in the Workplace

The hearing conservation program requires employers to monitor noise exposure levels in a manner that will accurately identify employees who are exposed to noise at or above 85 decibels (dB) averaged over 8 working hours, or an 8-

hour time-weighted average (TWA.) That is, employers must monitor all employees whose noise exposure is equivalent to or greater than a noise exposure received in 8 hours where the noise level is constantly 85 dB. The exposure measurement must include all continuous, intermittent, and impulsive noise within an 80 dB to 130 dB range and must be taken during a typical work situation. This requirement is performance-oriented since it allows employers to choose the monitoring method that best suits each individual situation. Monitoring should be repeated when changes in production, process, or controls increase noise exposure. Such changes may mean that additional employees need to be monitored and/or their hearing protectors may no longer provide adequate attenuation.

Under this program, employees are entitled to observe monitoring procedures and they must be notified of the results of exposure monitoring. The method used to notify employees is left to the discretion of the employers.

Instruments used for monitoring employee exposures must be carefully checked or calibrated to ensure that the measurements are accurate. Calibration procedures are unique to specific instruments. Employers have the duty to ensure that the measuring instruments are properly calibrated. They may find it useful to follow the manufacturer's instructions to determine when and how extensively to calibrate.

From *"Hearing Conservation."* U.S. Department of Labor, Occupational Safety and Health Administration. OSHA 3074, 1995, Revised. http://www.osha-slc.gov/Publications/osha3074.html#THREE1 (June 10, 2003)

Did You Know?

What are the two different types of hearing loss?

Sensorineural hearing loss is the result of damage to the inner ear and accounts for over 90% of hearing loss in adults. This type of hearing loss is generally permanent.

Conductive hearing loss occurs when there is damage or blockage in the outer or middle ear, preventing sound from travelling normally through the ear canal to the inner ear. This type of hearing loss can often be corrected.

Adapted from *"Facts About Hearing Loss."* Electronic Shooters Protection. http://www.espamerica.com/facts211b.html (June 10, 2003)

Did You Know?

Galileo investigated the inverse square law for sound.

Galileo was involved in music primarily because of his father, Vincenzo Galileo, a lutist who conducted experiments with music. Galileo was also a lutist and composed music for it. Galileo's interest in musical experiments started at a young age. Although Galileo is known for his other experiments, he also conducted experiments with music.

Stillman Drake believes that Galileo actually did conduct experiments in which he measured the weights tied onto similar strings of the same length and measure the musical interval between the two strings. He observed that the interval between the two notes was related to the inverse squares of the length of the string when the same weight was attached and the same interval was observed.

From The Galileo Project—Music History. http://es.rice.edu/ES/ humsoc/Galileo/Student_Work/Experiment96/music-theory.html (June 10, 2003)

ACTIVITY 16.4

Speaking of Speakers

Getting In Gear

What's the difference between those huge speakers that seem to fill the room and the tiny ones that come in a computer or in a boom box? Is bigger always better? And how does that little microphone musicians use make such a big sound on stage? You will create your own microphone and speakers.

Getting To Work!

To complete Project Milestone Two, you will

1. Discuss with your teacher and classmates how you think speakers and microphones work. What energy transfers must be taking place?

2. Follow the directions on | **Job Sheet 16.5** | Speaking of Speakers. Check in with your teacher when you reach Step 4 to obtain your coil wire.

Job Sheet

3. Ask your teacher to check your speaker circuit; then continue on to Step 16 and design a circuit that will act as a microphone.

4. Read Getting the Point sections *How Speakers Work* and *How Microphones Work* after you have finished testing your microphone. Complete the Focus Questions for both of the readings.

5. Answer Question 21 (for milestone two) on your job sheet. Hand in your job sheet, or engage in a class discussion about energy transfer, if directed to do so by your teacher.

6. Check out the Did You Know? readings as time permits.

7. Review the concepts and answer the questions in What Have You Learned? for homework.

Ever wonder about the power of speakers? Read Concept Connection: *The Power of Audio.*

Getting The Point.

How Speakers Work

A speaker is actually a linear motor. Loudspeakers are really very simple devices from an operational standpoint. An amplifier generates electrical energy that alternates constantly from positive to negative in a pattern of waves that vary in size and frequency. The output from the amplifier is connected to the speaker. There is a fine braided wire that carries the signal from the terminals to the conductors leading to the Voice Coil Assembly. These wires are extremely flexible, to enable the Cone to move back and forth without restriction or stress, and to do so without breaking these wires. The Voice coil itself is mounted on a rigid cylinder, to which it is firmly glued.

All the moving parts operate as a single unit, and are suspended by the surround, or outer edge of the cone at the front, and by the "Spider" at the rear. At its natural resting point, the voice coil is centered within a narrow magnetic Field Gap. This gap constitutes the north and south poles of the Magnet Structure, whose energy is derived from a powerful permanent Magnet, sandwiched between the two pole pieces. Essentially, the speaker operates by responding to positive and negative waves from the amplifier, passing through the voice coil, causing it to be moved back and forth by attraction to one pole of the magnet, and repulsion by the other. Since the voice coil is rigidly mounted to the cone, the resulting energy is transmitted to the cone producing a piston like motion that alternately compresses and evacuates the adjacent air, thus producing sound. If there is a high degree of conformity between the original recorded sound, and the sound produced from the speaker system as a whole, we then have high fidelity. If we do this for two channels of discrete sound information, we have stereo, and if there are four or more channels being activated, we have surround sound.

Figure 16.2
Cutaway of the
Inside of a Speaker

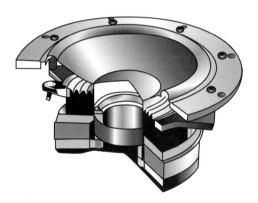

From *"How Do Speakers Work?"* Copyright © 2001 The Speaker Store. By Metrodirect Communications, Clearwater, FL. Reprinted with permission. http://www.thespeakerstore.com/glossary/howspeakerswork.htm (June 10, 2003)

Focus Questions

Name three important components of a speaker.

In what way do speakers rely on magnets for sound production?

Getting The Point.

How Microphones Work

A microphone is an example of a *transducer,* a device that changes information from one form to another. In a real sense, a microphone is a reverse speaker, operating on very similar principles. Sound information exists as patterns of air pressure; the microphone changes this information into patterns of electric current. In a speaker, patterns of electrical current are changed into patterns of air pressure—longitudinal wave—known as sound. The recording engineer is interested in the accuracy of this transformation, a concept he thinks of as fidelity.

A variety of mechanical techniques can be used in building microphones. The two most commonly encountered in recording studios are the magneto-dynamic and the variable condenser designs.

THE DYNAMIC MICROPHONE

In the magneto-dynamic, commonly called dynamic microphone, sound waves cause movement of a thin metallic diaphragm and an attached coil of wire. A magnet produces a magnetic field, which surrounds the coil, and motion of the coil within this field causes current to flow. The principles are the same as those that produce electricity at the utility company, realized in a pocket-sized scale. It is important to remember that the motion of the diaphragm produces current, and that the amount of current is determined by the speed of that motion. This kind of microphone is known as velocity sensitive.

THE CONDENSER MICROPHONE

In a condenser microphone, the diaphragm is mounted close to, but not touching, a rigid backplate. (The plate may or may not have holes in it.) A battery is connected to both pieces of metal, which produces an electrical potential, or charge, between them. The amount of charge is determined by the voltage of the battery, the area of the diaphragm and backplate, and the distance between the two. This distance changes as the diaphragm moves in response to sound. When the distance changes, current flows in the wire as the battery maintains the correct charge. The amount of current is essentially proportional to the displacement of the diaphragm, and is so small that it must be electrically amplified before it leaves the microphone.

From *"Microphones,"* by Peter Elsea, Director of Electronic Music Studios, University of California, Santa Cruz. Copyright © 1996 Peter Elsea. Reprinted with permission. http://arts.ucsc.edu/EMS/Music/tech_background/TE-20/teces_20.html (June 10, 2003)

Focus Questions

What produces the sound waves in a speaker?

Why are magnets an important component of speakers?

Why is a microphone much like a speaker?

What is the basic difference between a dynamic and a condenser microphone?

What is speaker "feedback?"

For a microphone to convert sound waves into electrical signals, it must be connected to an amplifier. The amplifier is connected to a speaker. When a microphone comes close to a speaker, feedback occurs. The sound wave radiated from the speaker becomes an electrical signal which is boosted through the amplifier and comes back out as a sound wave. This cycle happens so quickly that it creates a frequency of its own.

From *"How Things Work: Audio Speakers,"* by Edward Teaw and Jenny Ng. http://www.sinc.sunysb.edu/Stu/eteaw/types.html (June 10, 2003)

Concept Connection: The Power of Audio

If you were around in the early 70's, you undoubtedly remember the race to see who could make the biggest HIFI power amp and how much they stretched the truth about their power output rating. They finally standardized on an RMS (root-mean-square, a measure of the average power level of a signal rating at a certain impedance and distortion). Well, speaker companies didn't standardize on anything and still haven't. The official or accepted design technical standards are:

RMS—RMS power the driver can safely handle.
Peak Power—The amount of power the driver can handle for 20% of the time.
System Power—The amount of power required to burn the voice coil.
Excursion Limit Power—The power required to move the voice coil to its mechanical limit.

The published power ratings and how they are determined vary among manufacturers. One thing is for sure, though, they are usually higher than any of the technical design ratings. For instance, some speaker manufacturers rate their speakers at twice the RMS value, while others use up to four times the RMS value for their rating. They make the assumption that no one would put a steady tone (RMS power) into the speaker for very long, and also realize that music is transient in nature. Another big problem with truth in power rating is the fact that copper has a positive temperature coefficient. The voice coil wire is copper, so as soon as it starts heating up its resistance goes up. All electromagnetic devices are current devices, that is to say, they respond to the current through them, not the voltage across them.

For many reasons, speakers have always been driven by amplifiers that have voltage source outputs rather than current source outputs. This means that for a given input, the amp will put out a certain voltage, and the assumption is made that the load (the speaker) resistance won't change much. In reality, as the amp puts out enough voltage to put, say 40 watts into the speaker, the speaker voice coil begins to heat up, its resistance goes up, and before you know it, the speaker is only drawing 20 watts from the amp. Speaker manufacturers are well aware of this fact, and make use of it in determining their published power ratings. Of course, if you had an amp whose output was a true current source, it would keep pumping 40 watts, regardless of the resistance change in the voice coil.

The common term used to describe this effect is Power Compression. An example of this is after you've gigged for a lengthy period of time and you notice the speakers in your amp seem to lose attack, the loudness drops, and they get kind of mushy, you are experiencing the effect of power compression.

Some manufacturers rate their speakers based on a mechanical limit rather than an electrical one. WeberVST for instance, rates its model P10Q at 20 watts, because at around 30 to 35 watts the voice coil will bottom out and cause a cracking sound. The voice coil itself would handle much more than 20 watts of electrical power, however.

Did You Know?

WHY SPEAKERS BREAK

Loudspeaker drivers typically fail to operate because of two types of failure—thermal and excursion.

Thermal failure occurs when the heating capacity of the electrical signal is beyond the capability of the loudspeaker voice coil. The result is overheating and burning of the voice coil.

Excursion failure occurs when the loudspeaker cone or diaphragm is forced to physically move beyond its limits. The result is physical destruction of the loudspeaker cone, diaphragm and/or surround. This usually occurs when the electrical signal contains more low frequency content than the loudspeaker was intended to handle.

From *"Understanding Loudspeaker Power Handling & Selecting the Proper Power Amplifier."* Audio Video & Broadcasting Studio Systems. http://www.studio-systems.com/audiofeatures/janfeb99/120.htm (June 10, 2003)

Adapted from *"Power Rating."* Copyright © 1996 Weber Vintage Sound Technology. Reprinted with permission. http://www.webervst.com/spterm.html#power (June 10, 2003)

KEY CONCEPTS

Joule. A Joule is the fundamental unit of energy equal to 1 kgm²/sec².

Power. The rate at which you expend work or energy is called power, and its units are either Joules/second or watts.

Horsepower. This unit of power is named after the amount of work a horse (a Scottish farm horse in 1746) could do. One horsepower is equal to 746 watts.

Calorie. One calorie is the amount of heat required to heat 1 gram of water by 1° Celsius.

Law of Conservation of Energy. The total amount of energy in a system always remains constant. Energy within the system can change from one form to another, but is never created or destroyed.

Joule's law. James Prescott Joule, a leading physicist in the 1800s, formulated an equation that relates heat energy in a system to electric energy in that system. Joule's law says that a given amount of work is always equivalent to a particular amount of energy transferred.

Inverse square law. As energy moves away from a point source, its intensity diminishes by the square of the distance. This is true for sound, light, and gravity, for example.

Transducer. A transducer converts energy from one form to another.

Specific heat. Specific heat is a constant for each material that describes how much heat energy (Joules) it takes to heat 1 gram of water 1° Celsius.

Heat energy. Heat energy is the name we use for a particular band of the electromagnetic spectrum centered in the infrared. The quantity of heat energy is calculated by multiplying mass times specific heat times change in temperature.

Decibel. A relative scale of sound intensity logarithmic in nature is measured in decibels.

CONCEPT QUESTIONS

1. How does the concept of work differ from that of power?

2. Who expends more power: Jodi, who lifts a 40-pound weight over her head six times in 6 seconds, or Jimmy, who lifts a 60-pound weight over his head four times in 10 seconds? Assume both Jodi and Jimmy lift the weight to the same height.

3. How was the horsepower derived by James Watt?

4. What form of energy goes into a microphone, and what form of energy comes out of it?

5. What form of energy goes into a speaker, and what form of energy comes out of it?

Continued

1. A simple circuit has a 6-volt battery hooked in series with a 4-ohm resistor. What should the power rating of the resistor be so that overheating and circuit failure do not result?
   a. 1 watt
   b. 10 watt
   c. .5 watt
   d. It doesn't matter

2. If the velocity of a moving train is doubled, its total kinetic energy
   a. doubles.
   b. triples.
   c. quadruples.
   d. is halved.

3. If a cat is lifted from a height of .25 meters to a height of 1.0 meters, its potential energy is
   a. halved.
   b. doubled.
   c. tripled.
   d. quadrupled.

4. If a diver has 15,000 Joules of kinetic energy just prior to hitting the water, what is her speed if her mass is 50 kilograms?
   a. 600 meters/second
   b. 6 meters/second
   c. 24.5 meters/second
   d. 17.8 meters/second

5. From what height did the diver in Question 4 dive?
   a. 3 meters
   b. 15 meters
   c. 24.5 meters
   d. 30.6 meters

6. A 750-kilogram car moving at 100 kilometers/hour has approximately 290,000 Joules of kinetic energy. What is the kinetic energy of the same car if it is moving at 50 kilometers/hour?
   a. 72,500 Joules
   b. 145,000 Joules
   c. the same
   d. 580,000 Joules

Continued

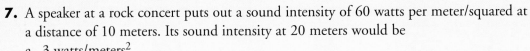

7. A speaker at a rock concert puts out a sound intensity of 60 watts per meter/squared at a distance of 10 meters. Its sound intensity at 20 meters would be
   a. 3 watts/meters^2
   b. 15 watts/meters^2
   c. 30 watts/meters^2
   d. unchanged

8. What will be the increase in temperature of 50 grams of water if a 50-ohm resistor carrying 2 amps of current is submerged in the water for 20 seconds? (*Specific heat capacity* = 4.2 J/g° C)
   a. 19° C
   b. 49° C
   c. 1.9° C
   d. The water will boil
   e. 9.5° C

Sending Signals

OVERVIEW

GETTING ON THE AIR

Now that you can make sound, and make it as loud as you want, it is time to share your waves with others. Chances are you have some kind of radio receiver in your home or your school, but did you ever think you'd have a radio transmitter?

In this chapter, you are going to build a radio transmitter that will send signals. It may not be as powerful as SunFM or KISS radio, but it should get your message out.

So get ready for some electronics and start building. After that, all you'll have to do is decide what it is you want to say to your waiting public!

Your last milestone:

Project Milestone 3

Building and Testing a Radio Transmitter and Operating the Radio Station

You will build a radio transmitter that converts sounds into radio waves. You will then test and adapt your radio "station" for the clearest signal and maximum possible range, and send your thumb piano notes to an FM receiver (and your audience!). You will explain the energy transfers that occur from the playing of a note to the brain's recognition of the note coming from the receiver's speaker.

By the end of this chapter, you will have put together the components of your classroom radio station. Beginning with a study of the electromagnetic spectrum, you will build an FM receiver and explore the world of radio communication. Then you will undertake your final project milestone.

To help you accomplish Project Milestone Three, you will do the following activities:

Activity 17.1 Mapping the EM Spectrum
You will study the electromagnetic (EM) spectrum and learn how radiation is transmitted through space.

Activity 17.2 Building an FM Receiver
You will build a receiver that you will use later for your radio broadcast.

Activity 17.3 A Visit to a Radio Station
You will witness how the principle of electronics and the concepts of sound and energy you have been studying actually play out in the world of radio communication. Your visit will also give you the opportunity to find out about careers in this field.

Activity 17.4 Building and Testing a Radio Transmitter
You will build a device (a radio transmitter) that converts sounds into radio waves, and transmit them through space to a receiver, where they can be interpreted as music or words. You will adapt components of the transmitter to optimize the broadcast signal and its reception. You will put on a "performance" using your thumb piano, and transmit the performance to a receiver and to an audience, whose brains will interpret the sounds as notes. Then you will explain the energy transfers that occur.

ACTIVITY 17.1

Mapping the EM Spectrum

Getting In Gear

Why can't you hear with your ears the waves that a radio station emits? Why is all this electric equipment necessary to receive them? Many times people confuse radio waves with sound waves and think that they should be able to "listen" to radio waves. Not so. Radio waves are a form of electromagnetic waves that need to be transformed into sound waves if we want to hear music or someone speaking. You will create a model electromagnetic spectrum to understand more about radio waves.

Getting To Work!

To explore the electromagnetic spectrum, you will

1. Read the overview scenario and project milestone for Chapter 17, and discuss the scenario with your class.

2. Participate in a class discussion about the electromagnetic spectrum.

3. Read Getting the Point: *The Biggest and the Smallest—Scientific Notation,* and complete the Focus Questions. Complete │ **Job Sheet 17.1** │ **The Biggest and the Smallest,** as directed by your teacher.

Job Sheet

4. Read Getting the Point: *Electromagnetic Waves,* and complete the Focus Questions.

5. Assist your teacher in completing the large spectrum chart posted in your classroom. Read │ **Job Sheet 17.2** │ **Mapping the Electromagnetic Spectrum,** and follow the directions to finish the chart. Answer the questions on the job sheet.

Job Sheet

6. Check out the Did You Know? reading as time permits.

Ever wonder about images used to study outer space? Read Concept Connection: *Studying Outer Space.*

Getting The Point

The Biggest and the Smallest—Scientific Notation

In science, and particularly in physics and astronomy, we often deal with very large and very small numbers. Presenting numerical information in visual form is an important task for people working in business, finance, or science. Numbers, along with other information, can be displayed and organized in tables, graphs, charts, and spreadsheets. And when the numbers themselves are very large or very small, scientists write them in a shorthand version called *scientific notation.*

The need for a shorthand version of writing numbers is obvious. For instance, on the large end of the scale there are 10,000,000,000,000,000,000,000 copper atoms in one penny. On the small end of the scale, the nuclei of these copper atoms are 0.00000000000001 meters in diameter. To simplify these kinds of numbers and to make them more understandable, scientists have devised a way of expressing them using *powers of ten*—a method that shortens any number, no matter how large or small, to just six or seven keystrokes.

Large Numbers. In the case of large numbers, scientific notation starts with the fact that the number 10 can be expressed as 10^1, 100 can be expressed as 10×10 or 10^2, and so on as the size of the numbers increases. Note that using this system, 10^0 is equal to 1. To write a large number in scientific notation, follow these steps:

1. Count the number of decimal places that are required to move the decimal point to a position in which only one digit remains to its left. (For example, given 36,000., move the decimal point four places to the left, to convert the number to 3.6.)

2. Write down the number, a multiplication sign, and the number 10 (for example, 3.6×10).

3. The number of places the decimal point was moved should be written as an exponent on the 10 ($3.6 \times 10^4 = 36,000$).

Converting a scientific notation number back to an integer number requires reversing the process as follows:

1. Write down the numbers before the multiplication sign (for example, given 7.2×10^{11}, write 7.2).

2. Move the decimal point to the right the number of places indicated by the exponent. For example, move the decimal point, adding zeroes, 11 places right to arrive at 720000000000., or 720,000,000,000.

The common names for large numbers are thousand, million, billion, and trillion, such as in describing amounts of money. In scientific notation, it is often convenient to know what these numbers look like in exponent form. They are 1 thousand = 10^3, 1 million = 10^6, 1 billion = 10^9, and 1 trillion = 10^{12}. So a number like 8.0×10^6 is "8 million," and 1.5×10^9 is "1.5 billion."

Small Numbers. In the case of small numbers, scientific notation starts with the fact that the number .1 can be expressed as 1/10 or 10^{-1}, .01 can be expressed as 1/ (10×10) or 10^{-2}, and so on for even smaller decimal numbers. To write a small decimal number in scientific notation, follow these steps:

1. Count the number of decimal places that are required to move the decimal point to a position in which only one digit remains to its left. For example, given .000000036, move the decimal point eight places to the right, to convert the number to 3.6.

2. Write down the number, a multiplication sign, and the number 10 (for example, 3.6 × 10).

3. The number of places the decimal point was moved should be written as a negative exponent on the 10 (3.6 × 10^{-8}).

Converting scientific notation numbers back to a small decimal number requires reversing the process as follows:

1. Write down the numbers before the multiplication sign (for example, given 7.2 × 10^{-6}, write 7.2).

2. Move the decimal point to the left the number of places indicated by the exponent. For example, move the decimal point, adding zeroes, six places left to arrive at .0000072.

Focus Questions

Give common names to the following large numbers (thousand, million, etc.) and convert to scientific notation:

1,100

2,000,000

445,000,000

4,500,000,000,000

Getting The Point.

Electromagnetic Waves

The light and heat energy streaming from the sun is absorbed, reflected, and reemitted by the Earth. The sun's energy is being transferred in a different way from the sound waves produced by tuning forks or by your voice. Traveling through the void of space, these types of waves have nothing to "wave" through. The energy from the sun moving through a vacuum is called *electromagnetic radiation.* This is really a continuum of waves with varying wavelengths and frequencies. Yet all electromagnetic waves travel at the same speed—the speed of light—186,000 miles per second, or 3 × 10^8 meters/second. Our eyes, which seem perfectly adequate for seeing the world around us, can only detect the tiniest sliver of the enormous range of this spectrum of radiation.

Figure 17.1

The Electromagnetic Spectrum

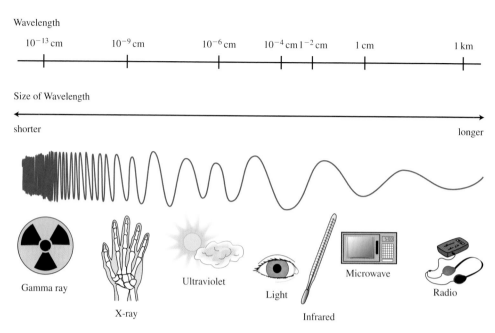

Image Courtesy of NASA.

We can detect many other types of electromagnetic (EM) waves by using specialized receivers. By turning on a television, for example, you receive EM waves a satellite is broadcasting—a program that has been transmitted to the satellite by the TV station. Similarly, in your final milestone, you will build a radio station to broadcast music and news using radio waves, and the antenna of a receiver will pick them up so the radio can translate the signals into the music and voices your lab partners will hear. These waves are always present in the air around us, but only when we tune our TV or radio to the correct frequencies do we have the opportunity to listen in.

The speed of light, frequency, and wavelength of electromagnetic waves is related through the general wave equation. Instead of $v = f\lambda$, we write

$c = f\lambda$ where c = speed of light in a vacuum $= 3 \times 10^8$ m/sec

Example problem: A local radio station broadcasts at a frequency of 98 MHz. What is the wavelength of the radio waves?

$c = f\lambda$ or $\lambda = c/f = 3 \times 10^8$ m/sec$/9.8 \times 10^7$ MHz

$(M = \text{million} = 10^6) = 3.06$ m

Focus Questions

How do electromagnetic waves differ from sound waves?

How do we know that electromagnetic waves are all around us?

What is the frequency of a microwave with a wavelength of .003 meters?

Concept Connection: Studying Outer Space

By studying the electromagnetic emissions of objects such as stars and galaxies, astronomers hope to come to a better understanding of the universe. Although many astronomical puzzles can only be solved by comparing images of different wavelengths, telescopes are only designed to detect a particular portion of the electromagnetic spectrum. Astronomers therefore often use images from several different telescopes to study celestial phenomena. Shown below is the Milky Way Galaxy as seen by radio, infrared, optical, X-ray and gamma ray telescopes.

Figure 17.2

What Our Own Milky Way Galaxy Looks Like in Ten Different Bands of the Electromagnetic Spectrum

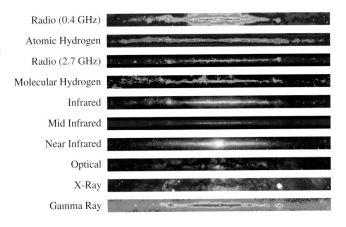

Radio (0.4 GHz)
Atomic Hydrogen
Radio (2.7 GHz)
Molecular Hydrogen
Infrared
Mid Infrared
Near Infrared
Optical
X-Ray
Gamma Ray

Image from *"MultiWavelength Milky Way."* Astrophysics Data Facility, NASA Goddard Space Flight Center. Courtesy of NASA. http://adc.gsfc.nasa.gov/mw/mmw_sci.html (June 10, 2003)

Each image shows the same view, looking into the center of our galaxy. However, astronomers attached different instruments to the telescope each time. Each instrument looked at only one portion of the electromagnetic radiation present in the galaxy. Because the galaxy produces different amounts of electromagnetic radiation, each image looks different.

Different types of telescopes usually don't take simultaneous readings. Space is a dynamic system, so an image taken at one time is not necessarily the precise equivalent of an image of the same phenomena taken at a later time. And often, there is barely enough time for one kind of telescope to observe extremely short-lived phe-

Did You Know?

What does a kite have to do with the first radio broadcast?

On the 12th of December 1901, Guglielmo Marconi realized a dream, when an electronic message was sent across the Atlantic from England to a receiving station on top of a mountain with an aerial kept aloft by a giant kite at St. John's Newfoundland.

Without that achievement where would our commonplace use of radio, television and mobile phones have been?

Adapted from THE WORLD TODAY. "100th Anniversary of First Radio Broadcast." http://www.abc.net.au/worldtoday/s438744.htm (June 10, 2003)

nomena like gamma-ray bursts. By the time other telescopes point to the object, it has grown too faint to be detected.

So why haven't scientists created a telescope designed to look at everything at once?

"Nature has determined the design of our telescopes," says Dr. Martin Weisskopf, an astrophysicist at NASA's Marshall Space Flight Center. The differing wavelengths among the various energies create different instrumental needs. This results in dissimilar, incompatible detecting devices like tuning a radio to receive your favorite TV channel.

Adapted from *"It Takes More Than One Kind of Telescope to See the Light: Why We Need Different Types of Telescopes to See the Light."* By Lesley Mullen. Science @ NASA. Courtesy of NASA. http://science.nasa.gov/newhome/headlines/features/ast20apr99_1.htm (June 10, 2003)

ACTIVITY 17.2

Building an FM Receiver

Getting In Gear

What does that button on your radio do that switches the stations from AM to FM? What is the difference in AM and FM? (Well, everyone knows the better music is on FM, right?) Both the radio transmitter and the receiver have to be tuned into each other for you to get the signal, so we better straighten this out. You will build an FM receiver to receive the radio waves in your final project.

Getting To Work!

To build an FM receiver, you will

1. Participate in a class discussion about radio receivers.

2. Obtain your FM radio kit, and build your FM receiver. Be sure to follow the instructions on | **Job Sheet 17.3** | **Building an FM Receiver,** as well as the directions enclosed in your kit.

Job Sheet

3. Read Getting the Point: *FM Radio,* and answer the Focus Questions.

4. Finish building your radio, test its signal clarity, and modify its antenna to get the best reception. (This radio will receive your thumb piano radio transmission in your final milestone.)

5. Answer Questions 10–14 on Job Sheet 17.3 and discuss as a class.

6. Check out Workplace Connection: *Technical Careers in Radio* and the Did You Know? readings if time permits.

Ever wonder how sound effects are made for the radio audience? Read Concept Connection: *Sound Effects in Radio.*

FM Radio

A radio wave contains an electric field that pushes on any electric charge it encounters. That's why, when a radio wave passes the antenna of your radio, it causes electric charges in that antenna to accelerate up and down. There is also a resonant circuit connected to the antenna—a circuit that oscillates strongly only when charge is pushed up and down the antenna at exactly the circuit's resonant frequency. If the circuit's resonant frequency is the same as that of the radio wave, the small pushes exerted on charges in the antenna add up so that charge moves more and more vigorously through the resonant circuit. But if your radio isn't tuned to the frequency of the radio wave, the overall motion of charge on the antenna and this resonant circuit is small. That's why your radio only responds to the radio transmission of one station and not others.

To understand this effect, imagine pushing a child on a swing. If you push rhythmically at just the right frequency, the child will swing higher and higher. But if you push rhythmically at the wrong frequency, the child will just jitter about a bit.

Once charge is moving strongly through the resonant circuit in your radio, the radio can monitor various features of that moving charge. If the station is using the AM or amplitude modulation technique to represent sound, your radio studies the amount of charge moving back and forth through the resonant circuit. When that flow of charge—that current—is strong, it moves the speaker cone toward you and produces a compression of the air. When that current is weak, it moves the speaker cone away from you and produces a rarefaction of the air. These changes in air density and pressure reproduce the sound that the station is transmitting.

If the station is using the FM or frequency modulation technique to represent sound, your radio studies the frequency at which charge moves back and forth in the resonant circuit. Very small changes in this frequency, caused by frequency changes in the radio wave itself, are used to control the speaker cone in your radio. When the frequency is raised slightly above normal, your radio moves the speaker cone toward you and produces a compression of the air. When the frequency is lowered slightly below normal, your radio moves the speaker cone away from you and produces a rarefaction of the air. Again, this change in air density and pressure produces sound.

Adapted from HOW THINGS WORK: RADIO, by Louis Bloomfield, Professor of Physics, The University of Virginia. Reprinted with permission. http://howthingswork.virginia.edu/radio.html (June 10, 2003)

Focus Questions

What is the difference between AM and FM radio, aside from the frequencies at which they broadcast?

How does the loudspeaker of an AM radio reproduce sound? How does an FM radio differ in its reproduction of sound?

Concept Connection: Sound Effects in Radio

Sound effects in radio broadcasting did not leap full-grown into this new medium in the 1920s. In its infancy, radio then was evolving from what was primarily a military communication tool into a vast system of popular entertainment, culture and news.

The few sound effects used in the early days were simple, unsophisticated, and often not very convincing. Anyone near a microphone who was available could supply a make-shift sound effect. The lid of a piano might be dropped to imitate a door closing. A wooden match stick could be snapped near the mike to simulate a baseball hitting a bat. Gun shots could be either a dowel hitting a leather couch or a drumstick striking the edge of a drum.

Realism was neither expected nor obtained through these efforts. In the early days, radio stations filled their air time with orchestra music, poetry readers, singers, and preachers, nearly all of whom were unpaid. Only when the drama shows began pushing out the "free talent" was it necessary to create better sound effects.

The first sound men, of course, had no training. Some had backstage theater experience where they had shaken a metal sheet to replicate thunder or slapped one board against another to create gunshots. A few others played percussive instruments in a band and they were used to producing a variety of unusual sounds on cue.

But most of them had neither experience nor training; they were designated to be the sound man because they were the junior man on the radio staff. Some were not even paid; Ted Robertson began at WXYZ in Detroit (home of The Lone Ranger, The Green Hornet, etc.) as a unpaid sound man and worked for several months with no salary. It would be three decades before the highly trained and specialized sound man was an integral part of network broadcasting.

By the 1930s, there were plenty of drama shows (kids' serials, detectives, mysteries, and soaps) most of which required realistic sound effects. The sounds basically fell into two broad categories: a) those that advanced the action or helped move the story line, and b) background or mood setting sounds. And all of these were produced with a combination of manual and recorded sounds.

Among the purists in old-time radio nostalgia, there exists a misconception that there was a time in which only manual sounds were used, and only much later did the recorded devices encroach. But recorded sound, in many forms, predated the Golden Age of Radio and the versatile transcriptions were used from the beginning.

In addition to a large stock of recorded music (usually classical and therefore free of copyright restriction) to fit every scene, there were sound effects records to replace the "real thing". That would usually be sounds of objects too large or too expensive for a radio studio, i.e. car engine, airplane, cannon, large crowds, explosions, and an ocean liner.

Also necessary would be records of sounds of creatures who couldn't read a cue: crickets, frogs, cows, elephants, etc. However, many good soundmen could, and did, imitate with their own voices the sounds of dogs, cats, horses, parrots, and others. Horses galloping could even be imitated by using coconut halves and an old board.

In addition to the size limitations of a radio studio (the earliest contraption to make the sound of rain was a series of 4 ft. by 4 ft. panels stacked six ft. high), economy was a compelling reason for using records. They were relatively cheap and could be used over and over, to the delight of the tight-fisted producers of both network and syndicated radio shows.

A few old radio buffs are still convinced that the manual sounds were more authentic and that their gradual replacement by recorded sounds was capricious, unnecessary, and perhaps even motivated by the American love of electronics. But in historical fact, the sounds on disk superseded the manual ones for three reasons, in addition to economy:

- As radio fidelity improved, the simulated sounds were revealed as inadequate imitations.
- A record library of hundreds of sounds took up less space than one large manual effect (most of the early wind machines were larger than a stuffed chair).
- The flexibility and versatility of the turntable with multiple arms would permit one sound man to do the work of three using only manual effects.

For example, one sound man with three turntables and four to six pickup arms could easily create the below sounds that were almost impossible manually:

- The speed of an automobile or industrial engine could be accelerated or slowed by varying the speed of the turntable.
- With two arms on the same record, one set of horse hooves could be doubled or one auto could pass another.
- The length, distance away, or size of any sound could be changed instantly by adjusting the volume.

Adapted from *"Sound Effects,"* by Jack French, Editor: *"Radio Recall."* Copyright © 1997 by Jack French. Reprinted with permission. http://www.old-time.com/sfx.html (June 10, 2003)

Workplace Connection: Technical Careers in Radio

International Broadcasting Bureau, Voice of America (IBB/VOA, Washington, DC, Office of Broadcast Operations)

Announcement Period: January 13, 2003–December 31, 2003

Title, Series, and Grade: **Radio Broadcast Technician** (WB-3940-2)

Salary: $21.42–$34.21 per hour

DUTIES: Technicians operate studio equipment for the control and regulation of English

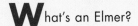

Did You Know?

What's an Elmer?

An "Elmer" is one who gives encouragement and assistance to newcomers to the hobby of radio. It may be someone who showed you how to solder, helped you build your first radio, or the person who always had an extra receiver or a spare part they weren't using, and let you borrow it for 40 years. Details concerning a contest ("Elmer Memorial Crystal Radio DX Contest") dedicated to the memory of the Elmers who helped people get started in radio-related hobbies can be found at the Crystal Radio Resources website (see below).

Adapted from *"The Fourth Annual Elmer Memorial Crystal Radio DX Contest: Rules,"* by Owen Pool. http://www.thebest.net/wuggy/rules.htm (June 10, 2003)

CB or citizens band radio refers to some parts of the electromagnetic spectrum that have been set aside for public use. You can operate a CB radio without training and without serious legal constraints, although the power of your transmitted wave is strictly limited. The principle band for CB radio is around 27 MHz and I think that the transmissions use the AM audio encoding scheme. As you talk, the power of your transmission increases and decreases to represent the pressure fluctuations in your voice. The receiving CB radio detects the power fluctuations in the radio wave and moves its speaker accordingly.

From HOW THINGS WORK: RADIO, by Louis Bloomfield, Professor of Physics, The University of Virginia. http://howthingswork.virginia.edu/radio.html (June 10, 2003)

and foreign language radio programs. They perform recording operations using professional, high quality tape-recording equipment, and are responsible for the maintenance, circuit design, testing, modification, and installation of all types of electronic broadcast equipment. Technicians use Bureau-owned, portable, technical equipment and facilities to control, record, regulate, and feed program materials from remote areas to IBB/VOA. Technicians work closely with program producers to present high-quality broadcasts.

EXPERIENCE REQUIREMENTS:

Applicants must have technical experience in professional radio or the audio portion of television which clearly demonstrates a good knowledge of the principles, practices, and methods of radio broadcasting. The experience must have been progressively responsible and must clearly demonstrate the applicant's competence in at least two of the following areas: studio control, tape or disc recording, field operations, or broadcast equipment maintenance.

KNOWLEDGE, SKILLS, AND ABILITIES:

1. Demonstrated experience in the operation of digital and/or analog equipment in broadcast studios/control rooms for live on-air and production of radio programs. (e.g., multi-channel audio consoles, reel-to-reel and cassette audio recorders, professional compact disc machines, mini-disc, audio cart machines, microphones, telephone hybrids)

2. Demonstrated knowledge of the operation of multi-channel and multi-path broadcasting equipment and knowledge in audio mixing, production and editing techniques, associated with the mixing of program material from multiple audio sources including studio and remote locations into live and pre-recorded radio programs.

3. Demonstrated ability to operate a variety of professional recording equipment, including audio tape, cassettes, R-dat, compact disc, mini-disc, and high speed duplication systems.

4. Basic knowledge of computer operations, specifically in relation to broadcast automation systems.

5. Demonstrated ability to follow instructions and operate as a team member with radio production personnel or radio producer during live broadcasts and the production of pre-recorded programs.

Adapted from International Broadcasting Bureau: Office of Personnel. Radio Broadcast Technician WB-3940-2 (position announcement). http://www.voa.gov/vacancies/personnel.html (June 10, 2003)

ACTIVITY 17.3

A Visit to a Radio Station

WWouldn't it be cool to work at a radio station? You'd get to choose all the music to play, could hear your favorite song anyting you want, and play it as loud as you want all the time! Well, maybe not. There are many jobs at a radio station that don't have to do with the music they play at all. You will visit a radio station and see all the different things that go on there. Maybe, you will be able to request that song though.

To explore this workplace, you will

1. Participate in a class discussion about your visit to the radio station. Review the questions on **Job Sheet 17.4** **A Visit to a Radio Station.** (You will answer these questions after you return from the station.)

Job Sheet

2. Work in your groups to develop questions about the radio communication industry and about the work people do at a radio station.

3. Meet with your tour leader at the radio station for a tour of the facility.

4. Listen to the tour leader and take notes. Ask questions if you need more information about the questions on the job sheet or other questions you might have.

5. Complete the job sheet after you return to class, and turn it in to your teacher.

6. Write a thank-you letter to your tour leader.

ACTIVITY 17.4

Building and Testing a Radio Transmitter

Are you ready to pump out some sound? Let's put it all together and create your radio transmitter. Your device should transmit the clearest possible signal over the maximum possible range. Are you up to the challenge? Go for it!

To complete Project Milestone Three, you will

1. Participate in a class discussion about the five major parts of a radio transmitter.

2. Read Getting the Point: *How a Radio Station Transmits a Signal,* and answer the Focus Questions.

3. Discuss with your teacher the teamwork necessary to accomplish your final milestone.

4. Build your transmitter, following the instructions carefully in Job Sheet 17.5 **Building an FM Radio Transmitter,** together with the instructions that accompany your kit.

Job Sheet

5. Answer Questions 13–16 on Job Sheet 17.5.

6. Read Job Sheet 17.6 **How to Solder.** Your teacher will give you a resistor and some wire with which to practice making connections.

Job Sheet

7. Use Job Sheet 17.7 **Testing Your Transmitter for Optimal Use** to test and alter components of your transmitter and receiver system to obtain the clearest signal and maximum range.

Job Sheet

8. Have your teacher evaluate your final attempt to send a signal from your thumb piano to your FM receiver, as explained in Job Sheet 17.7 Item 12.

9. Have your teacher also evaluate your understanding of energy transfers (see Job Sheet 17.7 Item 12). Prepare to explain the energy transfers that take place in all "steps," from using the thumb piano to produce a note through the brain's perception of the note you transmitted. Discuss with your teacher the way that you will demonstrate your understanding, that is, by a brief presentation, a written description, and/or a properly labeled diagram.

10. Check out the Did You Know? reading as time permits.

11. Review the concepts and answer the questions in What Have You Learned? for homework.

Wonder where it all began? Read Concept Connection: *The First Wireless Transmission.*

Getting The Point.

How a Radio Station Transmits a Signal

A radio station launches a radio wave by moving electric charges rhythmically up and down their antenna. As this electric charge accelerates back and forth, it produces a changing electric field—a structure in space that pushes on electric charges—and a changing magnetic field—a structure in space that pushes on magnetic poles. Because the electric field changes with time, it creates the magnetic field and because the magnetic field changes with time, it creates the electric field. The two travel off across space as a pair, endlessly recreating one another in an electromagnetic wave that will continue to the ends of the universe. However, when this wave encounters the antenna of your radio, its electric field begins to push electric charges up and down on that antenna. Your radio senses this motion of electric charges and thus detects the passing radio wave.

To convey audio information (sound) to your radio, the radio station makes one of several changes to the radio wave it transmits. In the AM or Amplitude Modulation technique, it adjusts the amount of charge it moves up and down its antenna, and hence the strength of its radio wave, in order to signal which way to move the speaker of your radio. These movements of the speaker are what cause your radio to emit sound. In the FM or Frequency Modulation technique, the radio station adjusts the precise frequency at which it moves charge up and down its antenna. Your radio senses these slight changes in frequency and moves its speaker accordingly.

From HOW THINGS WORK, by Louis A. Bloomfield, Professor of Physics, The University of Virginia. Reprinted with permission. http://rabi.phys.virginia.edu/HTW/radio.html (June 10, 2003)

Focus Questions

What exactly is transmitted by a radio transmitter?

What in an FM radio actually "receives" the signal transmitted by a radio station?

Concept Connection: The First Wireless Transmission

In a landmark experiment on December 12, 1901, Marconi, who is often called the "Father of Wireless," demonstrated transatlantic communication by receiving a signal in St. John's, Newfoundland that had been sent from Cornwall, England. Because of his pioneering work in the use of electromagnetic radiation for radio communications, Marconi was awarded the Nobel Prize in physics in 1909.

Marconi's famous experiment showed the way toward world-wide communication, but it also raised a serious scientific dilemma. Up to this point, it had

Did You Know?

Why do Amateur Radio enthusiasts call themselves "hams"?

Although the origin of the word "ham" is obscure, every ham has his or her own pet theory. One holds that early Amateurs were called hams because they liked to "perform" on the air, as in "hamming it up". Another theory proposes that the name came from the "ham-fisted" way some Amateurs handled their code keys. The easiest opinion to accept is that "hams" is a Briticism of "Ams", as in Amateurs. And one of the most exotic holds that "hams" is an acronym, the call sign H.A.M. from the initials of three college students who were among the first Radio Amateurs.

From *"Introduction to Amateur Radio."* South East Iowa Technical Society. http://www.seits.org/business/whatis1.htm (June 10, 2003)

been assumed that electromagnetic radiation travelled in straight lines in a manner similar to light waves.

If there were no objects in the path, the maximum distance would be determined by the transmitter and receiver antenna heights and by the bulge (or curvature) of the earth. Drawing from light as an analogy, this distance is often called the "Line-of-Sight" (LOS) distance. In Marconi's transatlantic demonstration, something different was happening to cause the radio waves to apparently bend around the Earth's curvature so that the communication signals from England could be heard over such an unprecedented distance.

In 1902, Oliver Heaviside and Arthur Kennelly each independently proposed that a conducting layer existed in the upper atmosphere that would allow a transmitted EM signal to be reflected back toward the Earth. Up to this time, there was no direct evidence of such a region and little was known about the physical or electrical properties of the Earth's upper atmosphere. If such a conductive layer existed, it would permit a dramatic extension of the "Line-of-Sight" limitation to radio communication.

Adapted from *"Why Conduct Ionospheric Research?"* High Frequency Active Auroral Research Program (HAARP). http://www.haarp.alaska.edu/haarp/io2.html (June 13, 2002)

What Have You Learned?

KEY CONCEPTS

Electromagnetic radiation. Electromagnetic radiation is emitted in the form of electromagnetic waves, such as light, radio, and gamma rays.

Radio waves. The lowest energy waves on the electromagnetic spectrum are called radio waves. They are characterized by large wavelengths and low frequencies.

FM. The commonly known band of radio is named for the initials of frequency modulation, a process which lowers or raises the frequency of a radio wave to move the diaphragm of a radio speaker.

AM. The initials for amplitude modulation give the name of the other common radio band, AM. Amplitude modulation is a process that lowers or raises the power of a radio wave to move the diaphragm of a radio speaker.

CONCEPT QUESTIONS

1. How do we "see" the bands in the electromagnetic spectrum other than visible light?

2. What kind of energy is produced by a microphone when you speak into it?

3. What are the five basic components of a radio receiver?

4. What are the five basic components of a radio transmitter?

5. What is the purpose of the antenna in a transmitter?

APPLYING WHAT YOU KNOW

1. If you see a bolt of lightning at a distance of 2,000 meters, how long did it take for the light to reach your eyes?
a. 2 seconds
b. 5.9 seconds
c. .0006 seconds
d. .0000067 seconds

2. Which of the following components can be found in both radio receivers and transmitters? (You may choose more than one.)
a. oscillator circuit
b. antenna
c. tuner
d. microphone
e. speaker
f. amplifier
g. power source

Index